Physiology
A Student's Self-test Colouring Book

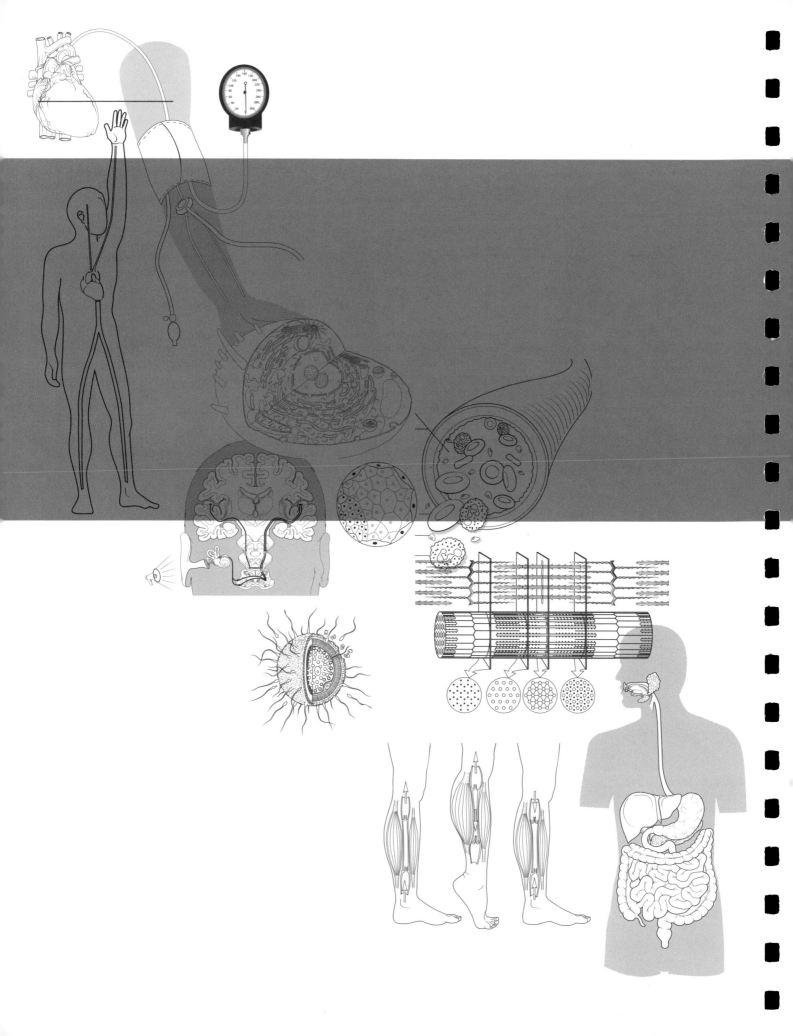

Physiology
A Student's Self-test Colouring Book

Chief Consultant:
James W. Hicks, Ph.D.

Department of Ecology and Evolutionary Biology
University of California, Irvine

QUAD BOOKS

Quarto is the authority on a wide range of topics.

Quarto educates, entertains and enriches the lives of our readers—enthusiasts and lovers of hands-on living.

www.QuartoKnows.com

First published in 2016 by
Global Book Publishing Pty Ltd
Part of The Quarto Group
Level 1, Ovest House, 58 West Street,
Brighton, BN1 2RA

ISBN 978-0-85762-462-8

Printed and Bound in China

Conceived, designed, and produced by Global Book Publishing Pty Ltd

Edited and designed by D & N Publishing, Baydon, Wiltshire, UK

Illustrations by Medical Artist Ltd (www.medical-artist.com)

Additional illustrations Mike Gorman, Thomson Digital, Glen Vause

CONTRIBUTORS

Brian Bagatto, Ph.D.
Tamatha Barbeau, Ph.D.
Alastair J. Barr, D.Phil.
Dorothy L. Buchhagen, Ph.D.
Anne R. Crecelius, Ph.D.
Terry L. Gleave, Ph.D.
Helen S. Goodridge, Ph.D.
Lynn Hartzler, Ph.D.
Ashley Lauren Juavinett, B.S.
Yvonne Mbaki, Ph.D.
Deborah Merrick, Ph.D.
Adrian O'Hara, Ph.D.
David Peeney, Ph.D.
Jennifer C. Richards, Ph.D.
Alix Warburton, Ph.D.

Contents

Introduction

Physiology focuses on understanding how living organisms work, and integrates molecular, cellular, anatomical, biomechanical, and biophysical concepts to reveal how all body systems work together to support life. Consequently, physiology is the cornerstone of medicine, with its early origins dating back more than a thousand years to Hippocrates (c. 460–c. 370 BC) and Aristotle (384–322 BC) in ancient Greece. The field of experimental physiology expanded in the 19th century with classic works by Claude Bernard (1813–1878), and major advances in understanding the functioning of the body occurred throughout the 20th century. Physiology continues to be a major field of study in the biological sciences, and the rapid advances in molecular and cellular biology taking place in the 21st century are providing a deeper understanding of physiological processes and leading to improvements in biomedicine.

Many resources are available to medical students, doctors, nurses, health professionals, fitness trainers, nutritionists, artists, and others who desire to learn about human physiology, or who need to brush up on their knowledge of the human body from time to time. What sets this book apart from the exhibitions, Internet sites, CD-ROMs, and other material is that it is an *active* learning experience – by colouring in the elements illustrated, the shape and location of each becomes firmly fixed in your mind, and writing the name of each part in the space provided and checking it against the answers at the bottom of the page impresses the word and its spelling on the mind far more readily than if you had simply viewed a diagram in a textbook. The unique connection between hand, eye, and mind makes this physiology colouring book an invaluable study tool for people of all ages and education levels.

How This Book is Organised

Featuring more than 200 computer-rendered line-drawings in a clean design, this book is divided into 14 comprehensive chapters. It covers the major body systems – from the skeletal and muscular to the circulatory and endocrine systems – and also includes an overview of the body, cells and tissues, and special sense organs, and how these systems are integrated. Integration is an important facet in the study of physiology – not only learning the names and locations of the parts of the body, but also discovering how these parts relate to each other and function together.

As you work your way through the book, you will gain both a clear understanding of physiology and a deeper appreciation for the human body – an amazingly complicated yet perfectly coordinated organic machine.

How to Use This Book

This book is designed to help students and professionals identify various aspects of physiology, and the coloured leader lines aid the process by clearly pointing out each feature. The functions of colouring and labelling allow you to familiarise yourself with individual parts of the body and then check your knowledge.

Colouring is best done using either pencils or ballpoint pens (not felt-tip pens) in a variety of dark and light colours. Where possible, you should use the same colour for the same structures, so that all completed illustrations can be utilised later as visual references. According to anatomical convention, the

colour green is usually reserved for lymphatic structures, yellow for nerves, red for arteries, and blue for veins.

Labelling the coloured leader lines that point to separate parts of the illustration enables you to test and then check your knowledge using the answers that are printed at the bottom of the page.

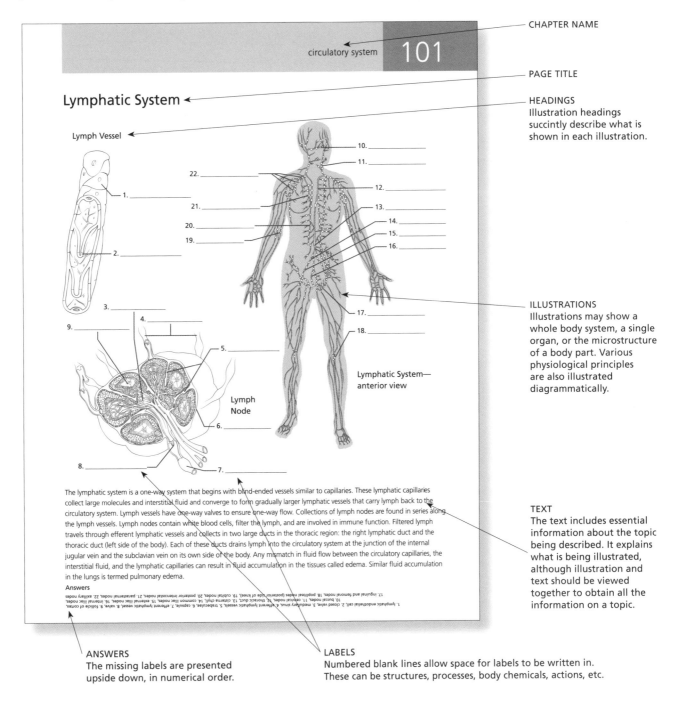

CHAPTER NAME

PAGE TITLE

HEADINGS
Illustration headings succintly describe what is shown in each illustration.

ILLUSTRATIONS
Illustrations may show a whole body system, a single organ, or the microstructure of a body part. Various physiological principles are also illustrated diagrammatically.

TEXT
The text includes essential information about the topic being described. It explains what is being illustrated, although illustration and text should be viewed together to obtain all the information on a topic.

ANSWERS
The missing labels are presented upside down, in numerical order.

LABELS
Numbered blank lines allow space for labels to be written in. These can be structures, processes, body chemicals, actions, etc.

Body Fluid Compartments

All cell types that are present in higher multicellular organisms arise from a single totipotent cell (a cell with the ability to differentiate into any type within the body). In humans, this is represented by the fertilisation of a female oocyte (egg) by a male sperm cell, giving rise to a single totipotent cell, referred to as a zygote. This zygote can then divide into many cell types that become more specialised as development progresses, giving rise to the three primary germ layers: mesoderm, ectoderm, and endoderm.

In the human body, there are several fluid compartments whose total composition needs to be tightly regulated. The largest of these is the intracellular (inside the cell) compartment, which takes up around two-thirds of the body's water. The remaining third is present in the extracellular (outside the cell) compartment, which can be split into the intravascular or plasma (fluid portion of blood) and interstitial (fluid between cells) compartments. On average, the human body is made up of 50–60 per cent water.

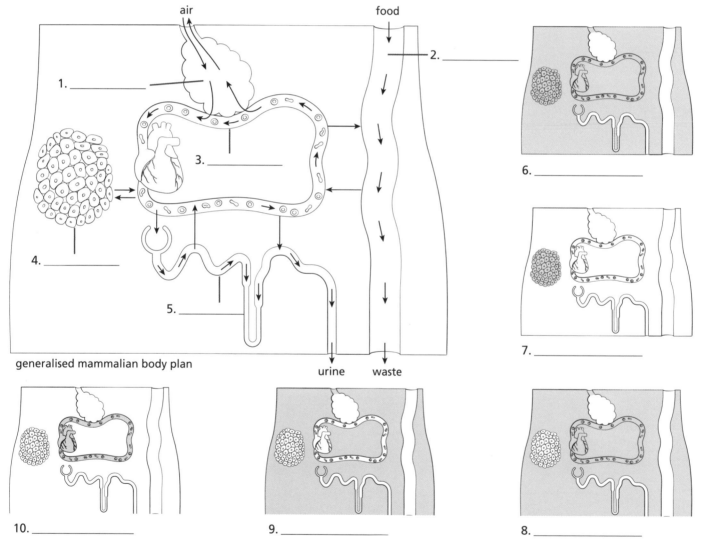

air

food

1. _____

2. _____

3. _____

4. _____

5. _____

6. _____

7. _____

generalised mammalian body plan

urine   waste

10. _____

9. _____

8. _____

Major Fluid Compartments

Label the type of fluid found in the areas shaded grey.

Answers

1. lungs, 2. gastrointestinal tract, 3. blood vessels, 4. cells, 5. kidneys, 6. total body water, 7. intracellular fluid, 8. extracellular fluid, 9. interstitial fluid, 10. plasma

Body Organisation

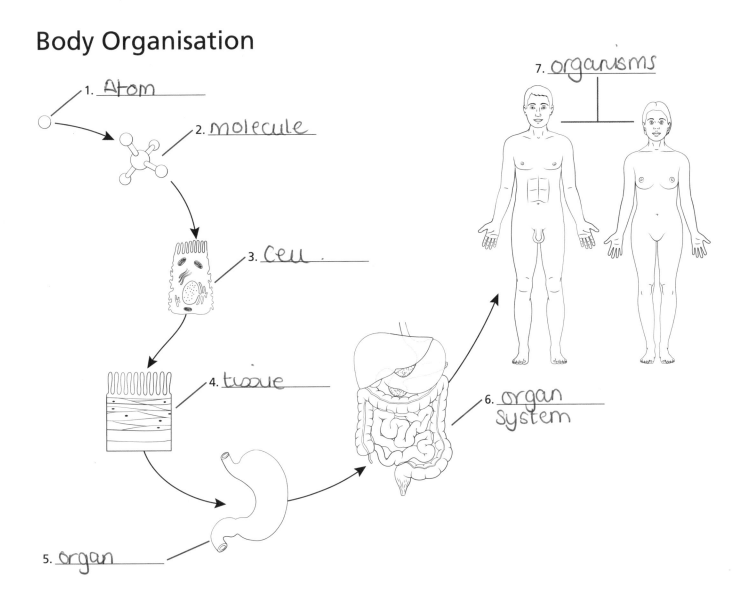

1. Atom
2. molecule
3. Cell.
4. tissue
5. organ
6. organ system
7. organisms

Cells are the basic structural units of all living organisms. They consist of simple molecules and macromolecules, which form the functional elements – referred to as organelles – that perform the basic biological processes that allow the organism to survive. The human body consists of hundreds of types of cells that can be divided into two fundamental groups: germ cells and somatic cells. Germ cells give rise to gametes, which are the cells required for sexual reproduction; somatic cells give rise to the three primary germ layers during development.

A group of connected cells that have similar and complementary functions are referred to as tissue. Tissue can be grouped into four basic types: epithelial, connective, muscle, and nervous tissues. When two or more of these tissue types work together they produce an organ, and when organs combine they form organ systems. An example of an organ system is the cardiovascular system, which is made up of the heart, blood vessels, and blood. The human body consists of a number of organ systems, which work together to create a functional human being.

Answers

1. atom, 2. molecule, 3. cell, 4. tissue, 5. organ, 6. organ system, 7. organism

Homeostasis: Keeping the Balance

Homeostasis – the maintenance of internal conditions within ranges that are compatible with life – is a biological phenomenon whereby the organism's regulatory systems maintain stable conditions within the body in response to changes in the external and internal environment. The compensatory mechanisms involved in homeostasis, which can be defined as structural, functional, and behavioural responses, are vital for the survival of multicellular organisms. The major conditions that are under human homeostatic control are body temperature (depicted in the illustration), blood composition, energy, extracellular fluid composition, and psychology. The inability to maintain homeostasis is referred to as homeostatic imbalance and is associated with many human diseases. If left untreated, homeostatic imbalance may lead to organ damage, organ failure, and ultimately death.

Compensatory mechanism	Response to hot	Response to cold
1. _____	Blood vessels at the skin surface 4. _____ so more heat is lost. This change in blood vessel diameter is called 5. _____	Blood vessels at the skin surface 9. _____, reducing surface heat loss. This change in blood vessel diameter is called 10. _____
2. _____	6. _____ Sweat glands secrete sweat to increase heat loss through evaporation. 7. _____ Hairs flatten out on skin surface, resulting in less air trapped between skin and external environment, and thus less insulation.	11. _____ Small and rapid contractions of skeletal muscle generate heat. 12. _____ Hairs stand up on skin surface, resulting in more air trapped between skin and external environment, and thus more insulation.
3. _____	Stretching out to 8. _____ body surface area.	Curling up to 13. _____ body surface area.

Answers

Control Systems – The Key to Homeostasis: Phenotypic Plasticity vs. Adaptation

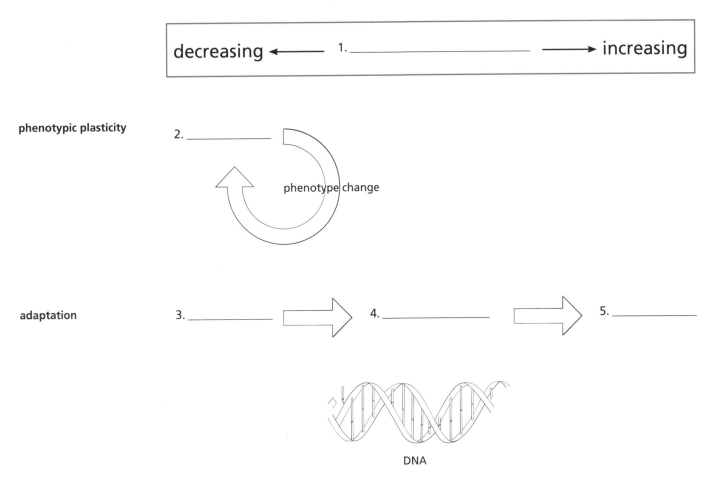

decreasing ← 1. _____ → increasing

phenotypic plasticity

2. _____

phenotype change

adaptation

3. _____ 4. _____ 5. _____

DNA

Phenotypic plasticity is best described as a change of phenotype (the set of observable characteristics in an organism resulting from the interaction between its genetic make-up and the environment leading to a steady state) in response to the environment (internal and external) that is plastic, or dynamic, in nature. Adaptation is defined by a genetic change, often as a result of generations of environmental (internal and external) pressure, which does not respond to immediate changes in the environment. The most obvious example of phenotypic plasticity and adaptation in humans is the skin's response to ultraviolet (UV) radiation. UV radiation is a DNA mutagen, a process that can cause ageing and disease. In response to extended exposure to UV light, the skin increases its production of the pigment melanin, which can absorb UV radiation and minimise DNA damage. This temporary change in phenotype is an example of phenotypic plasticity. On the other hand, there is a direct correlation between human demographics and skin colour/pigmentation. Geographical areas with higher UV exposure generally tend to have darker-skinned populations and vice versa, an occurrence that is thought to have come about as humans migrated to areas of different UV exposure. These permanent differences in human phenotype are defined as genetic adaptation.

A number of environmental pressures can induce phenotypic plasticity and adaptation in humans, such as climate change and alterations in the oxygen content of air; however, genetic adaptation generally takes many generations to occur.

Answers

1. environmental pressure, 2. normality, 3. normality, 4. genetic change, 5. normality

Control Systems – The Key to Homeostasis: Negative Feedback

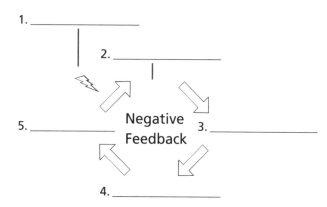

1. _____

2. _____

5. _____

Negative Feedback

3. _____

4. _____

Negative feedback is an automatic regulatory mechanism that minimises disturbances within body systems. Changes to a system under homeostatic control are sensed by the control centre, which in turn activates an effector to oppose or 'negate' the change in order to restore normal physiological conditions. Negative feedback is the primary regulatory mechanism of homeostasis. Systems that are controlled by negative feedback operate across a physiological range, meaning that fluctuations around a set point can occur throughout the day and from day to day. The homeostatic set point for a given system is determined by our environment or activity level, and variation between individuals is influenced by age, gender, genetic factors, and environmental conditions. Regulation of blood glucose levels (depicted in the illustration) is an example of a key homeostatic system controlled by negative feedback.

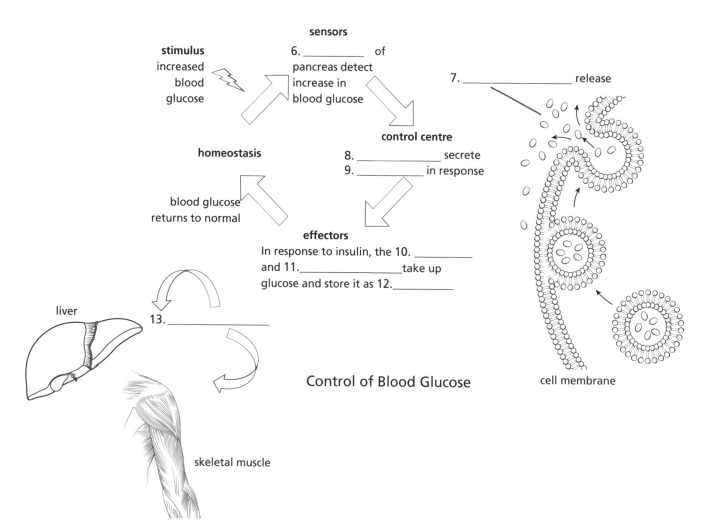

sensors

stimulus
increased
blood
glucose

6. _____ of pancreas detect increase in blood glucose

7. _____ release

control centre

8. _____ secrete
9. _____ in response

homeostasis

blood glucose
returns to normal

effectors
In response to insulin, the 10. _____
and 11._____take up
glucose and store it as 12._____

liver

13. _____

Control of Blood Glucose

cell membrane

skeletal muscle

Answers

Control Systems – Positive Feedback and Feed-Forward

In a positive feedback system, the initial stimulus potentiates a response rather than an opposing effect, as in the negative feedback shown opposite. This feedback mechanism is typical of stress responses in which a process must be quickly acted upon in order to restore homeostasis. This can be explained using an example of the body's response to blood loss, in which a positive feedback loop is essential for rapid blood clotting and cessation of bleeding.

Feed-forward control systems in human physiology are generally anticipatory responses that prepare the body for a pending change in the environment. This can be exemplified by the anticipatory increase in heart rate before physical activity, which is shown in the second diagram.

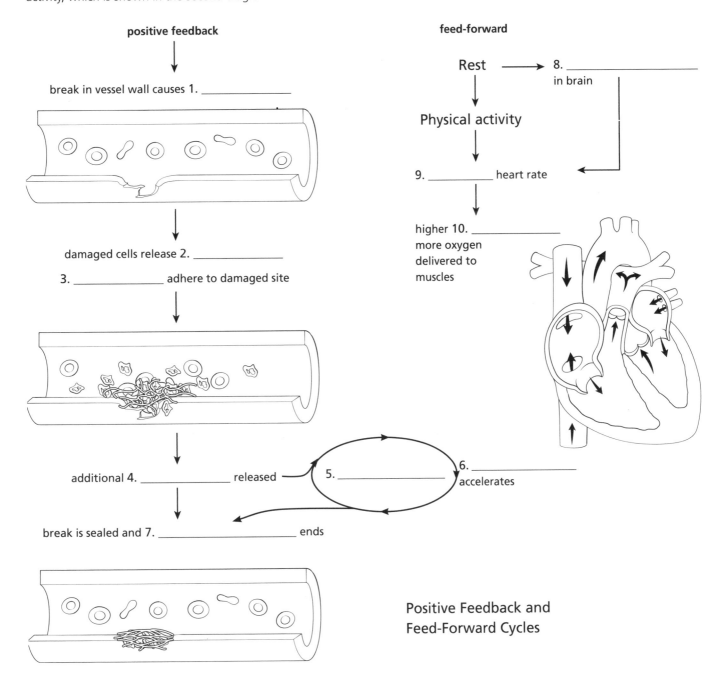

positive feedback

break in vessel wall causes 1. _____

damaged cells release 2. _____

3. _____ adhere to damaged site

additional 4. _____ released

break is sealed and 7. _____ ends

5. _____

6. _____ accelerates

feed-forward

Rest → 8. _____ in brain

Physical activity

9. _____ heart rate

higher 10. _____ more oxygen delivered to muscles

Positive Feedback and Feed-Forward Cycles

Answers

1. bleeding, 2. clotting agents, 3. platelets, 4. clotting agents, 5. positive feedback cycle, 6. clotting, 7. positive feedback, 8. anticipatory response, 9. increased, 10. cardiac output

Cell Structure and the Cell Membrane

For cells to function in an organism, the inside of the cell (cytoplasm) must be separate from the outside. A phospholipid bilayer forms the cell membrane, comprising hydrophilic phospholipid heads and hydrophobic fatty acid tails; thus, water and its solutes are in contact with both sides of the phospholipid bilayer but cannot pass through it. Integral membrane proteins span the phospholipid bilayer, allowing hydrophilic and charged molecules to move into or out of the cell. Phospholipid membranes must be fluid enough to allow membrane-bound proteins to be moved into and out of the membrane while remaining solid enough to prevent leaks. Proteins and lipids are sensitive to temperature, so membrane function changes as an animal's body temperature changes. Some animals replace their lipids and proteins as they acclimatise to changing ambient temperatures. Animals near their thermal maximum risk increases in body temperature that can irreversibly alter protein and lipid structure/function.

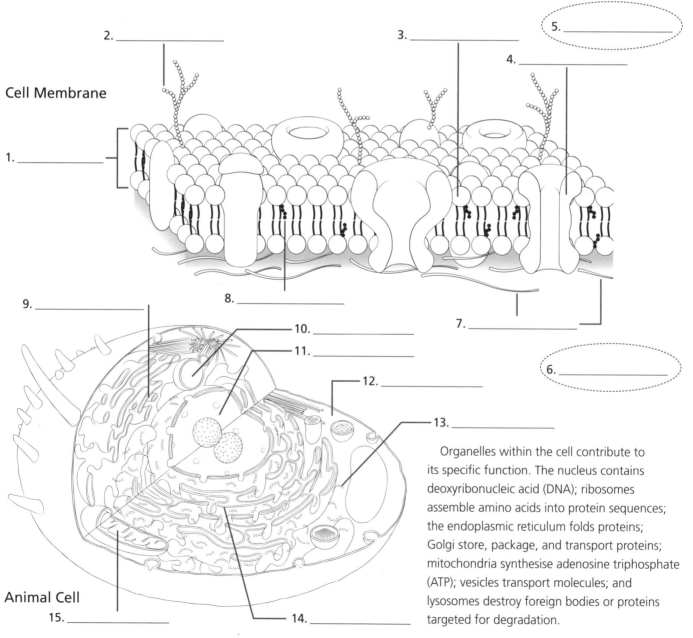

2. _____

3. _____

5. _____

4. _____

Cell Membrane

1. _____

8. _____

7. _____

9. _____

10. _____

11. _____

12. _____

6. _____

13. _____

Organelles within the cell contribute to its specific function. The nucleus contains deoxyribonucleic acid (DNA); ribosomes assemble amino acids into protein sequences; the endoplasmic reticulum folds proteins; Golgi store, package, and transport proteins; mitochondria synthesise adenosine triphosphate (ATP); vesicles transport molecules; and lysosomes destroy foreign bodies or proteins targeted for degradation.

Animal Cell

15. _____

14. _____

Answers

Cell Division

Cell division is the process by which new cells are created. Duplicate copies are made of the genetic information in a cell, and each new daughter cell receives one copy. Four steps in the cell cycle are necessary for cell division: gap (growth phase) 1, DNA synthesis (replication), gap 2, and mitosis. Interphase encompasses gap 1, DNA synthesis, and gap 2 phases of the cell cycle. The next stage of mitosis includes prophase, during which chromosomes condense, centrioles and spindles form, and the nuclear envelope dissolves. During metaphase, centrioles migrate to the poles and chromosomes line up on the equator. During anaphase, sister chromatids separate and migrate to the poles. Lastly, during telophase, the nuclear envelope re-forms, chromosomes decondense, and cytokinesis separates the cells. The cell cycle is regulated at each step with checkpoints to ensure no errors are made. Cell division can be initiated by the cell's 'internal clock' or by environmental stimuli. Unregulated cell division can lead to cancer. In some circumstances where energy, oxygen, or water are limiting, cells can undergo metabolic arrest. The cell cycle ceases until conditions improve, and some animals, such as brine shrimp, can be in metabolic arrest for years.

Mitosis, or Somatic Cell Division

phases of cell division

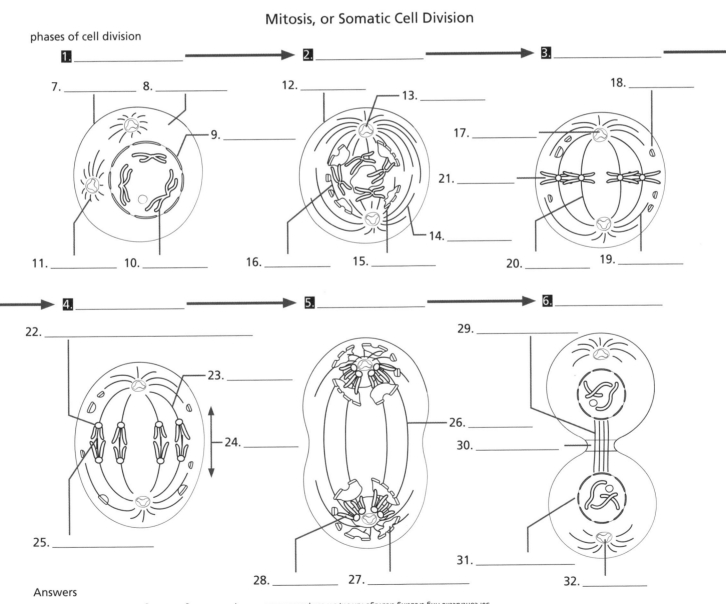

1. _____

7. _____ 8. _____

9. _____

11. _____ 10. _____

2. _____

12. _____

13. _____

17. _____

21. _____

14. _____

16. _____ 15. _____

3. _____

18. _____

19. _____

20. _____

4. _____

22. _____

23. _____

24. _____

25. _____

5. _____

26. _____

28. _____ 27. _____

6. _____

29. _____

30. _____

31. _____

32. _____

Answers

1. prophase, 2. prometaphase, 3. metaphase, 4. anaphase, 5. telophase, 6. cytokinesis, 7. intact nuclear envelope, 8. cytoplasm, 9. intact nuclear envelope, 10. condensing chromosome with two chromatids held together at kinetochore, 11. developing bipolar spindle, 12. cell membrane, 13. spindle pole, 14. nuclear envelope fragment, 15. polar microtubule, 16. kinetochore microtubule, 17. spindle pole, 18. nuclear envelope fragment, 19. polar microtubule, 20. kinetochore microtubule, 21. stationary chromosomes aligned at equator of spindle, 22. separated chromatid being pulled towards the pole, 23. shortening kinetochore microtubule, 24. increasing separation of the poles, 25. polar microtubule, 26. polar microtubule, 27. nuclear envelope re-forming around individual pund unravelling chromosomes, 28. unravelling chromosomes, 29. constricted remains of polar spindle microtubules, 30. contractile ring creating cleavage furrow, 31. completed nuclear envelope surrounding unravelling chromosomes, 32. centriole pair

DNA Replication

Deoxyribonucleic acid (DNA) is the coding molecule for the genetic information within eukaryotic cells. It is a double helix structure composed of polynucleotides of cytosine (C), guanine (G), adenine (A), thymine (T), deoxyribose, and phosphates. These strands are antiparallel (3' to 5' and 5' to 3'). Enzymes catalyse the process of DNA replication, from opening the strands with initiator proteins to bringing in new nucleotides to complement the strand using DNA polymerase. If a complement mistake is made, replication has to be stopped and corrected. The new DNA strand is assembled in the 5' to 3' direction, so the 5' to 3' strand is assembled continuously (leading strand) and the 3' to 5' strand is assembled discontinuously (lagging strand). The lagging strand is synthesised by short ribonucleic acid (RNA) primers; DNA segments on RNA primers are called Okazaki fragments.

Errors in DNA sequences can be caused by misreads during replication or by any number of environmental factors, such as temperature, radiation, oxidation, mutagenic chemicals, etc. Mutations in the DNA sequence can be deleterious, beneficial, or have no effect. Mutations in DNA are the source of variability in populations of organisms and are under selection pressure. Mutation rates have been used to estimate divergence times among species.

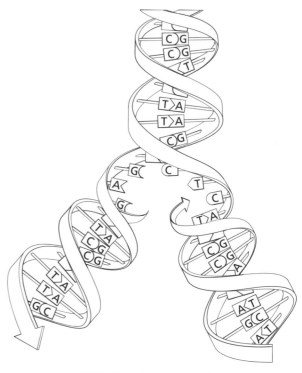

DNA Replication Split

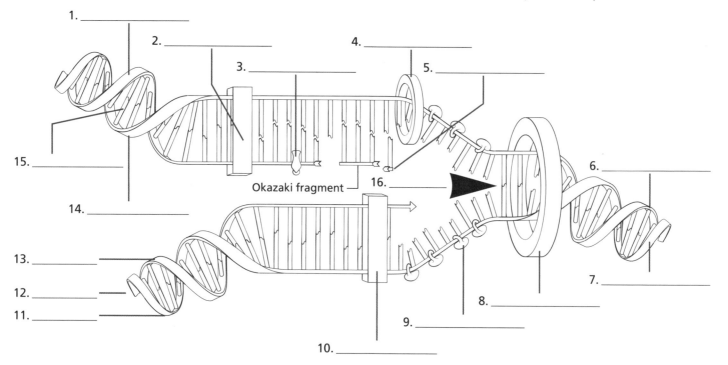

Okazaki fragment

Transcription and Translation

Transcription is the process by which DNA message is copied to RNA; the RNA message is then translated at the ribosomes. The messenger RNA (mRNA) copy is made in the nucleus where the DNA is housed. The nucleotide bases are the same as in DNA, except uracil replaces thymine. In the cell's cytoplasm, ribosomes read mRNA and assemble the appropriate sequence of amino acids. The AUG sequence (methionine) is the start codon, and as the reading frame shifts along the mRNA strand, amino acids coded for are attached in sequence. Stop codons (UAA, UAG, and UGA) end the sequence. With 20 amino acids involved, proteins with as few as five amino acid sequences could have more than 3 million different combinations making up that protein. This enables tremendous diversity of protein structures.

Transcription and translation are only the first two steps in making a functional protein. Once the amino acid sequence has been assembled, other molecules may be added to the protein, and the protein has to be folded. Proteins can be stored, packaged for transport, or inserted into the cell membrane. Activity of proteins depends on the conformation of the protein and can be altered to modify function.

Protein Structures

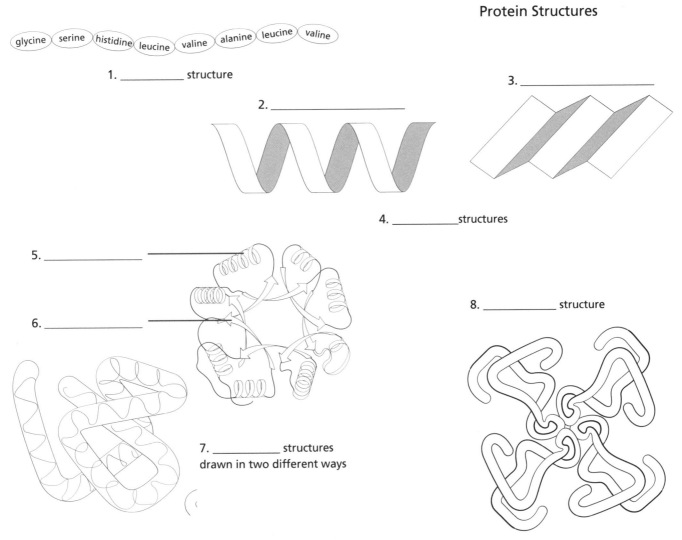

glycine — serine — histidine — leucine — valine — alanine — leucine — valine

1. _____ structure

2. _____

3. _____

4. _____ structures

5. _____ _____

6. _____

7. _____ structures drawn in two different ways

8. _____ structure

Answers

Movement Across the Cell Membrane

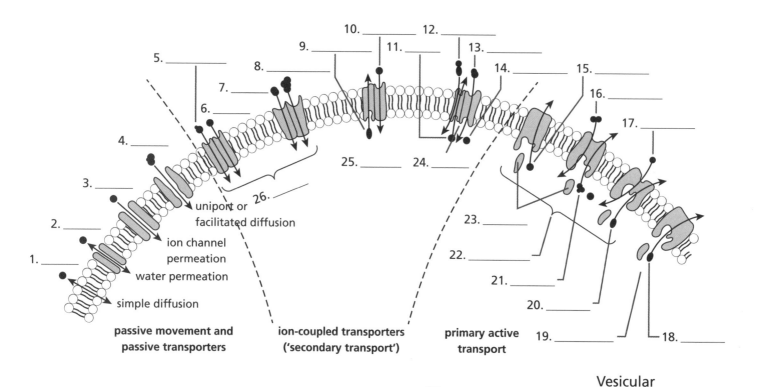

5. _____
4. _____
3. _____
2. _____
1. _____

6. _____
7. _____
8. _____
9. _____
10. _____
11. _____
12. _____
13. _____
14. _____
15. _____
16. _____
17. _____

uniport or
facilitated diffusion

ion channel
permeation

water permeation

simple diffusion

25. _____
26. _____
24. _____

23. _____
22. _____
21. _____
20. _____
19. _____
18. _____

**passive movement and
passive transporters**

**ion-coupled transporters
('secondary transport')**

**primary active
transport**

Since cell membranes are made of a phospholipid bilayer, they are hydrophobic and are not permeable to charged molecules. Integral membrane proteins form pores and channels through which large hydrophilic molecules and charged molecules can move. Gases such as oxygen and carbon dioxide can move passively across cell membranes down their partial pressure gradient. Lipid-soluble molecules can also diffuse through membranes. Water moves down its concentration gradient through aquaporins. Ions move down their electrochemical gradients through ion channels. Amino acids, glucose, urea, proteins, and other large molecules move down their concentration gradients through channels or through facilitated diffusion. Large molecules can be moved across membranes through secondary transport mechanisms, in which another molecule's gradient provides the energy to move that molecule. Co-transport can be in the same direction (symport), in the opposite direction (antiport), or both. Ions can be moved against their electrochemical gradient by primary active transport through P-ATPases (in cell membranes) or V-ATPases (in vacuoles). Molecules can be brought across a cell membrane through a vesicle formed by pinocytosis, endocytosis, or exocytosis. Because the cell membrane forms a vesicle, the molecule never actually passes through the phospholipid bilayer.

Vesicular Transport

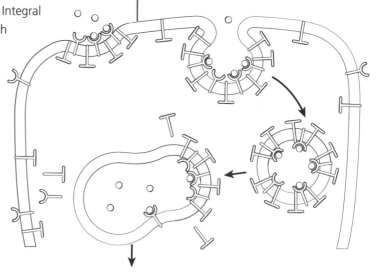

27. _____

28. _____
29. _____
30. _____

Sodium-Potassium Pump

Normally, sodium (Na+) concentration is high outside the cell and potassium (K+) is high inside the cell. In all cells, both sodium and potassium move down their electrochemical gradients whenever sodium channels or potassium channels are open. Sodium-potassium pumps (ATPase) are used to move both sodium and potassium against their electrochemical gradients. The sodium-potassium pump is, therefore, critical for establishing a voltage potential across a cell membrane. The sodium-potassium pump moves three sodium ions out and two potassium ions in, so it is an electrogenic pump (generating an electrical charge gradient). Sodium transport to establish an electrochemical gradient down which sodium can move is commonly used for secondary active transport to move other molecules across cell membranes. In cells that are permeable to water, the sodium-potassium pump may be used to control the volume of the cell. In circumstances where adenosine triphosphate (ATP) is not available, such as during anoxia or ischaemia, the sodium-potassium pump will fail to maintain the electrochemical gradients for sodium and potassium. This leads to depolarisation of excitable cells without subsequent repolarisation.

Sodium and Potassium Diffusion

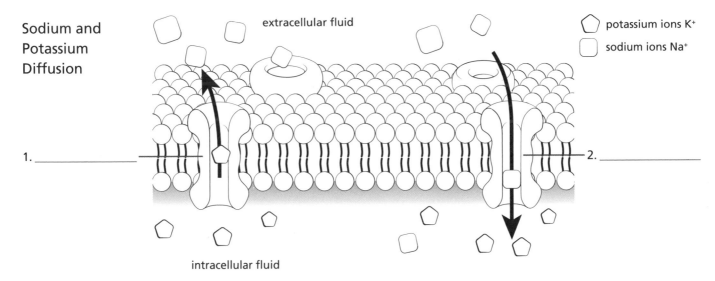

⬠ potassium ions K+

▢ sodium ions Na+

1. _____

2. _____

Sodium-Potassium Pump

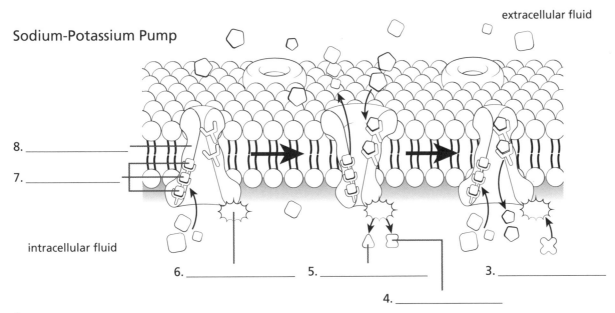

8. _____

7. _____

6. _____

5. _____

3. _____

4. _____

Answers

Membrane Potential

Selectively permeable cell membranes, in combination with ion channels and pumps, allow for the generation of a charge potential across a cell membrane. Typically, sodium (Na$^+$) and chloride (Cl$^-$) concentrations are high outside cells, and potassium (K$^+$) concentration is high inside the cell. Sodium-potassium pumps maintain this electrochemical gradient across the cell membrane. Membrane potentials in excitable cells can be reversed during an action potential. At resting membrane potential, the permeability of the cell membrane to potassium exceeds its permeability to sodium. Once a depolarising threshold for voltage-gated sodium channels is reached, the permeability to sodium becomes much higher than the permeability to potassium. Sodium moves down its electrochemical gradient, further depolarising the cell. Once the cell is depolarised, voltage-gated potassium channels open, allowing potassium to move down its electrochemical gradient (outside the cell at this point), and thereby repolarising the cell. The sodium-potassium pump returns these ions back to their steady-state levels. The membrane potential of a cell is determined by the concentration gradient of charged ions inside and outside the cell, and by the permeability of the cell membrane to those ions. The Goldman equation describes the membrane potential produced by potassium, sodium, and chloride ions as follows:

Charged molecules cannot cross a lipid bilayer except through integral membrane protein channels. Whether a channel is open determines the
1. _____ for that ion across the membrane.

$$V_m = \frac{RT}{F} \ln \left(\frac{p_k [K^+]_o + p_{Na} [Na^+]_o + p_{Cl} [Cl^-]_i}{p_k [K^+]_i + p_{Na} [Na^+]_i + p_{Cl} [Cl^-]_o} \right)$$

The Goldman equation describes membrane potential based on ion concentration and permeability.

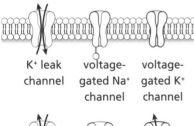

Excitable Cell

Ions move down their electrochemical gradient.
2. _____ is actively transported out of the cell; this creates a large inwards diffusional gradient.

3. _____ has a small outwards diffusional gradient and is actively transported into the cell.

Chloride diffuses into and out of the cell depending on 4. _____

Resting membrane potential

K$^+$ leak channel   voltage-gated Na$^+$ channel   voltage-gated K$^+$ channel

Falling phase

P_K 5. ____ P_{Na}

7. _____ much larger than 8. _____

Rising phase

Recovery

P_{Na} 6. ____ P_K

9. ____ larger than 10. ____

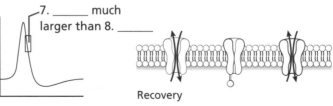
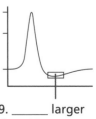

Receptors

Receptor proteins on the surface of cell membranes are critical to receiving signalling information from the cell's environment. Four primary types of receptors for chemical signals include ligand-gated channels, G-protein coupled receptors, enzyme-linked receptors, and intracellular receptors. Binding sites on these receptors can be blocked by competitive chemical signals or may lose their affinity for agonists by conformational changes to the protein itself. Touch reception is achieved through mechanosensors, such as the mechanoreceptors in mammalian skin. Light reception is achieved through photoreceptors and heat through thermosensors.

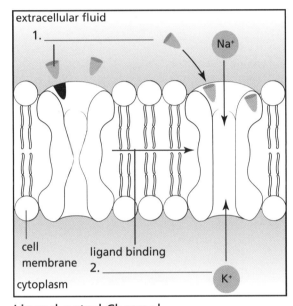

Ligand-gated Channel

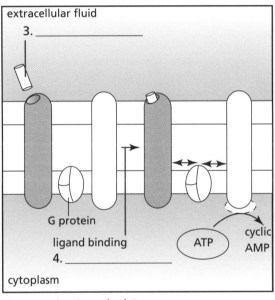

G-protein Coupled Receptors

For labels 2, 4, 6, and 8 write what effect ligand binding has.

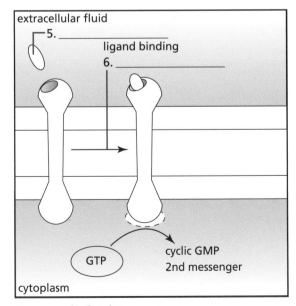

Enzyme-linked Receptor

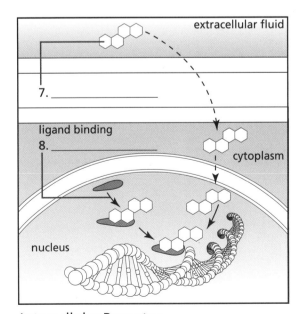

Intracellular Receptor

Answers

Cellular Communication, Including Axonal Transport

Cellular communication occurs through chemical and electrical signalling pathways. Communication pathways may be short, such as autocrine signalling, where the cell produces signals to which receptors on its own surface respond; paracrine signalling to neighbouring cells; or where gap junctions electrically couple two adjacent cells. Chemical signalling across synapses may involve neurotransmitters moving micrometres. Communication pathways may be longer when chemical signals are widely dispersed through the bloodstream or when electrical signals travel down long axons. For some animals, cells receive signals, such as pheromones, that have been dispersed several kilometres in the environment.

  Cells will respond to signals only if they have the receptors for that particular signal. If a signal is persistent or noxious, sometimes the receptor will inactivate and the communication will cease. Communication between cells requires a signal to be sent, a signal to be sensed (receptors), and a response to be elicited. Therefore, there are multiple ways cellular communication can be modulated. The strength of the signal can be increased or decreased, and the receptors can be activated, inactivated, removed from the cell surface, or otherwise altered. Finally, the signal can be received but not elicit any response from the cell if downstream signalling pathways are interrupted.

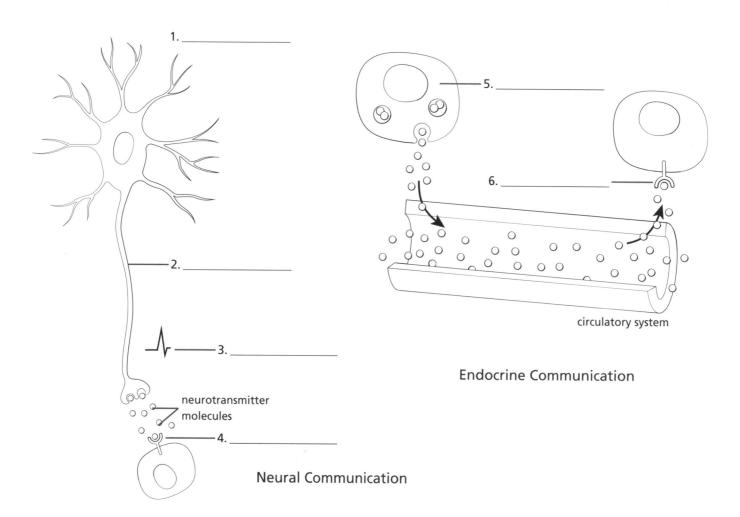

1. _____

2. _____

3. _____

neurotransmitter molecules

4. _____

Neural Communication

5. _____

6. _____

circulatory system

Endocrine Communication

Answers

7. _____

neural synapse

8. _____

9. _____

10. _____

11. _____

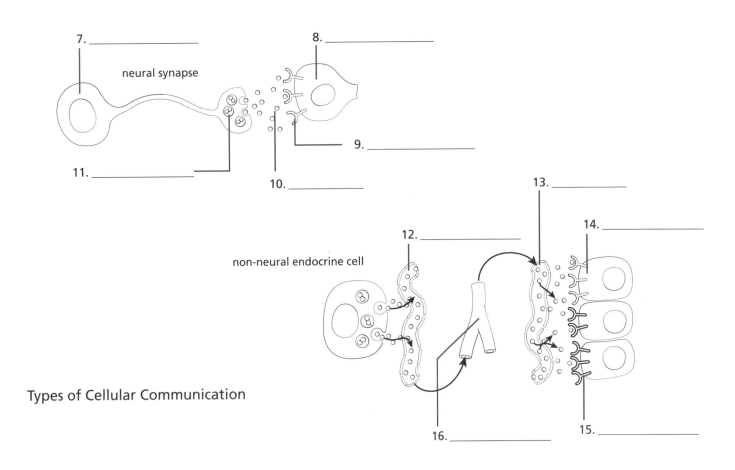

13. _____

14. _____

12. _____

non-neural endocrine cell

16. _____

15. _____

Types of Cellular Communication

18. _____

17. _____

neuroendocrine cell

19. _____

20. _____

21. _____

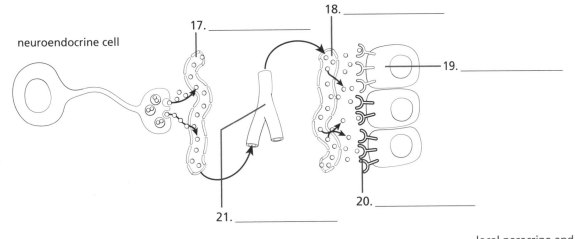

local paracrine and autocrine signals

22. _____

23. _____

24. _____

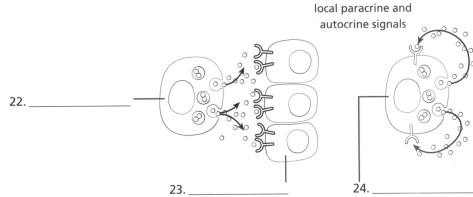

Answers

Cellular Communication, Including Axonal Transport

Communication within organisms can be across short distances (between adjacent cells) to long distances (kilometres between organisms). The principles of communication are the same: a signal is sent and is only received if appropriate receptors can accept and interpret that signal.

Communication Within and Between Organisms

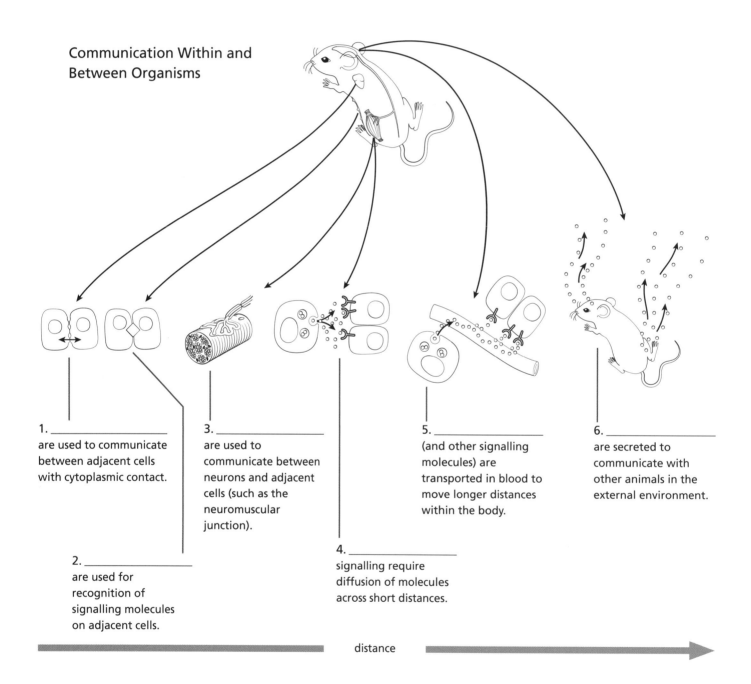

1. _____
are used to communicate between adjacent cells with cytoplasmic contact.

2. _____
are used for recognition of signalling molecules on adjacent cells.

3. _____
are used to communicate between neurons and adjacent cells (such as the neuromuscular junction).

4. _____
signalling require diffusion of molecules across short distances.

5. _____
(and other signalling molecules) are transported in blood to move longer distances within the body.

6. _____
are secreted to communicate with other animals in the external environment.

distance

Answers

1. gap junctions, 2. cell adhesion molecules, 3. neurotransmitters, 4. paracrine and autocrine, 5. hormones, 6. pheromones

Energy Production and Adenosine Triphosphate (ATP)

Adenosine triphosphate (ATP) is the energy 'currency' used by cells to carry out cellular processes. Chemical energy – stored as fats, carbohydrates, or proteins – is converted into chemical energy in the form of ATP in the mitochondria through the process of cellular respiration. ATP production uses the energy released from breaking carbon bonds through glycolysis and the citric acid cycle (or Kreb's cycle) to establish a proton gradient (proton motive force) in the inner-membrane space of the mitochondria. Protons move down their electrochemical gradient through the action of the enzyme ATP synthase, which catalyses the attachment of inorganic phosphate (P_i) to adenosine diphosphate (ADP).

If protons move down their electrochemical gradient through an alternative pathway such as uncoupling protein (UCP1), ATP is not synthesised and the energy used to move those protons against their electrochemical gradient is 'wasted.' Each time energy is converted from one form to another, some of that energy is lost as heat. Some animals take advantage of the UCP1 alternative pathway as a mechanism to generate heat. This is an important process for animals requiring high rates of heat production, such as human infants and other newborn mammals, who lose heat to their environment quickly, as well as hibernators generating heat during bouts of arousal.

Cellular Respiration in a Mitochondrion

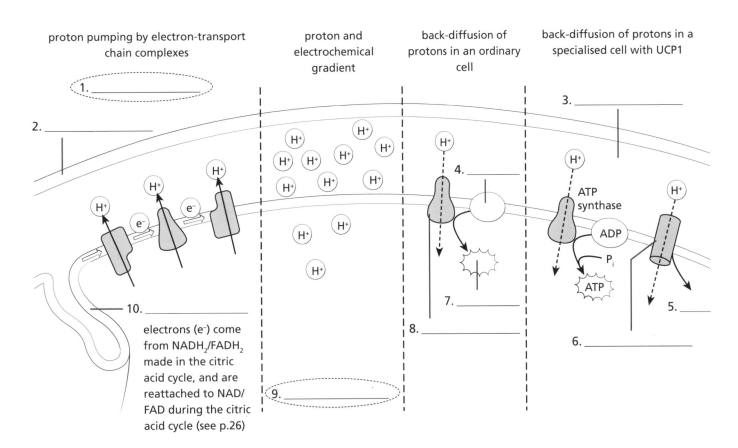

proton pumping by electron-transport chain complexes

proton and electrochemical gradient

back-diffusion of protons in an ordinary cell

back-diffusion of protons in a specialised cell with UCP1

1. _____

2. _____

3. _____

4. _____

H^+

ATP synthase

ADP

P_i

ATP

5. _____

6. _____

7. _____

8. _____

10. _____

electrons (e^-) come from $NADH_2/FADH_2$ made in the citric acid cycle, and are reattached to NAD/FAD during the citric acid cycle (see p.26)

9. _____

Answers

Aerobic/Anaerobic Metabolism

Metabolism refers to the chemical transformations within an organism. Energy is stored in carbon bonds and is made available to carry out physiological work through aerobic or anaerobic metabolic pathways that produce adenosine triphosphate (ATP). Glycolysis (lysis of glucose molecules) does not require oxygen for ATP production. Within the glycolytic pathway, glucose is broken down through a series of enzymatic reactions to pyruvic acid. If oxygen is present (aerobic metabolism), pyruvic acid can be further broken down to acetyl coenzyme A (acetyl-CoA) and enter the citric acid cycle, where guanosine diphosphate (GDP) is phosphorylated to guanosine triphosphate (GTP), and flavin adenine dinucleotide (FAD) and nicotinamide adenine dinucleotide (NAD) are reduced to $FADH_2$ and $NADH_2$, respectively. The energy in these molecules is used to establish the proton motive force used to generate ATP in the mitochondria.

If no oxygen is present, pyruvic acid will be converted to lactic acid. Lactic acid is removed from the cell or reconverted to pyruvic acid. Acetyl-CoA can also come from fat oxidation. The ratio of carbon dioxide (CO_2) produced to oxygen (O_2) consumed, referred to as the respiratory exchange ratio (RER), provides valuable insight into an animal's metabolic rate and fuel source. The RER will vary with breakdown of fats, carbohydrates, or proteins as the source of acetyl-CoA.

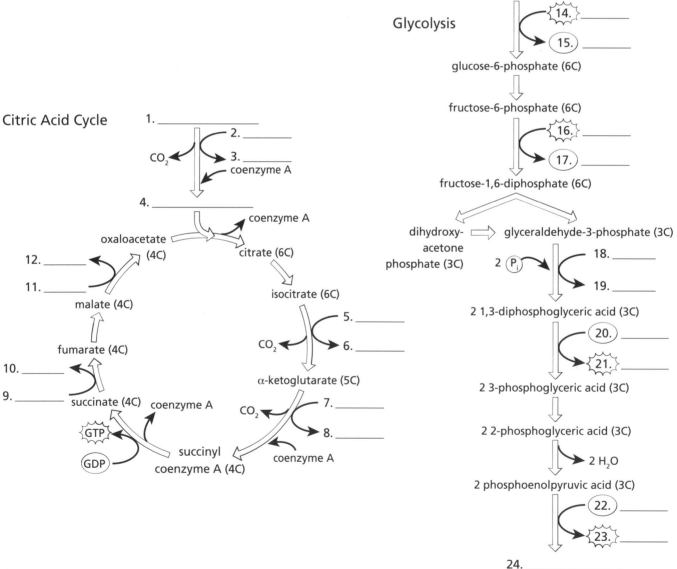

Glycolysis

13. _____

14. _____

15. _____

glucose-6-phosphate (6C)

fructose-6-phosphate (6C)

16. _____

17. _____

fructose-1,6-diphosphate (6C)

dihydroxy-acetone phosphate (3C) ⟹ glyceraldehyde-3-phosphate (3C)

2 P_i

18. _____

19. _____

2 1,3-diphosphoglyceric acid (3C)

20. _____

21. _____

2 3-phosphoglyceric acid (3C)

2 2-phosphoglyceric acid (3C)

2 H_2O

2 phosphoenolpyruvic acid (3C)

22. _____

23. _____

24. _____

Citric Acid Cycle

1. _____

2. _____

3. _____
coenzyme A

CO_2

4. _____

coenzyme A

oxaloacetate (4C)

citrate (6C)

12. _____

11. _____

malate (4C)

isocitrate (6C)

5. _____

CO_2

6. _____

α-ketoglutarate (5C)

fumarate (4C)

10. _____

9. _____

succinate (4C)   coenzyme A

CO_2

7. _____

8. _____

coenzyme A

GTP

GDP

succinyl coenzyme A (4C)

Composition and Function of Blood (1)

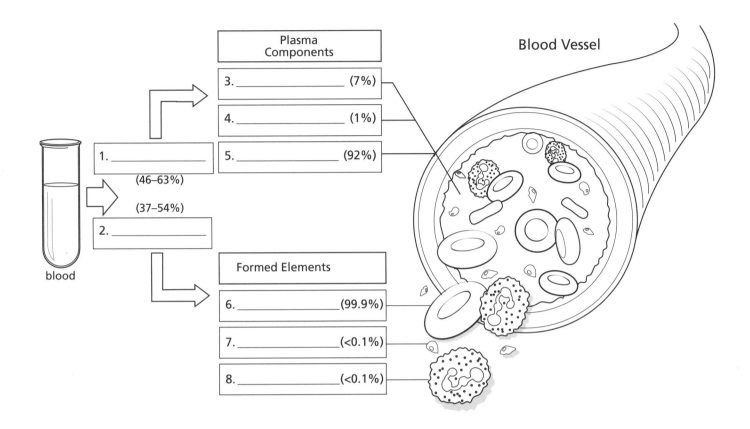

The cardiovascular system is made up of the heart, blood vessels, and its fluid component – blood. The average adult male has 5-6 litres of circulating blood, with females having around 1 litre less; this difference in blood volume primarily reflects differences in average body size. Blood can be divided into plasma, which constitutes 46–63 per cent of the blood volume, and formed elements, which make up the rest. The percentage of whole blood that is made up of formed elements is referred to as the 'haematocrit'. It is the erythrocytes, more commonly referred to as red blood cells (RBCs), that give blood its deep red colour; this is because the RBCs account for 99.9 per cent of the formed elements in whole blood. The remaining fraction of the formed elements is made up of platelets and white blood cells. The plasma fraction of blood consists mostly of water that contains plasma proteins and other solutes such as electrolytes, organic nutrients, and waste products.

Answers

1. plasma, 2. formed elements, 3. plasma proteins, 4. other solutes, 5. water, 6. red blood cells (RBCs), 7. platelets, 8. white blood cells

Composition and Function of Blood (2)

The cardiovascular systems is characterised by a vast network of arteries, capillaries, and veins, which supply the approximately 75 trillion cells of the human body with a ready flow of blood for the purposes of transport, protection, and regulation. The constant supply of blood to all core and peripheral tissues is essential for the transport of oxygen, nutrients, water, and biologically active molecules to tissues, and the removal of carbon dioxide, excess water, and waste to the appropriate organs for excretion. Blood also plays a central role in the protection against toxins, pathogens, and fluid loss as a result of injury. The key components of this protective function are the white blood cells, platelets, and the circulating protein fibrinogen. The final major function of blood is the regulation of interstitial fluid pH and ion composition and body temperature.

Vasculature of the Skin

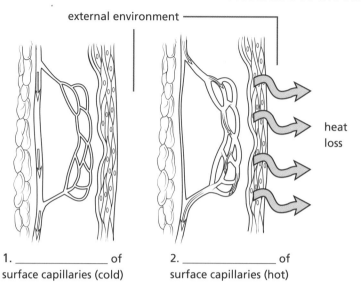

external environment

heat loss

1. _____ of surface capillaries (cold)

2. _____ of surface capillaries (hot)

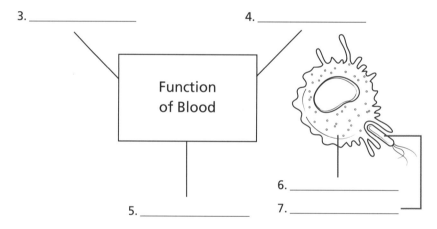

3. _____   4. _____

Function of Blood

6. _____

7. _____

5. _____

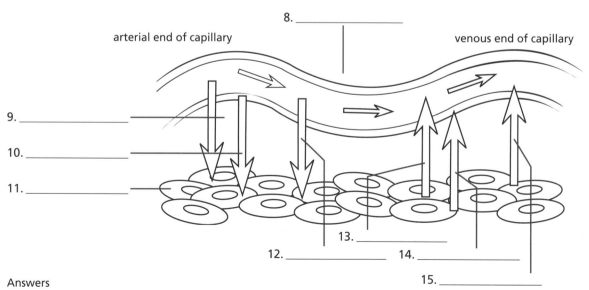

8. _____

arterial end of capillary   venous end of capillary

9. _____

10. _____

11. _____

13. _____

12. _____   14. _____

15. _____

Answers

Cellular Components of Blood and Plasma Proteins

Blood is made up of two broad types of cells – red blood cells (RBCs) and white blood cells (WBCs) – and specialised cellular fragments called platelets. RBCs are produced in the bone marrow and are the most numerous cells in the human body. Their shape is that of a biconcave disc, and they are essential for the transport of oxygen in blood. WBCs, or leukocytes, are much less numerous and are produced in the bone marrow and lymphatic tissues. They defend the body from viruses, bacteria, toxins, and other pathogenic agents. There are five major types of WBCs: neutrophils, eosinophils, basophils, monocytes, and lymphocytes. Platelets are the smallest structural units in the blood. They are formed in the bone marrow from the cytoplasm of giant cells known as megakaryocytes.

1. _____

2. _____

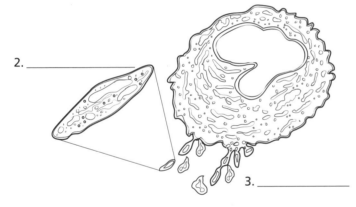

3. _____

Plasma Proteins	
4. _____	Maintain osmotic pressure of plasma and transport molecules such as lipids and hormones
5. _____	Transport ions, hormones, lipids; also have an immune function
6. _____	Major clotting component
7. _____	Proenzymes, enzymes, hormones, and cytokines

Blood Cells

8. _____

9. _____

10. _____

11. _____

12. _____

13. _____

Formation of Blood Elements

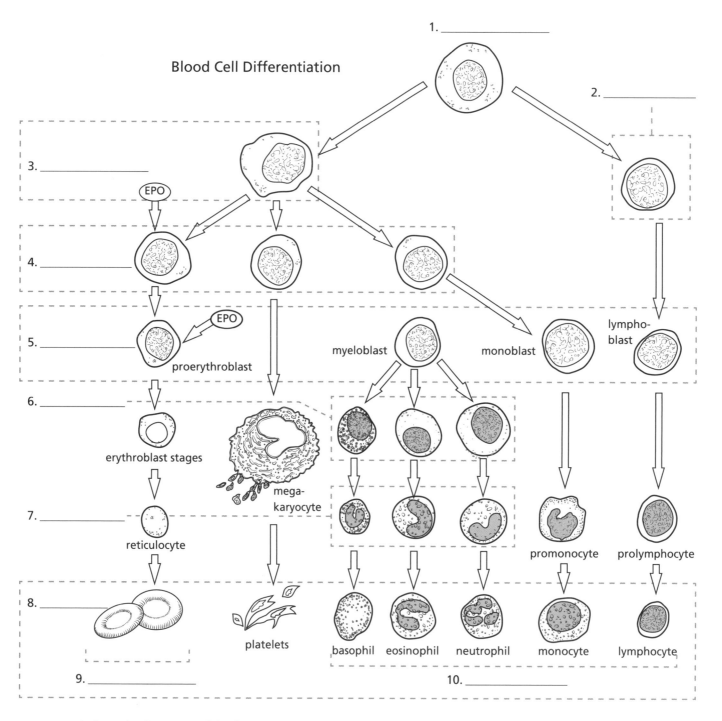

Blood Cell Differentiation

1. _____

2. _____

3. _____

4. _____

5. _____ proerythroblast

EPO

6. _____ erythroblast stages

myeloblast   monoblast   lympho-blast

mega-karyocyte

7. _____ reticulocyte

promonocyte   prolymphocyte

8. _____

platelets   basophil   eosinophil   neutrophil   monocyte   lymphocyte

9. _____

10. _____

Haematopoiesis, or the formation of the formed elements of blood, is a very complex process that involves multiple rounds of cellular differentiation. It begins with division of the haemocytoblast, or haematopoietic stem cell, which gives rise to myeloid or lymphoid stem cells. After each round of differentiation, the myeloid or lymphoid stem cells become more specialised and limited in their functional capabilities. Lymphoid stem cells go on to produce the various types of lymphocytes, whereas myeloid stem cells produce progenitor cells, which form all the classes of cells that make up the formed elements of blood.

Answers

Function of Red Blood Cells

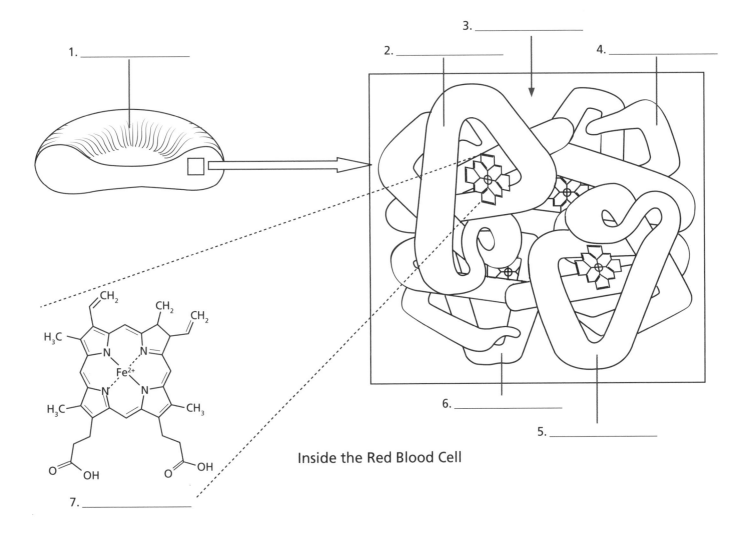

Inside the Red Blood Cell

1. _____

2. _____

3. _____

4. _____

5. _____

6. _____

7. _____

Red blood cells (RBCs) account for roughly 25 trillion, or one-third, of all cells in the human body and are among the most specialised. Each RBC is a biconcave disc, a shape that serves to increase the cell's surface area and enables it to bend, flex, and squeeze into tight capillaries. During their formation, RBCs lose most of their organelles, including their nuclei, retaining only their cytoskeleton and molecules of haemoglobin (Hb).

Hb accounts for more than 95 per cent of protein inside RBCs and is responsible for the cell's ability to transport oxygen and carbon dioxide. Each Hb molecule has a complex structure made up of four protein chains (two alpha and two beta chains), each of which contains a single molecule of haeme. Haeme is an iron ion-containing molecule that can readily bind to oxygen (O_2). When bound with O_2, haemoglobin is referred to as oxyhaemoglobin. At the peripheral tissues, oxygen dissociates with haemoglobin to form deoxyhaemoglobin. Hb molecules can also pick up carbon dioxide (CO_2) to form carbaminohaemoglobin via their alpha and beta chains, which is released at the lungs for gas exchange.

Control of Red Blood Cell Production and Blood Groups

Red blood cells (RBCs) have a life span of around 120 days, after which they will have travelled more than 620 miles (1,000 kilometres). Because RBCs are void of most of their organelles, they are incapable of protein synthesis and, thus, cell division. This means that the human body requires a constant supply of RBCs. RBC production, or erythropoiesis, begins with the generation of proerythroblasts in the bone marrow. After around four to five days of differentiation, the cells – now referred to as normoblasts – eject their nuclei to form reticulocytes. Reticulocytes contain around 80 per cent of the haemoglobin present in RBCs, yet they remain in the bone marrow for another two days until they form fully mature RBCs, which then enter the circulation.

Blood type is determined by the presence or absence of specific cell surface proteins (called antigens) on RBCs. Although RBCs have many kinds of antigens, there are two that are of particular importance: antigen A and antigen B. The human immune system ignores 'self' antigens. However, blood contains antibodies that will attack the antigens on RBCs with foreign antigens, thus explaining why knowing someone's blood type before a blood transfusion is vital.

Erythrocyte Maturation

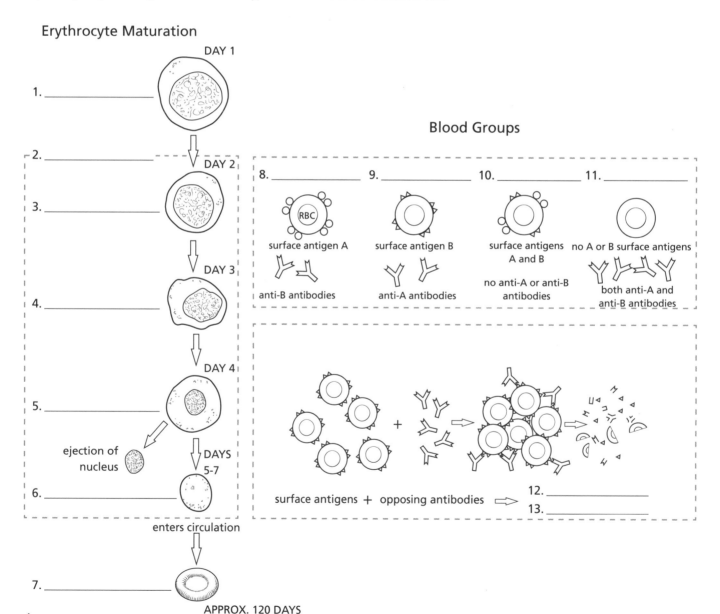

DAY 1

1. _____

2. _____

3. _____

DAY 2

4. _____

DAY 3

5. _____

ejection of nucleus

6. _____

DAYS 5-7

enters circulation

7. _____

APPROX. 120 DAYS

Blood Groups

8. _____   9. _____   10. _____   11. _____

RBC

surface antigen A

surface antigen B

surface antigens A and B

no A or B surface antigens

anti-B antibodies

anti-A antibodies

no anti-A or anti-B antibodies

both anti-A and anti-B antibodies

surface antigens + opposing antibodies ⟹

12. _____

13. _____

Haemostasis and Clotting Factors

Haemostasis is a biological sequence that functions to prevent excessive blood loss following damage to blood vessels and, at the same time, provides a scaffold to aid tissue repair. The process consists of three phases: the vascular phase, platelet phase, and coagulation phase.

Following damage to a vessel wall, its smooth muscle fibres immediately contract. This vascular spasm reduces the vessel diameter and can slow or even stop blood flow through the damaged vessel. Damage to the vessel wall stimulates cells within the vessel wall to release factors that allow platelets to adhere. This process occurs within 15 seconds after injury and leads to a homeostatic positive feedback cycle that stimulates further platelet aggregation and the formation of a platelet plug. The coagulation phase, or blood clotting, begins around 30 seconds after the initial injury. This phase is a complex sequence of steps that results in conversion of circulating fibrinogen into fibrin by the enzyme thrombin. A fibrin network is created over the platelet plug, trapping more platelets and other blood cells and effectively sealing the damaged area.

Phases following Vessel Injury

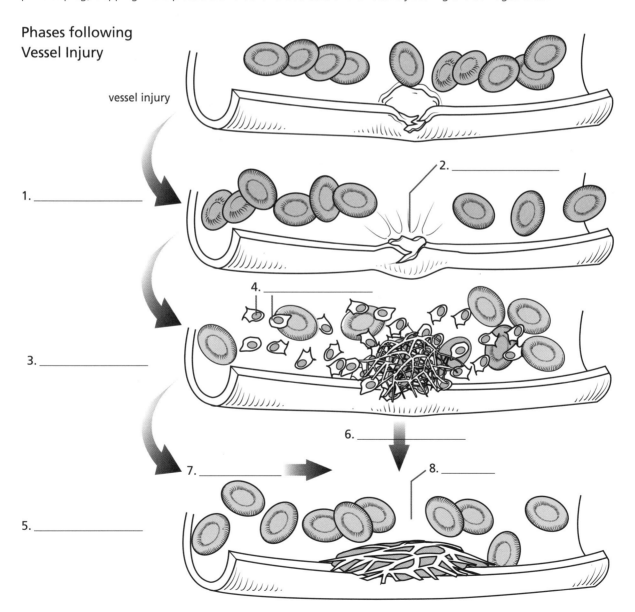

vessel injury

1. _____

2. _____

3. _____

4. _____

5. _____

6. _____

7. _____

8. _____

Answers

1. vascular phase, 2. vascular spasm, 3. platelet phase, 4. platelets, 5. coagulation phase, 6. thrombin, 7. fibrinogen, 8. fibrin

Organisation of the Nervous System

The nervous system (NS) is an organ system responsible for receiving and processing sensory information, motor control, learning, and regulation of internal organs and systems. The NS is composed of non-excitable specialised cells (glia), excitable nerve cells (neurons), and junctions (synapses). It can be split into two major divisions: the central nervous system (CNS), comprising the brain and spinal cord, and the peripheral nervous system (PNS), comprising afferent (sensory) and efferent (motor and autonomic) neurons. Neurons convey information along tracts and pathways, operating via excitation or inhibition depending on the type of neuron/synapse. The connections between neurons and also their immediate environments are important in determining their function.

The PNS reacts to both external and internal stimuli, conveying changes to the CNS via afferent sensory neurons. Communication from the CNS in response to information received is via efferent neurons, targeted typically to muscles or glands.

The CNS is a site of sensory information processing and integration with memories to produce an appropriate response to stimuli received. Sensory, motor, and association centres in the brain and spinal cord perform CNS functions. These centres are organised in a hierarchy: higher centres are linked to the lower centres, which are subsequently in direct communication with the PNS.

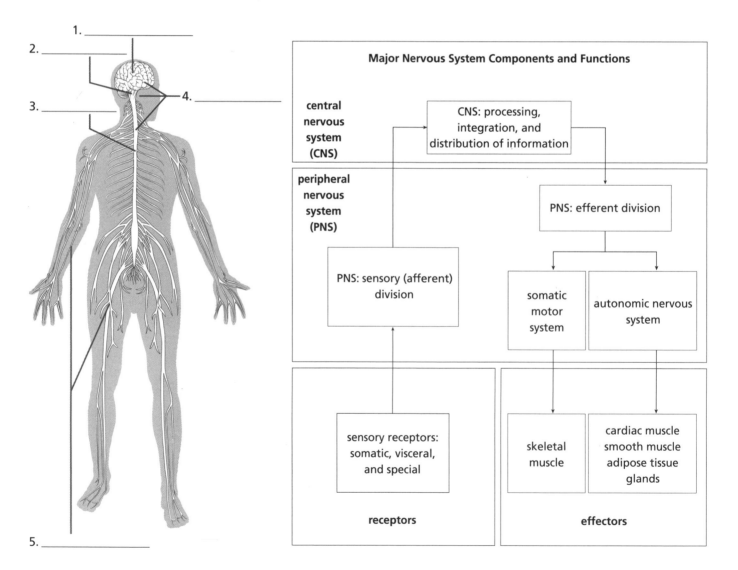

1. _____

2. _____

3. _____

4. _____

5. _____

Major Nervous System Components and Functions

central nervous system (CNS)

CNS: processing, integration, and distribution of information

peripheral nervous system (PNS)

PNS: efferent division

PNS: sensory (afferent) division

somatic motor system

autonomic nervous system

sensory receptors: somatic, visceral, and special

skeletal muscle

cardiac muscle
smooth muscle
adipose tissue
glands

receptors

effectors

Answers

Overview of Brain Structure and Function

The brain is part of the central nervous system, the control centre for everyday life that is responsible for everything from breathing and walking to memory. Sensory neurons deliver information from our internal and external environments to the brain, which processes this information and responds. The brain is made up of three main parts: the forebrain (cerebrum, thalamus, and hypothalamus), midbrain (tectum and tegmentum), and hindbrain (cerebellum, pons, and medulla). It is highly wrinkled, increasing its surface area and thereby its efficiency. The cerebrum (cortex) is the largest part of the human brain. It is made up of two hemispheres (halves), joined together by the corpus callosum. It is also divided into four lobes: frontal (reasoning, planning, movement, emotion, problem solving), parietal (movement, orientation, recognition, perception of stimuli), occipital (visual), and temporal (perception, audio recognition, memory, speech). The cerebellum also has two hemispheres. It is associated with regulation and coordination of balance, posture, and movement. The thalamus (sensory and motor information relay), hypothalamus (homeostasis), amygdala (emotion), and hippocampus (memory formation) together make up the limbic system, which is associated with emotion and memory. Below the limbic system is the brainstem, responsible for vital life functions, including controlling the respiratory and cardiovascular systems.

Lobes of the Brain – lateral view

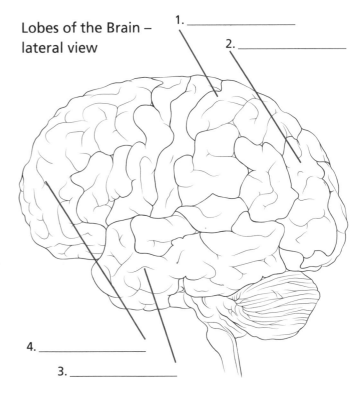

1. _____
2. _____
3. _____
4. _____

Functional Areas of the Brain – lateral view

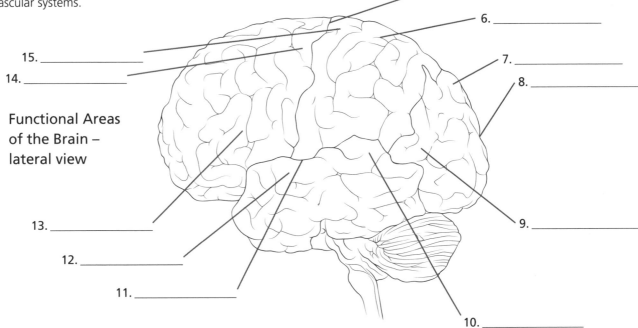

5. _____
6. _____
7. _____
8. _____
9. _____
10. _____
11. _____
12. _____
13. _____
14. _____
15. _____

Answers

1. parietal lobe, 2. occipital lobe, 3. temporal lobe, 4. frontal lobe, 5. central sulcus, 6. somatic sensory association area, 7. visual association area, 8. visual cortex, 9. reading comprehension area, 10. Wernicke's sensory speech area, 11. auditory cortex, 12. auditory association area, 13. motor speech (Broca's) area, 14. primary motor cortex, 15. primary sensory cortex

Autonomic Nervous System: Structure and Divisions

The autonomic nervous system (ANS) comprises both afferent and efferent pathways for involuntary control of most organs (excluding skeletal muscle motor control) in response to changes in environmental and emotional stimuli. The sympathetic and parasympathetic divisions make up the ANS. Both divisions originate with preganglionic neurons from the central nervous system that synapse with non-myelinated postganglionic neurons in their peripheral ganglia. Postganglionic neurons innervate the target organs or tissues.

Parasympathetic preganglionic neurons synapse at their peripheral ganglia with postganglionic neurons close to, or inside, their target organ/tissue. Sympathetic ganglia are typically found in two sympathetic chains adjacent to either side of the vertebral column. Sympathetic preganglionic neurons are very short compared with their postganglionic counterparts. Postganglionic sympathetic neurons are generally very long, whereas those of the parasympathetic system are short. An exception to this is sympathetic innervation of the adrenal glands, where sympathetic preganglionic neurons innervate the adrenal medulla directly. The adrenal medulla is specialised postganglionic tissue.

The sympathetic and parasympathetic systems work antagonistically and are coordinated centrally; increases in sympathetic activity will be commonly accompanied by a decrease in parasympathetic activity in the same organ. However, they may modulate different functions in the same organ, e.g. the 'fight/flight' response of the sympathetic system versus the 'rest/digest' response of the parasympathetic system.

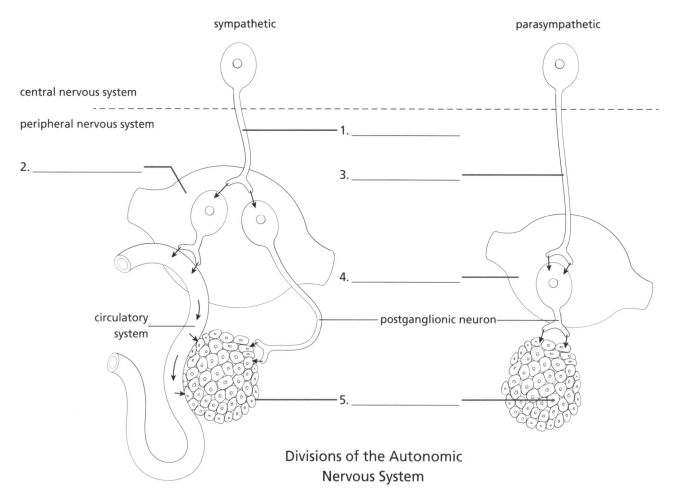

sympathetic   parasympathetic

central nervous system

peripheral nervous system

1. _____

2. _____

3. _____

4. _____

circulatory system _____

postganglionic neuron

5. _____

Divisions of the Autonomic Nervous System

Answers

1. sympathetic preganglionic neuron, 2. sympathetic ganglion, 3. parasympathetic preganglionic neuron, 4. parasympathetic ganglion, 5. target tissue/gland

Autonomic Nervous System: Neurotransmitters and Receptors

The autonomic nervous system utilises two major chemical synapses: cholinergic synapses (preganglionic neurons releasing acetylcholine) and adrenergic synapses (postganglionic neurons releasing noradrenaline, adrenaline, or dopamine). Both divisions of the ANS release acetylcholine from their preganglionic neurons, which acts upon cholinergic nicotinic receptors of the postganglionic neuron.

Parasympathetic postganglionic neurons release acetylcholine that acts upon cholinergic muscarinic receptors. There are three major muscarinic receptors: M_1 (neural), M_2 (cardiac), and M_3 (glandular/smooth muscle).

Sympathetic postganglionic neurons release noradrenaline (NE), adrenaline (E), or dopamine. The action of these is dependent on the adrenergic receptor type located on the target tissue. There are two main classes of adrenergic receptor: α (more sensitive to NE than E) and β (more sensitive to E than NE). These are further divided into four subtypes, each initiating a G-protein coupled second messenger sequence:

α_1 – formation of inositol trisphosphate (IP_3), leading to increased intracellular Ca^{2+}, vasoconstriction, energy mobilisation, and inhibition of gut motility.

α_2 – inhibition of adenylate cyclase, leading to inhibition of cyclic adenosine monophosphate (cAMP) production and consequently inhibiting Ca^{2+} channels (reducing Ca^{2+} influx); important in feedback control of NE secretion.

β_1 – increase in cAMP, leading to increased Ca^{2+} influx, and consequently increasing cardiac force and rate of contraction.

β_2 – decrease in cAMP, leading to decreased Ca^{2+} influx, and consequently causing bronchodilation, vasodilation, and visceral smooth muscle relaxation.

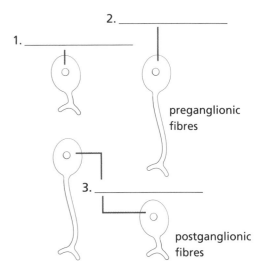

1. _____
2. _____
3. _____
preganglionic fibres
postganglionic fibres

Autonomic Nervous System – anatomy

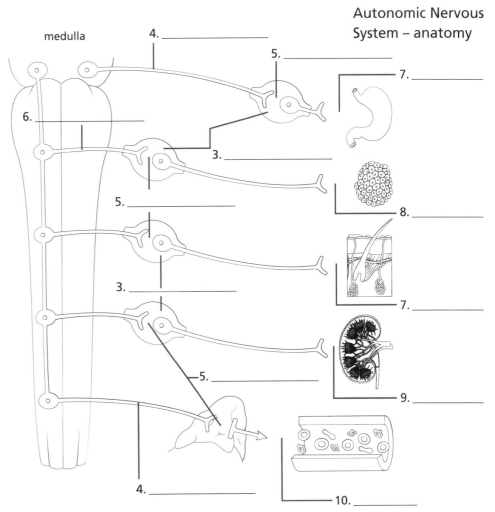

medulla

4. _____
5. _____
6. _____
3. _____
5. _____
3. _____
5. _____
4. _____

7. _____
8. _____
7. _____
9. _____
10. _____

Overview of Neuron Structure and Function

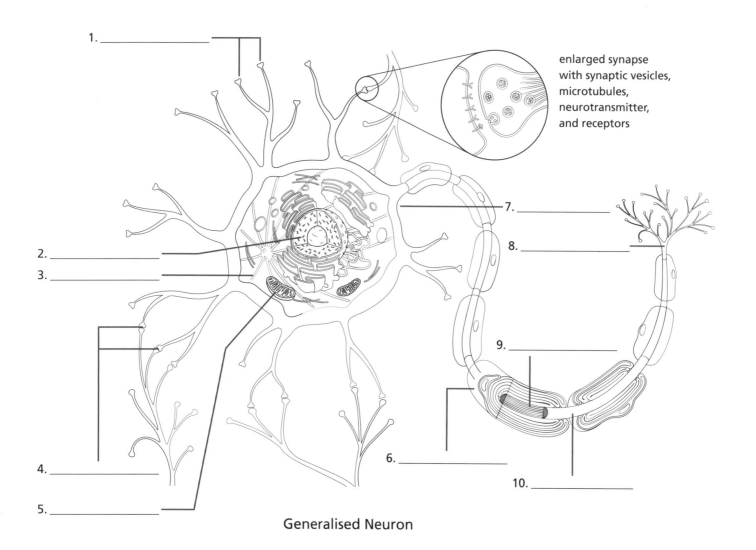

1. _____

enlarged synapse
with synaptic vesicles,
microtubules,
neurotransmitter,
and receptors

2. _____

3. _____

4. _____

5. _____

6. _____

7. _____

8. _____

9. _____

10. _____

Generalised Neuron

Although neurons may differ morphologically, they all contain four distinct regions, each of which has a different function. Dendrites are projections from the cell body and are designed to receive signals from axon terminals, converting them into electrical impulses. The cell body contains the nucleus and is the site of synthesis of virtually all neuronal proteins and membranes. The axons vary in diameter, can be myelinated or non-myelinated, and are specialised for the conduction of action potentials (APs) to the axon terminals. Axon terminals are the terminal branches of axons and sites of communication between neurons.

Newly synthesised proteins are transported down axons in membrane vesicles along microtubules via anterograde transport. Damaged membranes and organelles are transported in the opposite direction via retrograde transport, for degradation in lysosomes.

A single axon in the CNS can synapse with many neurons, inducing responses in all of them simultaneously. This principle is called divergence. One cell body can also receive a large number of signals from other neurons (convergence). Converging signals will spread through the dendrite and cell body, and can spread to the axon hillock – if these signals are collectively large enough, an AP will be generated. APs originate in the axon hillock (trigger zone) and can move at up to 150m/s (depending on the axon diameter and degree of myelination) down the axon to its terminals and synapses.

Answers

1. dendrites, 2. nucleus, 3. microtubules, 4. synapses, 5. mitochondrion, 6. myelin sheath, 7. axon hillock, 8. axon terminals, 9. microtubules, 10. axon

Control of Ion Channels by Membrane Potential

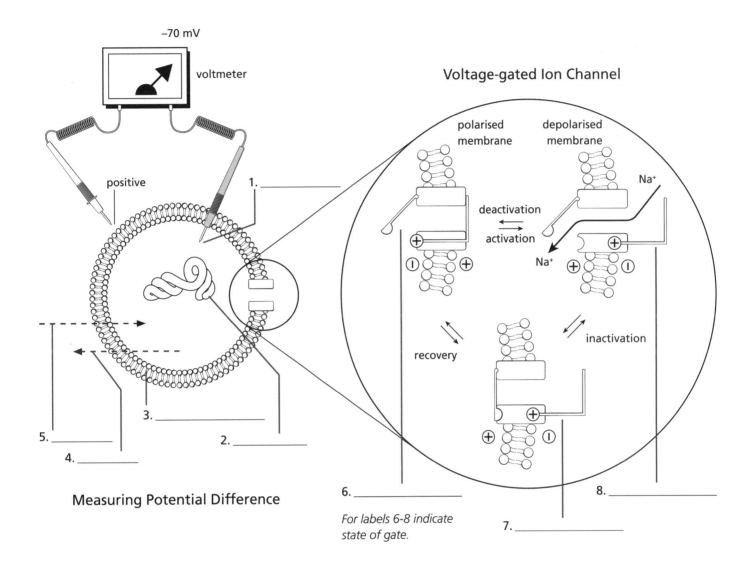

Measuring Potential Difference

Voltage-gated Ion Channel

For labels 6-8 indicate state of gate.

Differences in ionic composition of fluids across cell membranes lead to an electrical potential difference (measured in millivolts, or mV) across those membranes. For example, in a resting neuron the permeability of the membrane to K^+ at rest and the presence of the negatively charged proteins within the cell result in a potential difference of −70 mV. Ions are able to cross the cell membrane only by passing through specific ion channels, one class of which is 'voltage gated'. Changes in the membrane potential cause conformational changes of the channels, altering their open and closed state. As the membrane depolarises/repolarises, a set potential is reached (specific to the channel) and the channels open and become active, allowing ions to pass through. The subsequent change in membrane potential triggers a second conformational change of the gated channels, thus closing them.

Some voltage-gated channels are more complex in their activity and have a number of different states/conformations. For example, voltage-gated Na^+ channels have three states: closed, open, and closed and inactive. These three states allow the neuronal cell membranes to depolarise, repolarise, and enter a resting inoperable state.

Essentially, voltage-gated ion channels are controlled via changes in membrane potential, allowing movement of specific ions through their transmembrane pores.

Answers

Understanding an Action Potential

As dendrites receive stimuli, small electrical impulses (depolarisations) are generated that collect at the axon hillock (the trigger zone). If the depolarisation exceeds the threshold, an action potential (AP) will be generated. All APs are the same size, irrespective of the size of stimulus as long as the stimulus exceeds the threshold potential. This is called the all-or-none principle.

The threshold potential is the activation voltage, approximately −50 millivolts (mV), for voltage-gated Na⁺ channels; once these open there is a rapid influx of Na⁺ down the electrochemical gradient. Depolarising the membrane to around +50 mV, thus opening more voltage-gated Na⁺ channels along the way, is an example of positive feedback. Very soon after opening, the channels rapidly close and inactivate spontaneously.

Voltage-gated K⁺ channels open very slowly at threshold, allowing K⁺ efflux in accordance with its electrochemical gradients. Closure of the voltage-gated Na⁺ channels results in repolarisation as K⁺ leaves. Because of the slow-acting nature of K⁺ channels, the membrane hyperpolarises, overshooting its resting potential, as K⁺ channels close slowly once beneath threshold. The membrane potential returns to rest (−70 mV) as the Na⁺/K⁺ pump restores the ionic balance to the neuron.

When resting potential is restored, the inactivation of voltage-gated Na⁺ channels is removed and they revert to a closed state. The inactivation ensures the channels cannot be reopened – this is called the refractory period.

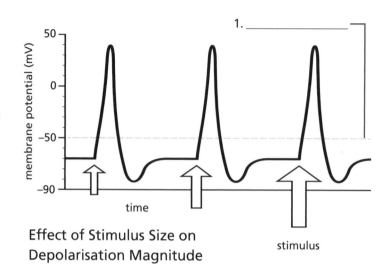

Effect of Stimulus Size on Depolarisation Magnitude

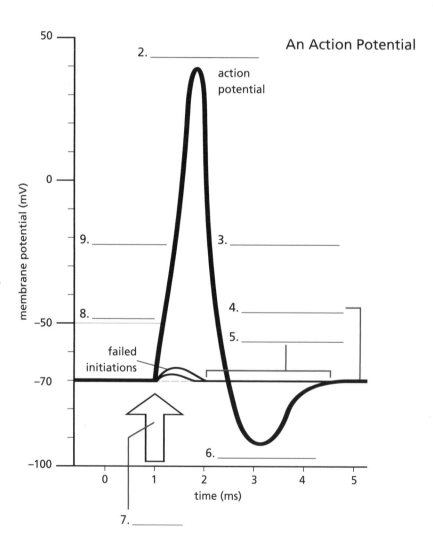

An Action Potential

Synaptic Structure and Function

Synapses are the junctions between axon terminals and target tissues/organs. They are bulbous regions at the end of the axon terminal and are surrounded by a presynaptic membrane. The target membrane is called the postsynaptic membrane. The gap between the membranes is the cleft. Within the membranes are ion channels and receptor proteins that are specific to the synapse and target. Synapses contain membrane-wrapped packages (vesicles) of neurotransmitter, which are released into the cleft upon arrival of an action potential (AP).

When APs arrive at the synapse, the presynaptic membrane is depolarised, opening voltage-gated Ca^{2+} channels and increasing intracellular Ca^{2+} concentration. This triggers the fusion of vesicles with the presynaptic membrane adjacent to the cleft and causes them to release their contents into the cleft. This is a process of regulated exocytosis.

The neurotransmitter diffuses across the cleft to interact with specific receptors on the postsynaptic membrane, the effect of which is dependent on the neurotransmitter and the receptor. Neurotransmitters are removed from the cleft by enzymes in the cleft or reuptake pumps in the presynaptic membrane.

Neurotransmitters can be excitatory or inhibitory. Excitatory postsynaptic potentials (EPSPs) result in depolarisations, whereas inhibitory postsynaptic potentials (IPSPs) lead to hyperpolarisations. The sum of these governs the generation of APs.

Generalised Synapse

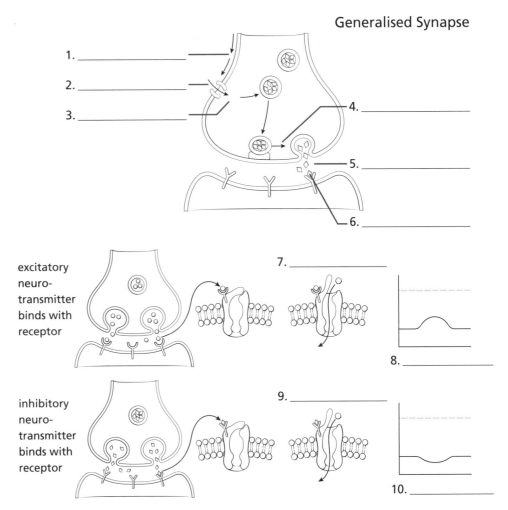

1. _____
2. _____
3. _____
4. _____
5. _____
6. _____

excitatory neuro-transmitter binds with receptor

7. _____
8. _____

inhibitory neuro-transmitter binds with receptor

9. _____
10. _____

Excitatory and Inhibitory Neurotransmitters

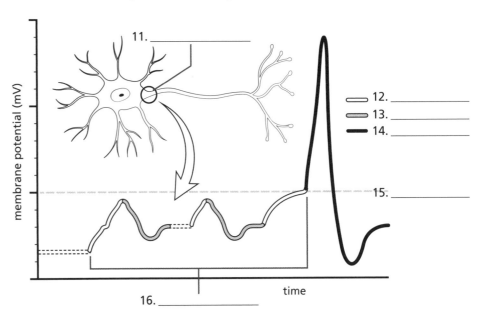

membrane potential (mV)

11. _____
12. _____
13. _____
14. _____
15. _____
16. _____

time

Answers

Types of Sensory Receptors

Sensory receptors are highly specialised cells that are vital to the sensory mechanisms of the nervous system. They detect the presence of, and changes in, various stimuli from both internal and external environments. These stimuli are then converted into action potentials, which are sent to the central nervous system.

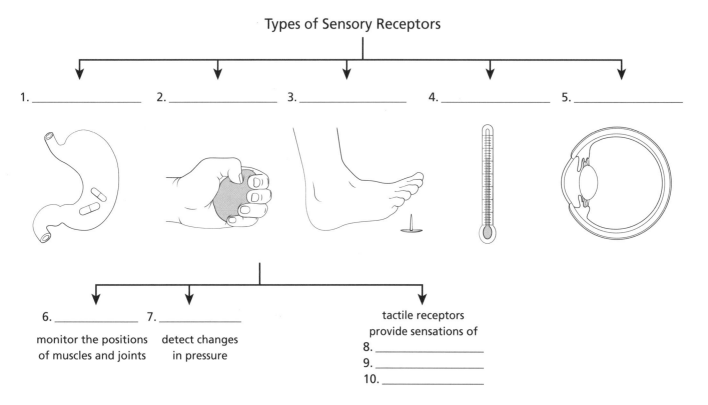

Types of Sensory Receptors

1. _____ 2. _____ 3. _____ 4. _____ 5. _____

6. _____ 7. _____

monitor the positions of muscles and joints

detect changes in pressure

tactile receptors provide sensations of

8. _____
9. _____
10. _____

Classes of sensory receptors:

Mechanoreceptors are the most diverse group of sensory receptors, found in skin, muscles, visceral organs, and joints. They are stimulated by mechanical deformation of the receptor through stretching, compression, or hair movement. Many mechanoreceptors are sensory nerve endings encapsulated in fibrous/connective tissue.

> **Muscle and tendon receptors (proprioceptors)** detect changes in muscle length and tension, with those found in the joints sensing limb position and movement.
>
> **Hair cells** are highly specialised mechanoreceptors (modified cilia) of the inner ear that respond to changes in fluid movement (balance) and mechanical sound waves (hearing).
>
> **Baroreceptors** are sensitive to distension in arterial walls, sensing changes in blood pressure.

Stretch receptors are located in the walls of many visceral organs and sense their distension.

Thermoreceptors and **nocioceptors** are types of free nerve endings in the skin that detect sensations of cold/warmth and pain, respectively.

Chemoreceptors are sensitive to the presence of chemical stimuli, while **photoreceptors** are sensitive with respect to light.

Answers

1. chemoreceptors, 2. mechanoreceptors, 3. nocioceptors, 4. thermoreceptors, 5. photoreceptors, 6. proprioceptors, 7. baroreceptors, 8. touch, 9. pressure, 10. vibration

Receptors and Sensory Transduction

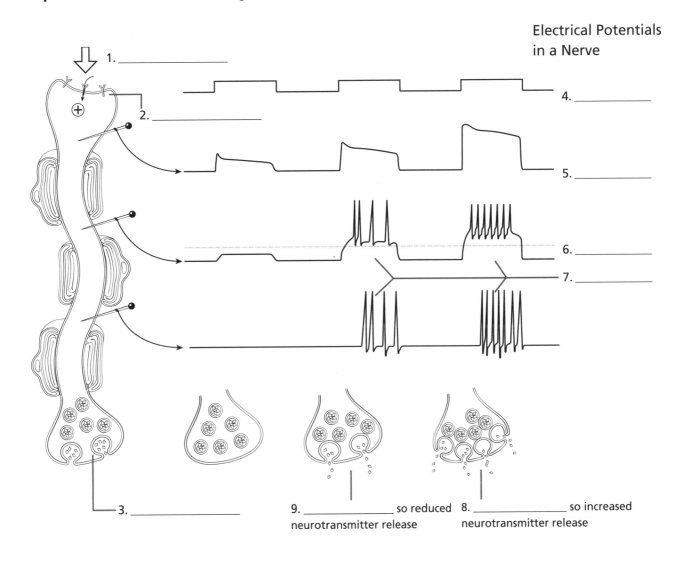

Electrical Potentials in a Nerve

1. _____

2. _____

3. _____

4. _____

5. _____

6. _____

7. _____

9. _____ so reduced neurotransmitter release

8. _____ so increased neurotransmitter release

Sensory transduction (by a sensory receptor) is the conversion of energy from a peripheral stimulus into action potentials (APs) that carry the information via axons to the central nervous system (CNS) for integration. The principles of signal transduction are simple: to convert energy (mechanical, light, chemical, temperature) into electrical impulses (sometimes called generator potentials), which can then lead to APs.

There are different mechanisms by which this transduction takes place, depending on the receptor type detecting the stimulus energy. Mechanotransduction is the conversion of mechanical energy (stretch, pressure, skin compression, vibration) into electrical impulses. When stimulated, mechanically gated ion channels open to produce a transduction current, changing the membrane potential of the cell. Similarly, chemoreceptors, photoreceptors, and thermoreceptors generate electrical impulses when triggered by the presence of chemicals, photons of light, and changes in temperature, respectively.

There is a direct link between the stimulus energy and the amplitude of the transduced electrical stimuli (generator potentials). Only when a stimulus is large enough to transduce a generator potential that exceeds the threshold will APs be fired and carried via axons to the CNS for integration. The larger the stimulus, the larger the generator potential, and so more APs will be fired.

Answers

1. stimulus, 2. sensory receptor, 3. axon terminal/synapse, 4. stimulus intensity, 5. receptor/generator potentials, 6. threshold, 7. action potentials (APs), 8. strong stimulus, 9. weak stimulus

Spinal Cord Structure and Function

The spinal cord extends from the medulla oblongata to the lumbar region of the vertebral column. It consists of a core of grey matter – nerve cell bodies, dendrites, and supporting cells – that is surrounded by white matter – columns of myelinated and non-myelinated axons (nerve fibres). These nerve fibres carry sensory information up through the central nervous system to the brain, and motor action potentials from the brain to the rest of the body. Each spinal nerve comprises sensory and motor nerve roots, which enter the back (dorsal roots) and leave the front (ventral roots) of the spinal cord, respectively. Therefore, two consecutive rows of nerve roots emerge on each side of the spinal cord. Each spinal cord segment innervates a dermatome, which is an area of skin supplied by peripheral nerve fibres from a single dorsal root ganglion.

Sensory pathways are divided into the dorsal column–medial lemniscus tract (proprioception, touch, vibration) and the anterolateral system (temperature, pain). Both of these pathways use three different neurons (primary, secondary, and tertiary) to convey information from receptors to the brain. An exception to this is proprioception of the lower limbs, which utilises a third neuron in the pathway.

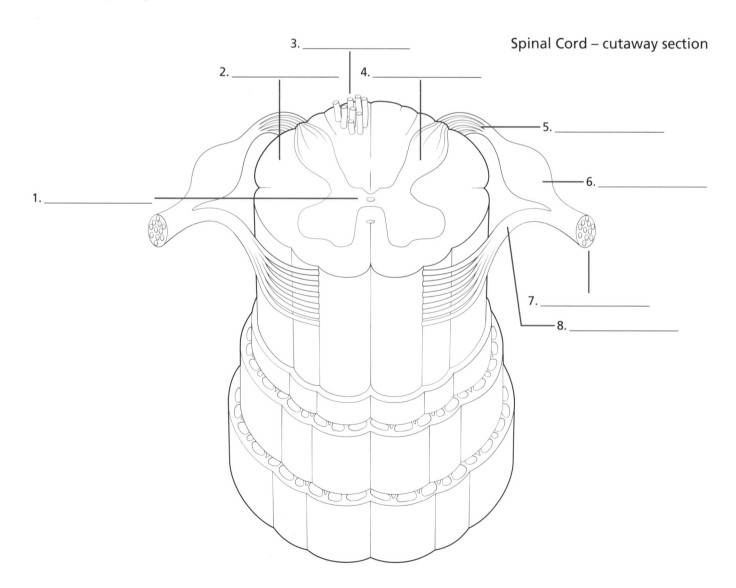

Spinal Cord – cutaway section

1. _____
2. _____
3. _____
4. _____
5. _____
6. _____
7. _____
8. _____

Peripheral Nervous System Components

The peripheral nervous system (PNS) contains all the nerves of the body that are outside the central nervous system (CNS). The PNS therefore includes all the nerves that go from the skin, organs, and muscles to the brain and spinal cord (sensory nerves), allowing the body to respond to its environment (efferent nerves).

The PNS consists of 12 pairs of cranial nerves and 31 pairs of spinal nerves; some of these are sensory, while others are motor nerves. There are some nerve pairs that comprise both sensory and motor cells, such as those involved in taste and swallowing.

The PNS is further subdivided into the somatic and autonomic nervous systems. Somatic sensory nerve cells carry action potentials from the sensory receptors of the outer areas of the body to the CNS. The autonomic nerves are divided into three further classifications: parasympathetic, sympathetic, and enteric. The somatic nervous system governs voluntary actions and reflexes (those that do not require brain input), while the autonomic nervous system regulates involuntary actions, i.e. digestion and respiration.

Somatic (voluntary) motor nerves innervate muscle via neuromuscular junctions. Autonomic (involuntary) efferent nerves can innervate muscle or secretory glands/tissues.

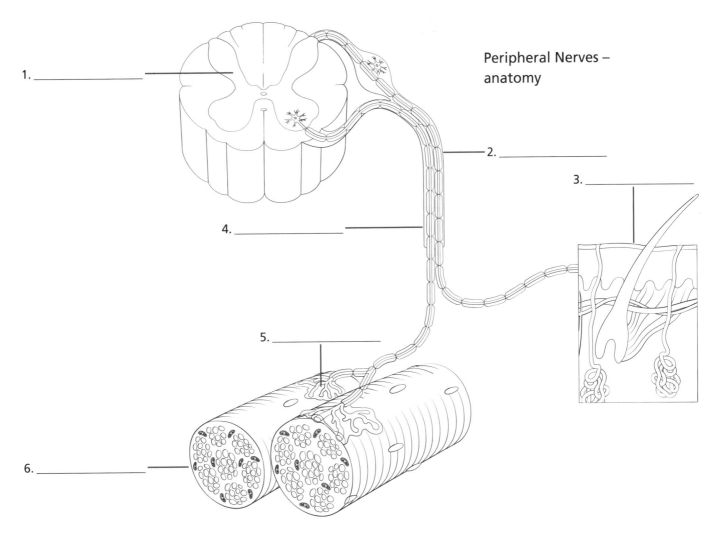

Peripheral Nerves – anatomy

1. _____

2. _____

3. _____

4. _____

5. _____

6. _____

Answers

1. central nervous system (CNS) or spinal cord, 2. sensory neuron, 3. sensory receptors, 4. motor neuron, 5. neuromuscular junction, 6. skeletal muscle fibre

Peripheral Nerves and Conduction Velocities

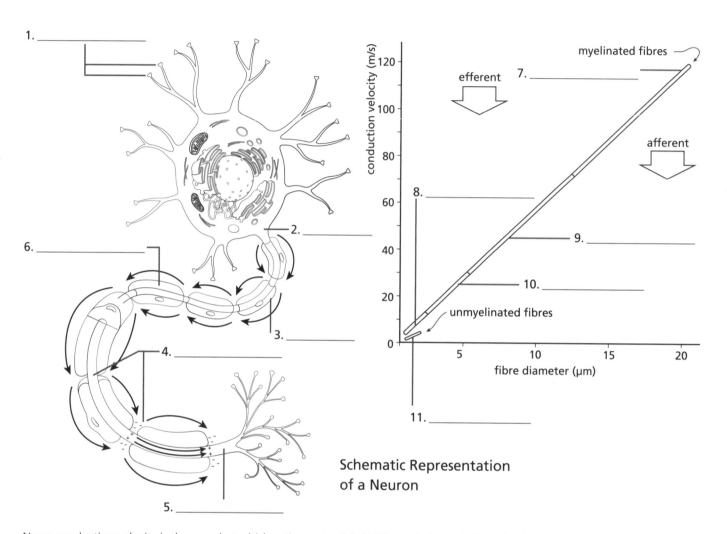

1. _____

2. _____

3. _____

4. _____

5. _____

6. _____

7. _____

8. _____

9. _____

10. _____

11. _____

efferent

afferent

myelinated fibres

unmyelinated fibres

conduction velocity (m/s)

fibre diameter (µm)

Schematic Representation of a Neuron

Nerve conduction velocity is the speed at which action potentials (APs) travel along the length of the axon. These velocities are affected by a number of factors, the main ones being nerve diameter, whether or not the nerve is myelinated, and how much is myelinated. Temperature, age, and various medical conditions can also influence the velocities.

While conduction velocities are specific to individuals, they can be estimated based on the class of the nerve involved and its structure. Myelinated fibres with a large diameter have among the fastest velocities, at approximately 150 m/s.

Motor fibre classes: α, 13–20 µm diameter, myelinated, 80–150 m/s conduction velocities; γ, 5–8 µm diameter, myelinated, 4–24 m/s conduction velocities.

Sensory fibre classes: Ia and Ib, 13–20 µm diameter, myelinated, 80–150 m/s conduction velocities; II, 6–12 µm diameter, myelinated, 33–75 m/s conduction velocities; III, 1–5 µm diameter, thin myelination, 3–30 m/s conduction velocities; and IV, 0.2–1.5 µm diameter, non-myelinated, 0.5–2.0 m/s conduction velocities.

A direct correlation exists between large axon diameter and high conduction velocities, and between the degree of myelination and the conduction velocity. Myelination insulates the axon, increasing the efficiency and speed of AP conduction. Through a process called saltatory (meaning 'to leap') conduction, the APs jump between the nodes in the myelin sheath along the axon.

Fibres that are narrower in diameter and non-myelinated are less efficient at conducting APs along the axon, thus, reducing their velocity.

Answers

1. dendrites, 2. axon hillock, 3. myelin sheath, 4. nodes of Ranvier, 5. axon, 6. Schwann cells, 7. Ia, Ib, and α fibres, 8. IV fibres, 9. II and Aβ fibres, 10. III and γ fibres, 11. C fibres

Cortical Sensory Regions

Cerebral Cortex

White numbers refer to lobes.

2. _____

1. _____ 3. _____

4. _____

14. _____ _____

5. _____

13. _____ _____

6. _____

7. _____

12. _____

8. _____

11. _____

10. _____ _____

9. _____

Sensory areas of the cerebral cortex receive and process information from sensory receptors (sound, sight, taste, touch, smell), the majority of which is initially routed through the thalamus (olfaction is the exception, as this bypasses the thalamus). The cortical region of the brain can be divided into three functionally distinct areas: sensory, associative, and motor. The sensory areas include primary cortices for auditory, visual, olfaction, gustation, and somatosensory (thermoreceptors, chemoreceptors, and mechanoreceptors) signals, which receive information from the thalamus. Information is also relayed between primary cortices and their corresponding association areas, aiding in their recognition.

Each primary cortex can be mapped topographically, illustrating the link between cortical organisation and the respective sensing organs. Points on the retina that correspond to points on the primary visual cortex are shown on a retinotopic map, the primary auditory cortex is shown on a tonotopic map, and the primary sensory cortex is shown on a somatotopic map.

The somatotopic map is commonly visualised in the form of a somatosensory homunculus, in which the size/surface area of each different body part depicted on the map reflects the density of the sensory receptors that innervate that region, which is in turn a reflection of the sensitivity of the area.

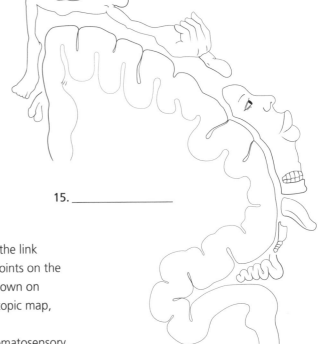

15. _____

Answers

Somatosensation: Pain and Nociception

Nociception is the sensing of potentially harmful stimuli. Sensory-free nerve endings (nociceptors/pain receptors) respond to tissue damage. Action potentials then propagate along afferent fibres of the peripheral nervous system to the central nervous system (CNS), where autonomic responses and the possible raised awareness/perception of the harmful stimulus are triggered. The intensity of the pain stimulus is translated into a train of action potentials, the frequency of which correlates directly with the stimulus strength.

There are three different types of nociceptors: cutaneous (skin), somatic (bones/joints), and visceral (organs). There are also two different types of pain transmission: fast and slow.

Fast pain is transmitted via fast myelinated Aδ fibres through the neospinothalamic tract and the thalamus to the somatosensory cortex. Fast pain is a response to mechanical or thermal stimuli and is felt as an acute, sharp pain.

Slow pain travels via slower non-myelinated C fibres, through the paleospinothalamic tract. Ten per cent of the fibres pass through the thalamus to reach the somatosensory cortex, while the rest terminate in the medulla, pons, and periaqueductal grey (PAG) in the midbrain. Slow pain is felt as a dull ache or throbbing tonic sensation.

Pain transmission can be modulated by descending pathways in the CNS before it reaches the thalamus.

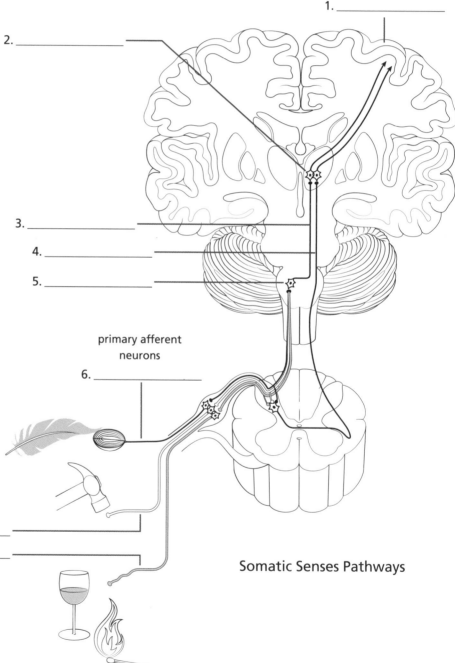

1. _____

2. _____

3. _____

4. _____

5. _____

primary afferent neurons

6. _____

7. _____

8. _____

Somatic Senses Pathways

Answers

Somatosensation: Touch, Pressure, and Vibration

Somatosensation of touch, pressure, and vibration is the detection, integration, and perception of tactile stimuli from external forces in contact with the skin. The receptors responsible for this are mechanoreceptors, which are found all over the body and are stimulated by mechanical deformation.

Receptor Distribution in Glabrous vs. Hairy Skin

2. _____

3. _____

1. _____

4. _____

5. _____

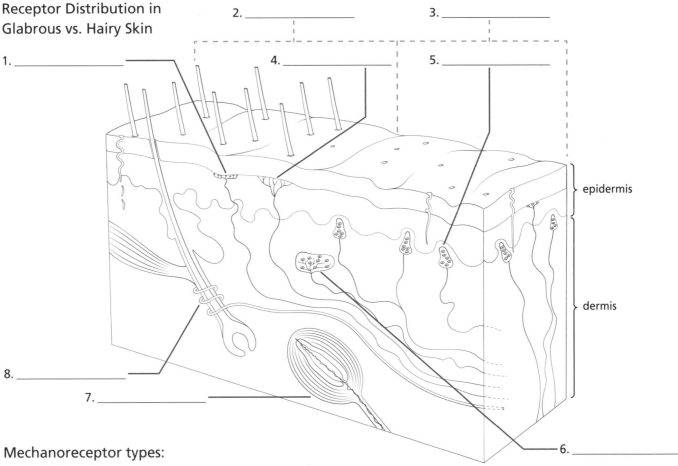

epidermis

dermis

8. _____

7. _____

6. _____

Mechanoreceptor types:

Merkel's discs: light touch and pressure, deep static touch, very low-frequency vibrations (5–15 Hz); detect shape (e.g. edges, Braille).

Meissner's corpuscles: light touch, low-frequency vibrations (30–50 Hz), localised movement on the skin; adapt to changes in texture (e.g. useful for reading Braille).

Pacinian corpuscles: deep pressure and vibration (100–300 Hz); detect vibrations and high-velocity joint movement.

Ruffini's endings: skin tension and stretch; useful for grip modulation and proprioception. These receptors have varying responses to constant stimuli:

> **Slowly adapting**: continuing to send action potentials (APs) while the stimulus is present (Ruffini's endings, Merkel's discs); detect intensity.

> **Moderately rapidly adapting**: sending APs for approximately 50–500 ms after stimulus onset, even when stimulus is maintained (hair follicle receptors, Meissner's corpuscles); detect velocity.

> **Very rapidly adapting**: firing only one or two APs (Pacinian corpuscles); detect vibration. Touch, pressure, and vibration signals follow the dorsal column–medial lemniscal pathway to the primary somatosensory cortex.

Answers

1. free nerve endings, 2. hairy skin, 3. glabrous skin, 4. Merkel's discs, 5. Meissner's corpuscle, 6. Ruffini's ending, 7. Pacinian corpuscle, 8. hair follicle receptor

Somatosensation: Proprioception

Proprioception is the unconscious and conscious perception of movement and spatial orientation arising from stimuli in the body. It is the ability to sense position, movement, and force generated by or in limbs and joints. Proprioceptors are located in joint capsules (joint receptors), tendons (Golgi tendon organs, or GTOs), and muscles (muscle spindle fibres, or MSFs).

Joint capsules are stimulated by compression or stretch of the receptors (slowly adapting Ruffini's endings) as a result of joint movement. This gives information on joint position and the direction and velocity of movement.

MSFs (intrafusal fibres) are grouped together and encapsulated in a connective tissue capsule and lie parallel to the contractile muscle fibres (extrafusal fibres). MSFs respond to change in muscle length. They consist of 'bag' (dynamic, speed of contraction) and 'chain' (static, stress and strain) fibres and respond to muscle stretch.

GTOs are stretch receptors located in the muscle tendons, encapsulated in connective tissue. They are in series with the extrafusal fibres, providing information on muscle tension and responding to both contraction and relaxation.

Conscious proprioceptive information is relayed to the central nervous system mostly via the dorsal column and, in part, the spinocervical tract. Unconscious proprioceptive information follows the spinocerebellar tract, terminating in the cerebellum.

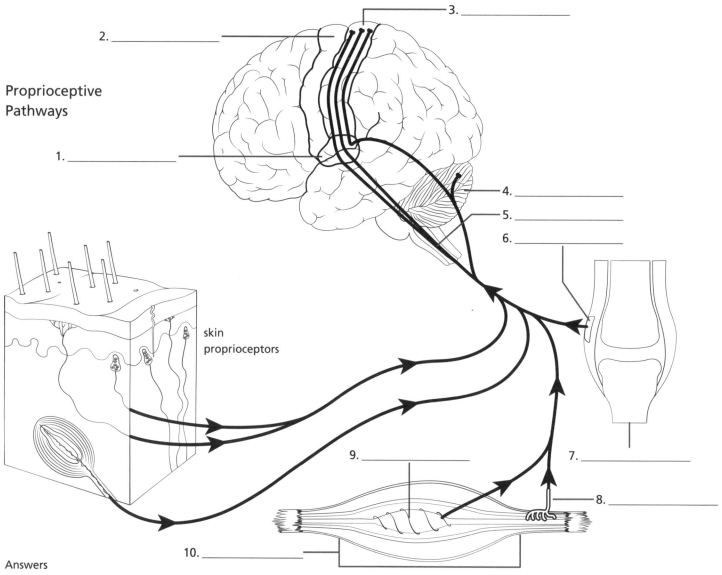

Proprioceptive Pathways

skin proprioceptors

1. _____
2. _____
3. _____
4. _____
5. _____
6. _____
7. _____
8. _____
9. _____
10. _____

Answers

Hearing: Structure and Function of the Ear

Sound is a travelling pressure wave, in which air molecules compress together to form the peaks and their absences form the troughs. These pressure waves are collected by the pinna of the ear and channelled down the external auditory canal. The force of the waves causes the tympanic membrane – which separates the external ear from the middle ear – to vibrate (buckle and yield) in relation to the peaks and troughs. Air is present on either side of the tympanic membrane and must be maintained at equal pressure. The Eustachian tube facilitates this equalisation.

Connecting the tympanic membrane to the oval window (the start of the cochlea) are the auditory ossicles (malleus, incus, and stapes); these span the middle ear and transfer energy to the inner ear. The lever action of these ossicles and larger surface area of the tympanic membrane compared to the oval window amplify the energy of the sound wave. Two skeletal muscles in the middle ear provide protection from loud sounds by contracting, thereby reducing the energy passage through this section.

The mechanical energy resulting from the vibration of the oval window is passed into the cochlea for transduction into electrical impulses.

The vestibular system (three fluid-filled semicircular canals) is located in the inner ear and is involved with balance, postural reflexes, and eye movements.

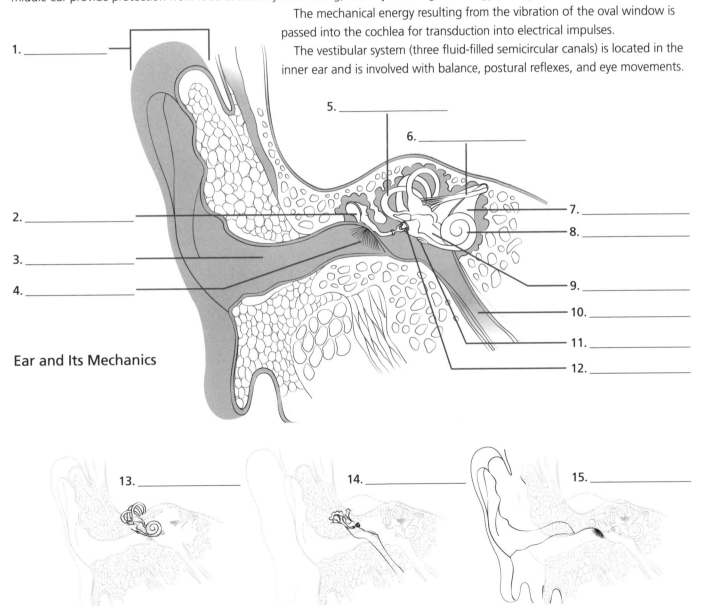

1. _____

2. _____

3. _____

4. _____

5. _____

6. _____

7. _____

8. _____

9. _____

10. _____

11. _____

12. _____

Ear and Its Mechanics

13. _____

14. _____

15. _____

Hearing: Physiology of the Organ of Corti

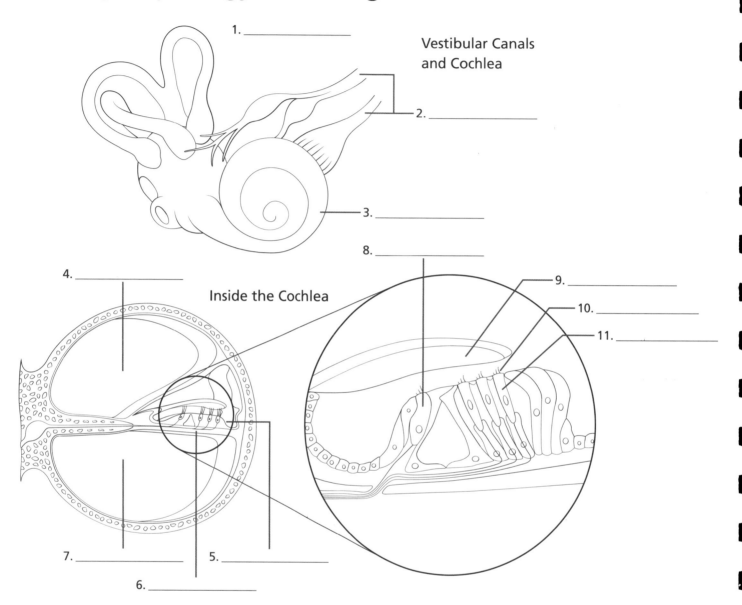

Vestibular Canals and Cochlea

1. _____

2. _____

3. _____

Inside the Cochlea

4. _____

8. _____

9. _____

10. _____

11. _____

7. _____

5. _____

6. _____

The cochlea comprises a coiled tube about 3 cm (1.2 inches) in length, containing three tubular canals (the scala vestibuli, scala media, and scala tympani) running parallel to each other. The scala tympani and scala vestibuli contain perilymph (low K^+), whereas the scala media contains endolymph (high K^+). At the base of the scala vestibuli is the oval window, and at the base of the scala tympani is the round window. The basilar membrane lies between the scala tympani and scala media.

The organ of Corti (the sensitive element of the cochlea) sits on top of the basilar membrane. It contains four rows of hair cells, above which is the tectorial membrane. The basilar and tectorial membranes move in relation to the vibrations/pressure variations in the fluids between the oval and round windows. Each hair cell in the organ of Corti possesses strands called stereocilia; together they are arranged in a tonotopic map between the basilar and tectorial membranes along the length of the cochlea.

Transduction occurs through vibration of the membranes and subsequent movement of the 'tuned' hair cells. This stimulus opens ion channels and results in depolarisation and neurotransmitter release at the synapse. In turn, this generates action potentials that propagate through the auditory nerve to the auditory cortex.

Answers

1. inner ear, 2. afferent nerves, 3. cochlea, 4. scala vestibuli, 5. organ of Corti, 6. basilar membrane, 7. Scala tympani, 8. inner hair cells, 9. tectorial membrane, 10. cilia, 11. outer hair cells

Hearing: Central Processing of Auditory Information

Following the transduction of sound waves into action potentials (APs), these electrical signals must now travel to the auditory cortex to be translated and perceived. During the journey, a degree of central processing occurs. The cochlear nuclei (ventral and dorsal) are the first site of this neuronal processing, where timing and patterns of activity from the numerous APs are identified, and spectral analysis takes place to identify the sound location/orientation.

Next is the superior olivary nucleus, which aids in accurately locating sounds on the left and right planes, thereby establishing the time difference of sound arrival at each ear.

The inferior colliculus is the first site of integration of horizontal and vertical sound location information. It is also involved in integration of other stimuli, related to the startle response and vestibulo-ocular reflex.

The medial geniculate nucleus is part of the auditory thalamus and is believed to be involved in direction and maintenance of attention. It relays sound frequency, intensity, duration, and binaural information to the cortex, linking auditory and somatosensory inputs.

The primary auditory cortex is the first part of the cerebral cortex to receive auditory inputs. Numerous links to the secondary auditory cortex and frontal lobe exist, which are important in perception and recognition, such as distinguishing speech, music, and noises.

Pathway from Ear to Auditory Cortex

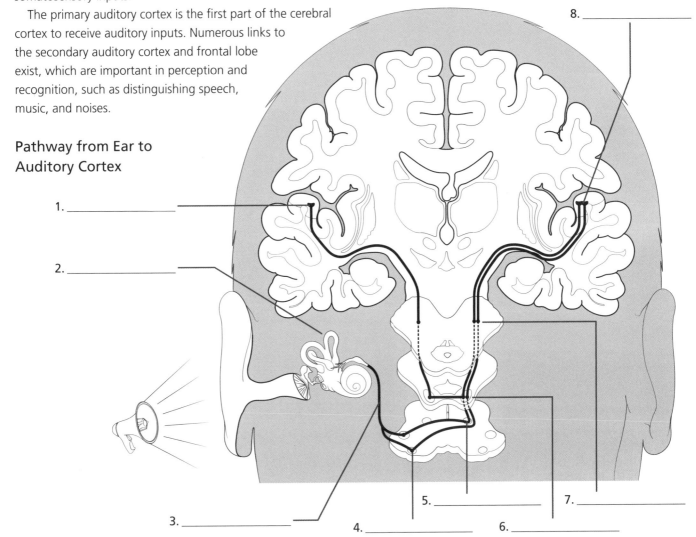

1. _____

2. _____

3. _____

4. _____

5. _____

6. _____

7. _____

8. _____

Vestibular Function and Balance

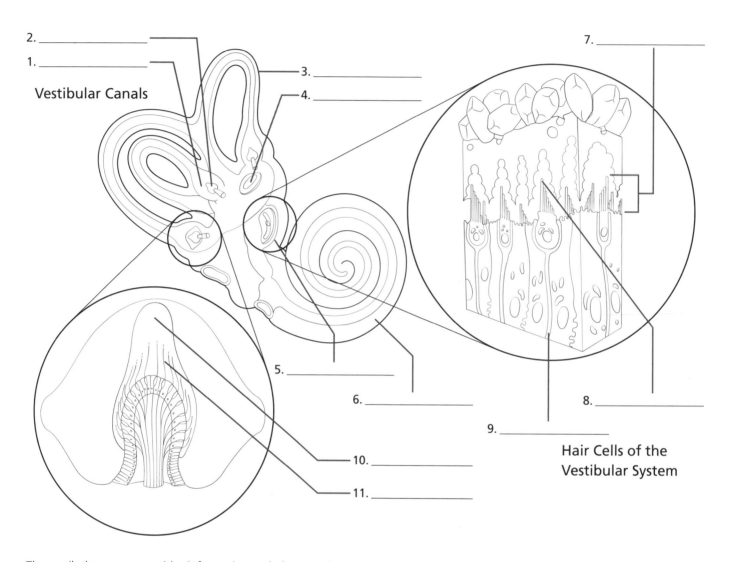

2. _____

1. _____

Vestibular Canals

3. _____

4. _____

7. _____

5. _____

6. _____

8. _____

9. _____

Hair Cells of the Vestibular System

10. _____

11. _____

The vestibular system provides information on balance and spatial orientation. A semicircular canal system (for rotational movement) and the otoliths (for linear accelerations) make up the system. Information from this system is used to control eye movements and body posture and to keep us upright. The system is also involved in proprioception, position, and acceleration.

The three semicircular canals are orientated horizontally (for rotational movement) and vertically (for nodding and cartwheeling). They are arranged almost parallel to one another on either side of the head, so they operate in a 'push-pull' manner: If one canal side is stimulated, the canal on the opposing side is inhibited.

Fluid movement in the canals (corresponding to physical movements) pushes on the cupula, which contains hair cells that transduce the mechanical movements to electrical impulses. Hair cell displacement opens and closes ion channels, causing depolarisations and hyperpolarisations. The resulting action potentials then travel to the cortex, thalamus, reticular formation, and cerebellum.

The vestibular system's otolithic organs sense linear acceleration. There are two on either side of the head, each possessing a saccule and macula (hair and support cells). Each hair cell has up to 70 stereocilia and one kinocilium. Movement stimulates the kinocilium, generating action potentials. These are then conveyed to the central nervous system, where they are integrated with visual information.

Answers

1. ampulla, 2. crista, 3. semicircular canal, 4. macula, 5. saccule, 6. cochlea, 7. stereocilia, 8. kinocilium, 9. nerve fibre, 10. cupula, 11. hair bundles

Structure and Function of the Eye

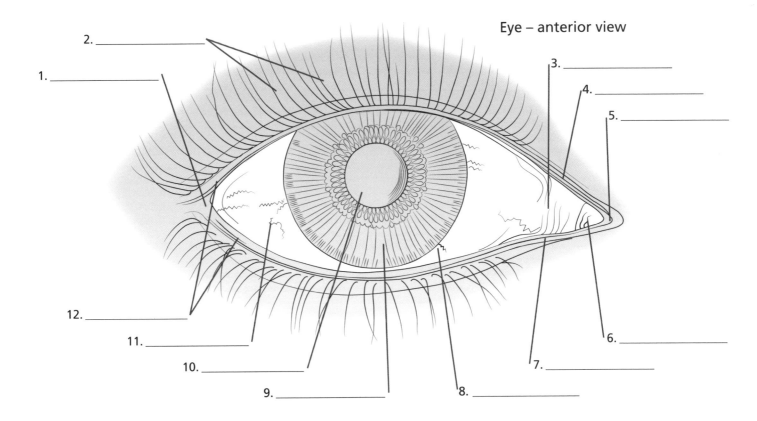

Eye – anterior view

2. _____

1. _____

3. _____

4. _____

5. _____

12. _____

11. _____

10. _____

9. _____

8. _____

7. _____

6. _____

As visual creatures, the eye serves as one of our primary sensory organs. Its main function is to receive light from the world and convert it to electrochemical signals that our brains can interpret. These signals allow us to perceive our visual surroundings as well as coordinate our bodily functions with the time of day.

The eyeball has three layers: the sclera and cornea comprise the outer layer; the lens, choroid, ciliary body, and iris comprise the middle layer; and the retina is the inner layer. The sclera gives the eyeball its spherical shape, with the front of the sphere covered by a thin membrane called the conjunctiva. The eyeball is divided into two fluid-filled cavities: the anterior cavity is filled with aqueous humour and lies in front of the lens. It is made up of the anterior and posterior chambers on the front and sides of the iris, respectively. The posterior cavity contains the vitreous body (a gelatin-like mass). The eyelids (palpebrae) protect the eyes and meet at the medial and lateral canthi. Each eyelid is covered on the outside by the skin and on the inside by the conjunctiva. The eyelid margin is lined with a few rows of eyelashes (cilia) and has openings for numerous glands that moisten the eyeball. The front of the eye is protected by the bulbar conjunctiva, which is thickest in the corner, where it folds into a structure called the plica semilunaris.

Answers

Optics of the Eye and Phototransduction

Light rays entering the eye strike the cornea, which refracts the rays, bending them closer together. The rays then pass through the lens and through the vitreous humour of the posterior cavity. The lens can adapt its shape depending on incoming light, helping to focus the light on the back of the retina. The ciliary bodies control the size of the iris, and consequently the amount of light that can enter the eye. The retina is a complex, multilayered structure, with its outermost part containing 130 million light-sensitive cells known as photoreceptors. There are two different types of photoreceptors: rods, which are active in low light and cannot distinguish colour, and cones, which are active in bright light and respond maximally to specific colours. While rods are equally distributed across the retina, cones are concentrated around the fovea. Light that strikes the rods and cones is converted to electrical signals in the form of action potentials, which are passed through the layers of the retina. These signals ultimately reach the retinal ganglion cells, which have axons that leave the back of the retina, forming the optic nerve.

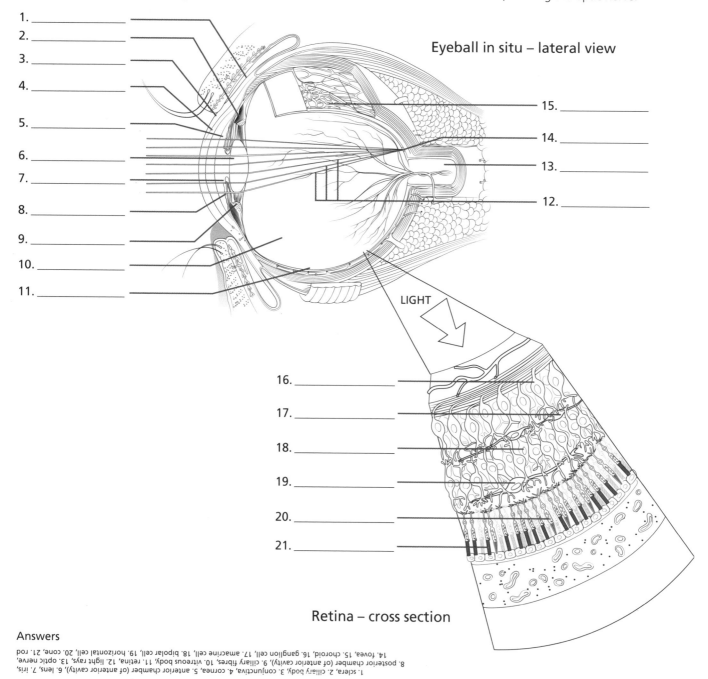

1. _____
2. _____
3. _____
4. _____
5. _____
6. _____
7. _____
8. _____
9. _____
10. _____
11. _____

Eyeball in situ – lateral view

15. _____
14. _____
13. _____
12. _____

LIGHT

16. _____
17. _____
18. _____
19. _____
20. _____
21. _____

Retina – cross section

Answers

1. sclera, 2. ciliary body, 3. conjunctiva, 4. cornea, 5. anterior chamber (of anterior cavity), 6. lens, 7. iris, 8. posterior chamber (of anterior cavity), 9. ciliary fibres, 10. vitreous body, 11. retina, 12. light rays, 13. optic nerve, 14. fovea, 15. choroid, 16. ganglion cell, 17. amacrine cell, 18. bipolar cell, 19. horizontal cell, 20. cone, 21. rod

Colour Vision

In most individuals, three different types of cones (red/long, blue/short, and green/medium) form the basis for colour vision. In the discs of its outer segment, each cone contains a different type of opsin (light-sensitive protein) and photopigment that is maximally activated by a specific range of light wavelengths, with sensitivities of 400–700 nanometres (nm) (the visual spectrum). Combining the activity of these cones allows us to see intermediate colours; for example, yellow light will activate both green and red cones. Subsequent stages of processing in the thalamus and visual cortex maintain separation between the different colour streams but ultimately colours are assigned based on a comparison of the readout of the three cones. Cones are most active in bright light, when the response to light in rods becomes completely saturated. In low light or dark conditions, rods provide additional information about the brightness of a colour.

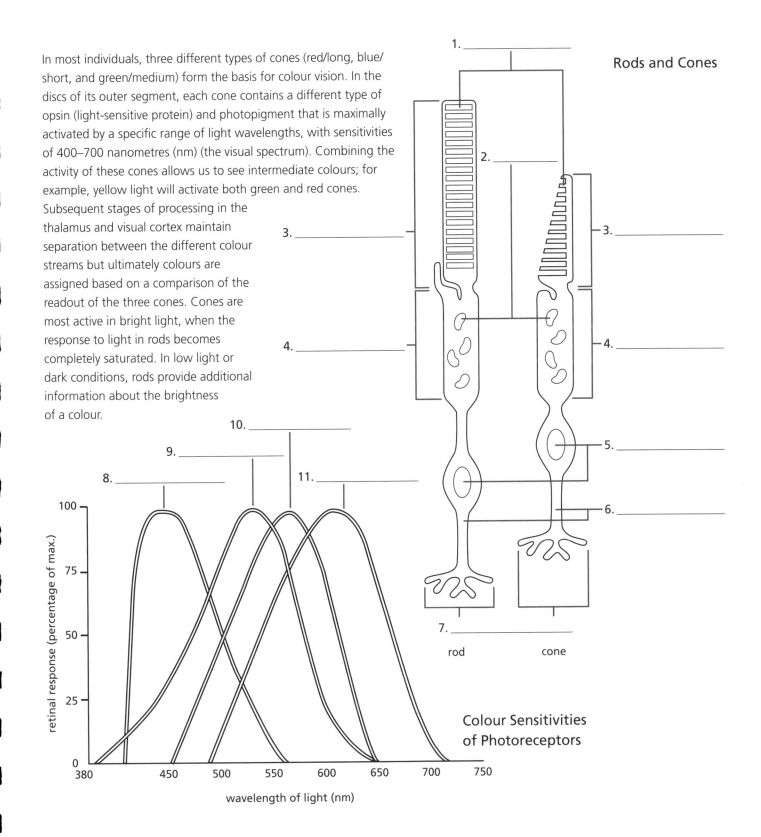

Rods and Cones

1. _____

2. _____

3. _____

3. _____

4. _____

4. _____

5. _____

6. _____

7. _____

rod   cone

Colour Sensitivities of Photoreceptors

8. _____ 9. _____ 10. _____ 11. _____

retinal response (percentage of max.)

100

75

50

25

0

380   450   500   550   600   650   700   750

wavelength of light (nm)

Visual Functions of the Brain

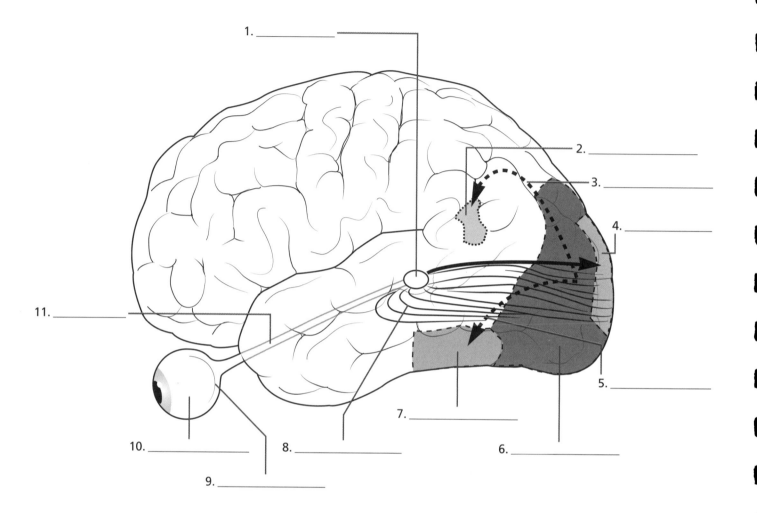

1. _____

2. _____

3. _____

4. _____

5. _____

6. _____

7. _____

8. _____

9. _____

10. _____

11. _____

While the retina computes details about the location, luminosity, and colour of an image, the brain is responsible for the remaining aspects of visual perception. Retinal ganglion cells send axons through the optic nerve and optic tract to the lateral geniculate nucleus (LGN) of the thalamus. Neurons in the LGN compute basic information about the motion and form of an object and then send this information via the optic radiation to the striate, or primary, visual cortex (V1), where each part of visual space is represented. Here, specific cells respond to particular orientations of lines – the beginning of a true representation of visual form in the brain. Depth information is computed by combining information from both left and right visual fields, a process known as stereopsis. From V1, information about the basic form of an object is sent through the ventral 'what' pathway to extrastriate areas such as the V4/ inferior temporal cortex, which combines this information to create a complex representation of an object. Alternatively, information is sent through the dorsal 'where' pathway, which contains areas such as the V5/middle temporal cortex (MT), largely responsible for computing the movement of an object.

Answers

1. lateral geniculate nucleus of the thalamus, 2. V5/middle temporal cortex, 3. dorsal 'where' pathway, 4. striate/primary visual cortex, 5. ventral 'what' pathway, 6. extrastriate, 7. V4/inferior temporal cortex, 8. optic radiation, 9. retina, 10. eye, 11. optic nerve

Sense of Taste

Sense of taste, or gustation, operates by chemoreception, whereby chemical compounds (tastants) are detected and translated into specific tastes. There are five main tastes: salty, bitter, sour, sweet, and umami (savoury). Taste sensations are transduced by gustatory cells located in taste pores, bunches of which are called taste buds. Found throughout the mouth, taste buds are highly concentrated on the tongue, where they can be mapped out in accordance with their predominant taste perception. Gustatory cells are replenished frequently due to their short life span.

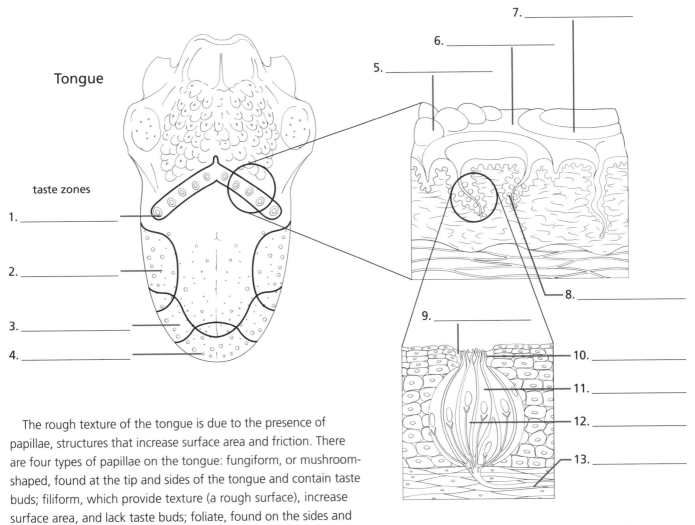

Tongue

taste zones

1. _____
2. _____
3. _____
4. _____

5. _____
6. _____
7. _____
8. _____
9. _____
10. _____
11. _____
12. _____
13. _____

The rough texture of the tongue is due to the presence of papillae, structures that increase surface area and friction. There are four types of papillae on the tongue: fungiform, or mushroom-shaped, found at the tip and sides of the tongue and contain taste buds; filiform, which provide texture (a rough surface), increase surface area, and lack taste buds; foliate, found on the sides and back of the tongue and possess taste buds; and circumvallate, which are dome-shaped and lead back in two rows to the midline, and are sensitive to rapid changes in taste sensation.

Sweet, bitter, and umami tastes are sensed by the binding of the related tastants to G-protein coupled receptors. Salt is detected through Na^+ channels, and sour tastes are perceived when H^+ ions enter taste buds.

Taste is only part of the flavour sensation – other factors detected in the mouth include texture, temperature, and spiciness. Humans have also developed an increased sensitivity to bitterness as a protective mechanism, as most poisons taste bitter.

From the gustatory cells, three cranial nerves convey taste impulses to the brainstem: the facial nerve, the glossopharyngeal nerve, and the vagus nerve.

Answers

1. bitter, 2. sour, 3. salty, 4. sweet, 5. fungiform papillae, 6. filiform papillae, 7. circumvallate papillae, 8. taste bud, 9. taste pore, 10. gustatory hairs, 11. gustatory receptor cell, 12. supporting cell, 13. sensory afferents

Sense of Smell

Sense of smell, or olfaction, is a form of chemoreception whereby chemical compounds (odorants) bind to specific sites on olfactory receptors. In order to increase the surface area for the detection of odorants, the olfactory receptors are located on olfactory hairs. These hairs are surrounded by a mucus, which provides protection and also further increases surface area. Odorants are carried into the nasal cavity in inhaled air, where concha create turbulence in the airflow, increasing the probability of odorant delivery to the mucus and therefore the olfactory receptors. The mucus acts as a solvent for the odorants and is replaced approximately every ten minutes.

Mucus also contains mucopolysaccharides, salts, enzymes, and antibodies. This is important, as the olfactory neurons potentially provide a direct route for infection to pass to the brain.

Odorants bind to specific receptors, generating action potentials (APs) via second messenger (cyclic adenosine monophosphate, or cAMP) pathways. The APs follow tracts to the olfactory cortex and mitral cells, from where they pass into regions of the cerebrum involved in compound recognition and memory association.

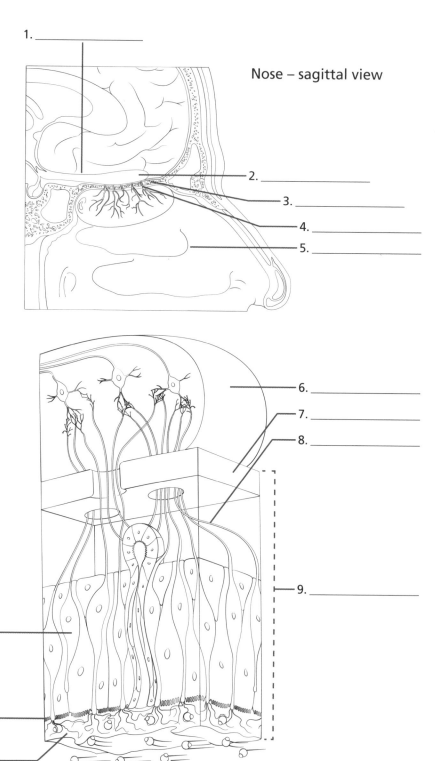

Nose – sagittal view

1. _____

2. _____

3. _____

4. _____

5. _____

6. _____

7. _____

8. _____

9. _____

10. _____

11. _____

12. _____

13. _____

Olfactory Receptors

Spinal Reflexes (1)

Spinal reflexes do not involve the brain but are instead mediated by the spinal cord. In a spinal reflex a stimulus is detected and relayed to neurons in the spinal cord via sensory afferent fibres. The spinal cord returns a signal along the efferent motor pathway, resulting in a movement in response to the stimulus. All this happens in a fraction of a second, prior to stimulus perception.

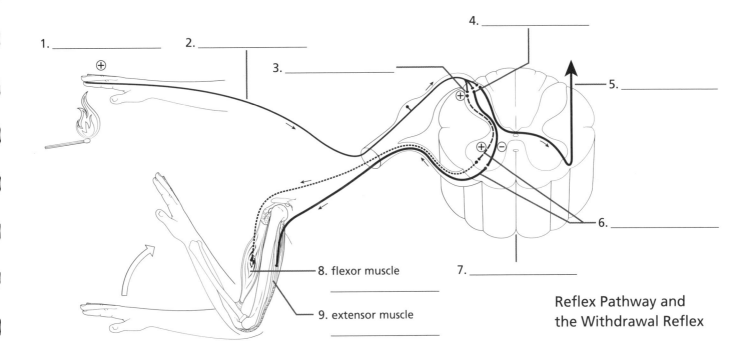

1. _____
2. _____
3. _____
4. _____
5. _____
6. _____
7. _____

8. flexor muscle _____

9. extensor muscle _____

Reflex Pathway and the Withdrawal Reflex

Types of spinal reflex:

The withdrawal reflex protects the body from noxious stimuli. It is a polysynaptic reflex, stimulating efferent, afferent, and association neurons. Sensory receptors that sense a potentially damaging stimulus are called nociceptors. When nociceptors are activated, action potentials (APs) propagate along afferent fibres to the central nervous system. From here, the signals pass to interneurons connected to efferent motor neurons, which then carry the signals to paired muscles – flexor muscles contract to withdraw the limb, and the antagonistic extensor muscle relaxes to aid withdrawal; this is called reciprocal innervation.

The Golgi tendon/inverse myotatic reflex protects muscles and tendons from damage resulting from excess tension. Sensory receptors in the tendons fire APs in response to an increase in tension. Afferent fibres relay messages to efferent fibres in the spinal cord, which are inhibited by the neurotransmitter glycine. This hyperpolarises the efferent fibres, resulting in the generation of inhibitory postsynaptic potentials (IPSPs) and relaxation of the muscle. Although less sensitive than the stretch reflex, the Golgi tendon reflex can override the stretch reflex.

Answers

1. sensory receptor, 2. afferent/sensory neuron, 3. excitatory interneuron, 4. inhibitory interneuron, 5. ascending pathway, 6. efferent/motor neurons, 7. spinal cord, 8. contracts, 9. relaxes

Spinal Reflexes (2)

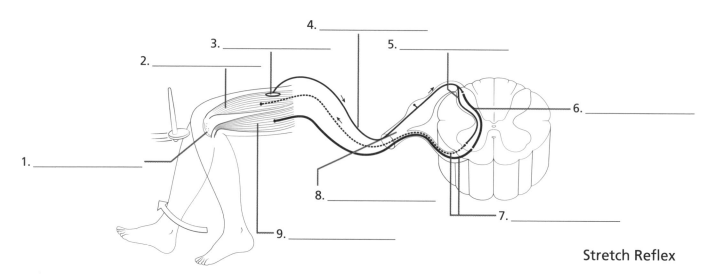

1. _____
2. _____
3. _____
4. _____
5. _____
6. _____
7. _____
8. _____
9. _____

Stretch Reflex

The stretch/myotatic reflex maintains appropriate muscle length, whereby a muscle contracts in response to stretching. It is a monosynaptic reflex, responsible for automatic regulation of skeletal muscle length. When a muscle is stretched, the muscle spindle fibres are stretched, at which point receptors detect the stretching and fire action potentials along afferent neurons to the spinal cord. This in turn stimulates efferent motor neurons, causing the muscle to contract. A secondary set of neurons causes relaxation in the antagonistic muscle.

The crossed extensor reflex occurs in the legs, whereby a withdrawal reflex takes place in one leg and the opposite happens in the opposing leg to allow it to take primarily the body's weight. This is a contralateral reflex, as it takes place on the opposite side of the body to the stimulus. Stimulated afferent fibres cross the spinal cord, synapsing with interneurons that then stimulate or inhibit the appropriate motor neurons on the opposing side to the stimulus. Efferent fibres control the hip muscles to maintain balance. This coordination is controlled by the cerebellum and cerebral cortex following the initial reflex.

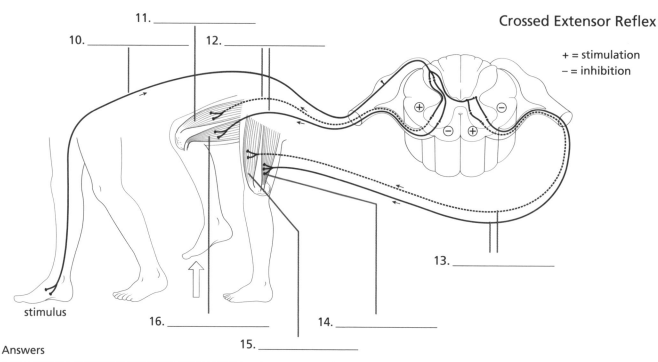

Crossed Extensor Reflex

+ = stimulation
− = inhibition

10. _____
11. _____
12. _____
13. _____
14. _____
15. _____
16. _____

stimulus

Answers

Motor Pathways

Pyramidal neurons are the most numerous cell type in the mammalian brain; they have a distinct anatomy (a pyramidal-shaped cell body and two distinct dendritic trees) and are found in forebrain structures, such as the cerebral cortex, hippocampus, and amygdala. Motor pathways originate in the pyramidal neurons of the precentral gyrus (motor cortex), with about 30 per cent of fibres arising from the primary motor cortex and another 30 per cent from the premotor cortex and supplementary motor area. The somatosensory cortex, cingulate gyrus, and parietal lobe provide the rest. Their cell bodies are in the cerebral cortex, with their axons projecting down the pyramids of the brainstem and then descending the spinal cord to control the α-motor neurons, which exit the central nervous system via the ventral horns.

There are two main motor pathways, the corticospinal and corticobulbar tracts, which terminate in the spinal cord and brainstem, respectively.

The corticobulbar tract conducts action potentials to the cranial nerves, controlling facial and neck muscles. It is involved in mastication, swallowing, and facial expression, among other functions.

The corticospinal tract conducts action potentials to the spinal cord; it consists of lateral and anterior tracts. The medulla is the crossing point for the majority of the fibres in the corticospinal tract, with the brain controlling muscle on the opposite side of the body. Betz cells (giant pyramidal cells) project their axons from the primary motor cortex down the corticospinal tract, synapsing in the ventral/dorsal horns with motor neurons. They are involved in controlling voluntary movements.

1. _____

2. _____

3. _____

**Motor Pathways
Through Spinal Cord**

4. _____   ____

5. _____   ____

6. _____   ____

7. _____

Answers

Motor Control and Coordination: Basal Ganglia

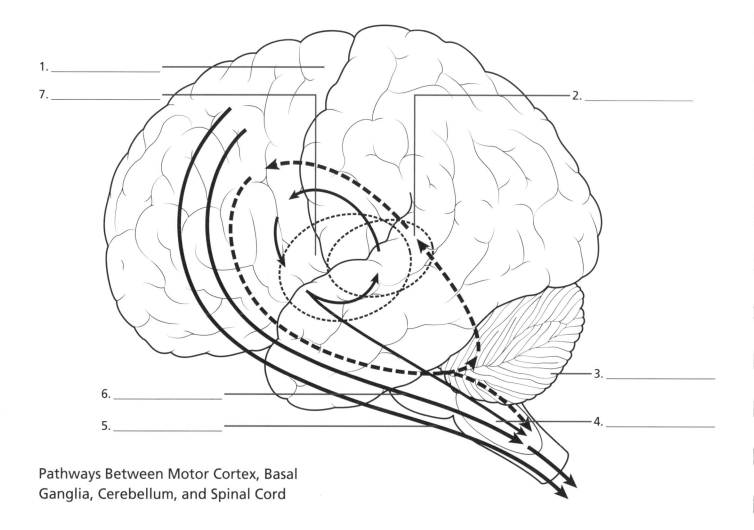

1. _____ _____
7. _____
2. _____
3. _____
6. _____
5. _____
4. _____

**Pathways Between Motor Cortex, Basal
Ganglia, Cerebellum, and Spinal Cord**

Basal ganglia are groups of nuclei found on both sides of the thalamus, outside and above the limbic
system but below the cingulate gyrus and within the temporal lobe. They play a role in planning,
coordination, learning, and selection of specific movements.

Basal ganglia are known to modify movements continually. The motor cortex sends impulses to the
basal ganglia, which return inhibitory impulses to the motor cortex via the thalamus. Basal ganglia are
inhibitory to motor systems; removal of this inhibition allows the activity to be fulfilled. Inputs from many
parts of the brain feed into the basal ganglia to influence the removal of the inhibitions.

For example, in order to sit still, all action potentials for motor movement must be inhibited, with the
exception of those required for maintenance of posture. To allow specific voluntary movement, some of
the postural impulses and reflexes must be inhibited, and at the same time specific inhibitions must be
removed.

Lesions in specific nuclei show as specific characteristics. Parkinson's disease is an example of this, with
usual symptoms including tremors, rigidity, and difficulty initiating voluntary movements.

Answers

Motor Control and Coordination: Cerebellum

The cerebellum, attached to the base of the brain and known as the 'little brain', is involved in the coordination of movement. It constantly analyses the information from the motor cortex and compares it to proprioceptive feedback, ensuring the movements made match the instructions given. It also plays a role in 'motor learning' and maintenance of balance and posture.

The cerebellum is subdivided into the vestibulocerebellum, involved with vestibular reflexes and postural maintenance; the spinocerebellum, responsible for integrating sensory information with motor commands to produce adaptive motor coordination; and the cerebrocerebellum, involved in planning and timing of movements.

There are four principles to cerebellar function:

Feed-forward processing: The cerebellum does not generate self-sustaining neural activity but receives signals, processes them, and then passes them on.

Divergence and convergence: Although the cerebellum has a limited number of inputs and exits, its internal processing is vast, with up to 40 billion granule cells processing the information received.

Modularity: The cerebellum is divided functionally into modules (neuron clusters and Purkinje fibre strips) that operate independently with shared input information.

Plasticity: The divergence and convergence of the cerebellum provides flexibility for fine-tuning the relationship between inputs and outputs.

In contrast to the output signals of the basal ganglia, which are inhibitory, the output signals from the cerebellum are excitatory.

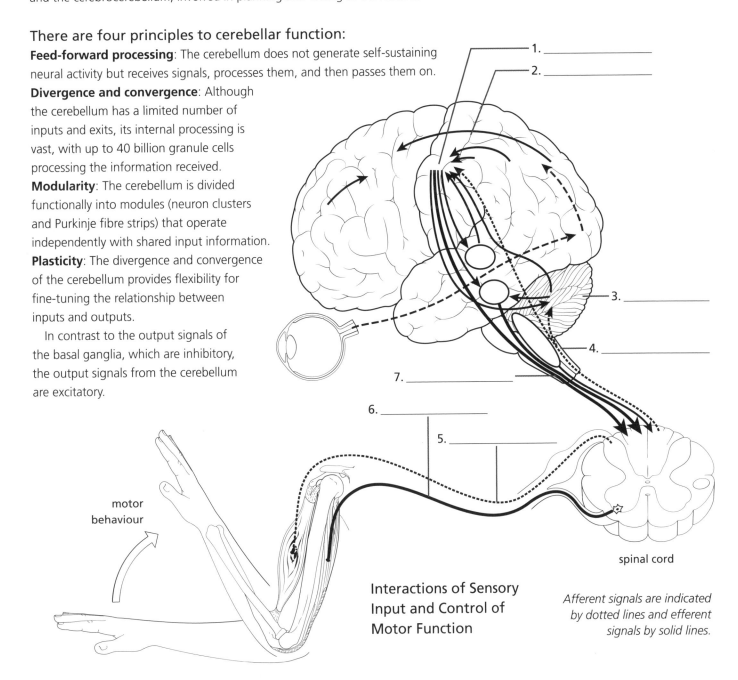

1. _____

2. _____

3. _____

4. _____

7. _____

6. _____

5. _____

spinal cord

motor behaviour

Interactions of Sensory Input and Control of Motor Function

Afferent signals are indicated by dotted lines and efferent signals by solid lines.

Sleep and Wakefulness

Sleep is a recurring condition of body and mind, during which almost all sensory activity and voluntary muscles are inhibited. Interaction with the environment and the ability to detect stimuli are reduced to help facilitate sleep. Both the hypothalamus (via orexin) and reticular formation are actively involved in the execution and timing of sleep and the regulation of phase transition. The circadian clock promotes sleep regularly at night, influenced heavily by daylight and darkness, which inhibits/promotes melatonin secretion from the pineal gland.

Sleep can be split into three phases: rapid eye movement (REM), non-REM (NREM), and waking. It occurs in repeating cycles, alternating between REM and NREM sleep, and entering REM approximately every 90 minutes.

During NREM (comprising around 80 per cent of sleep), the body reduces energy consumption and acetylcholine is less available in the brain. Brainwaves become slower and larger. Adenosine triphosphate (ATP) levels are replenished in depleted areas.

During REM (which makes up around 20 per cent of sleep), most muscles are paralysed, and thermoregulation, heart rate, and breathing are unregulated. REM is promoted by acetylcholine and inhibited by monoamines, including serotonin.

Waking involves increased electrical activation of the brain from the thalamus through to the cortex.

Wakefulness – the state of being awake – can be defined as engaging in coherent cognitive and behavioural responses to stimuli.

Brain – sagittal section

1. _____
2. _____
3. _____
4. _____
5. _____
6. _____
7. _____
8. _____

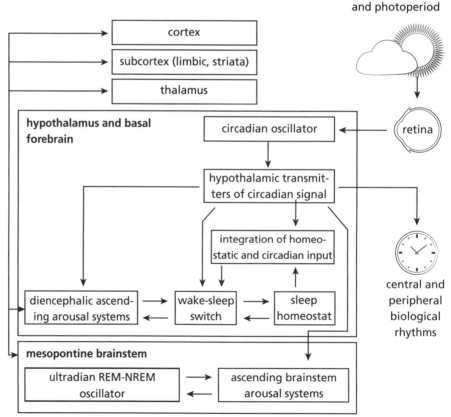

Sleep-Wake Control Systems

environmental light and photoperiod

cortex

subcortex (limbic, striata)

thalamus

hypothalamus and basal forebrain

circadian oscillator

retina

hypothalamic transmitters of circadian signal

integration of homeostatic and circadian input

diencephalic ascending arousal systems

wake-sleep switch

sleep homeostat

central and peripheral biological rhythms

mesopontine brainstem

ultradian REM-NREM oscillator

ascending brainstem arousal systems

1. prefrontal cortex (dreams), 2. thalamus, 3. hippocampus (memory), 4. visual association area (dreams), 5. pineal gland, 6. pons, 7. hypothalamus, 8. amygdala (dreams)

Emotions and the Limbic System

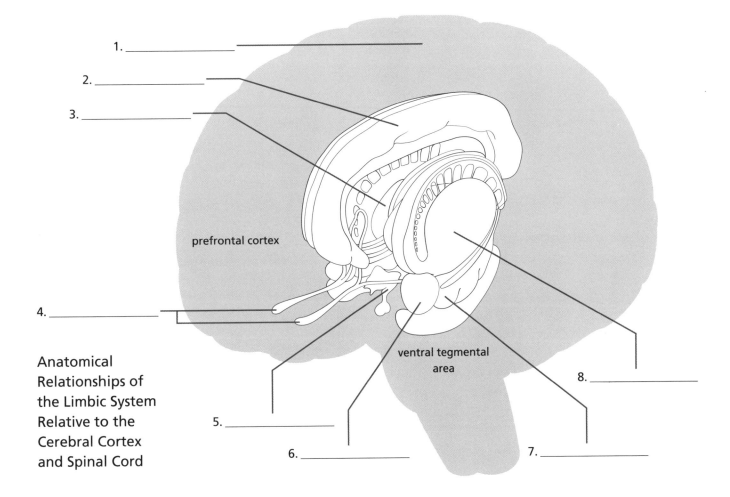

1. _____ _____
2. _____
3. _____

prefrontal cortex

4. _____

Anatomical Relationships of the Limbic System Relative to the Cerebral Cortex and Spinal Cord

ventral tegmental area

5. _____

6. _____

8. _____

7. _____

The limbic system is made up of the amygdala, hippocampus, thalamus, hypothalamus, basal ganglia, and cingulate gyrus. It is involved in emotion, motivation, learning and memory, and the regulation of many of the brain's processes.

The amygdala is the emotional centre of the brain, responsible for evaluating the emotional classification of situations. It aids in recognition of potential threats, stimulating the sympathetic nervous system. It also plays a role in learning through punishment and reward (via links with dopamine transmission). Emotion can also influence the strength of memories, a connection due in part to the amygdala's links with the hippocampus.

The hypothalamus plays an important role in the integration of sensory information from around the body, which influences emotion. It also has a role in the regulation of the autonomic nervous system and can be influenced by emotional inputs from the amygdala.

The ventral tegmental area and prefrontal cortex also play a role in emotion. They are both involved in the dopamine reward/pleasure pathways. Their links with the amygdala and other parts of the limbic system influence emotion.

Overall, the amygdala responds to a variety of emotional stimuli, especially those related to stress, anxiety, and fear.

Answers

1. cortex, 2. cingulate gyrus, 3. thalamus, 4. olfactory bulbs, 5. hypothalamus, 6. amygdala, 7. hippocampus, 8. basal ganglia

Learning and Memory

Long- and short-term memory classification is only half the story. There are two different types of long-term memory: semantic, which is split into declarative (explicit), conscious-type memories of learned cognitive tasks, e.g. words, names, and symbols; and procedural, unconscious (implicit) memories, formed following development of a new sensory or motor skill, e.g. riding a bicycle. In addition, explicit memories also include episodic memories, which are autobiographical events (emotions, times, and places).

Sensory information is held in the memory for less than a second after perception. Short-term memory (limited capacity) enables recall from seconds to minutes without the need for repetition. It takes the form of transient patterns of neural communication. Long-term memory can be stored for up to a lifetime. Its capacity is immeasurable, and it is in a stable form of neural connections spread throughout the brain.

The hippocampus is essential for the consolidation of short-term memories into long-term memories. The amygdala is known to be involved in emotional memory, while the hippocampus is believed to be involved in spatial and declarative learning.

Learning and memory are affected by changes in neuronal synapses (synaptic plasticity), mediated by long-term potentiation (LTP) and long-term depression (LTD). LTP is a persistent strengthening of synapses based on activity patterns. A high-frequency train of action potentials applied to a presynaptic fibre prior to an individual action potential results in prolonged excitatory postsynaptic potentials (EPSPs) at the synapse. Emotion is known to enhance memory.

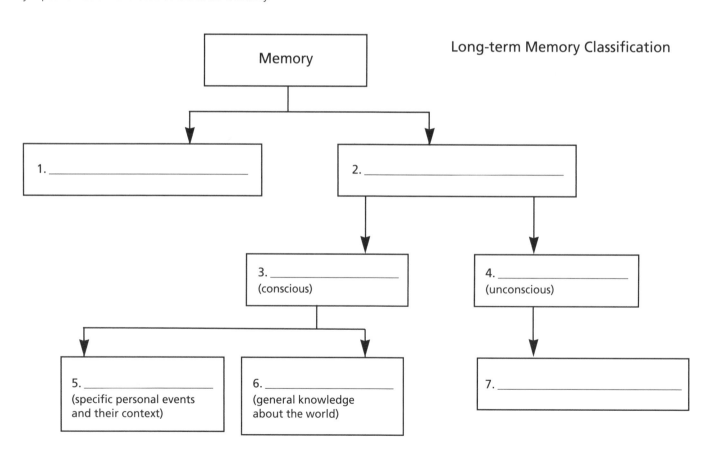

Long-term Memory Classification

Memory

1. _____

2. _____

3. _____ (conscious)

4. _____ (unconscious)

5. _____ (specific personal events and their context)

6. _____ (general knowledge about the world)

7. _____

Answers

1. short-term memory, 2. long-term memory, 3. declarative (explicit), 4. implicit, 5. episodic 6. semantic, 7. procedural

Cortical Specialisation and Asymmetry

The cerebral cortex can be divided in accordance with its layers into the neocortex, which is made up of six layers, and the allocortex, which has either three or four layers. The layers are characterised according to their cell types.

The cerebral cortex can also be subdivided in accordance with its numerous functional areas.

Sensory areas are those receiving and perceiving information from sensory receptors. Those parts receiving inputs from the thalamus are the primary sensory areas, such as the somatosensory (touch), visual (vision), and auditory (hearing) cortices. Adjacent association areas are interwoven with the primary sensory areas, enabling the processing of information for meaningful perception and interpretation. The two hemispheres of the brain receive information from the contralateral (opposite) side of the body.

Motor areas (primary and premotor) are found on both hemispheres; they are also contralateral to the areas they control. The posterior parietal and dorsolateral prefrontal cortexes are involved with voluntary movements.

The human brain demonstrates asymmetries, with an overall leftwards posterior and rightwards anterior torque. Large asymmetries exist in the frontal, temporal, and occipital lobes, suggesting increased connectivity between the motor and somatosensory cortices in the left side of the brain. Human male brains are more asymmetrical laterally than those of females.

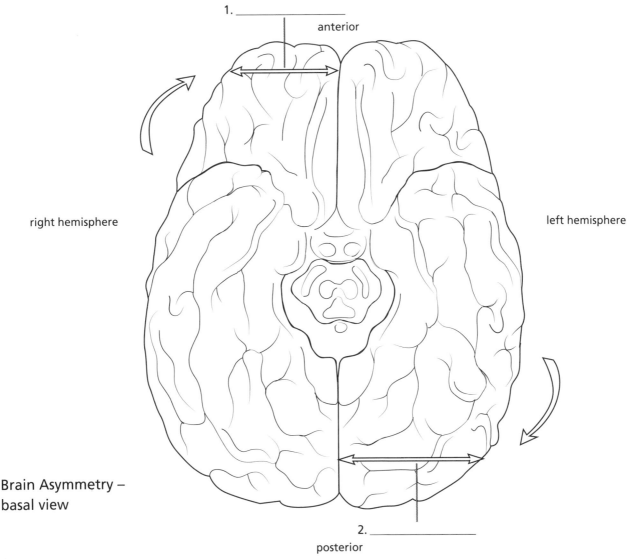

1. _____
anterior

right hemisphere

left hemisphere

Brain Asymmetry – basal view

2. _____
posterior

Answers

1. frontal cortex, 2. occipital cortex

Language

Language processing in the brain occurs mainly in the cerebral cortex and its association areas. Broca's and Wernicke's areas (located in the dominant hemisphere) are both thought to be the most important areas for processing language, along with the prefrontal cortex.

Broca's area is involved in language comprehension and production of speech, and its links with the motor cortex control the mouth, tongue, and larynx. Broca's area has also been linked with sound (through close association with the primary auditory cortex) and speech-associated gestures. Posterior to Broca's area is Wernicke's area, located between the auditory and visual cortices; it is also associated with receptive speech.

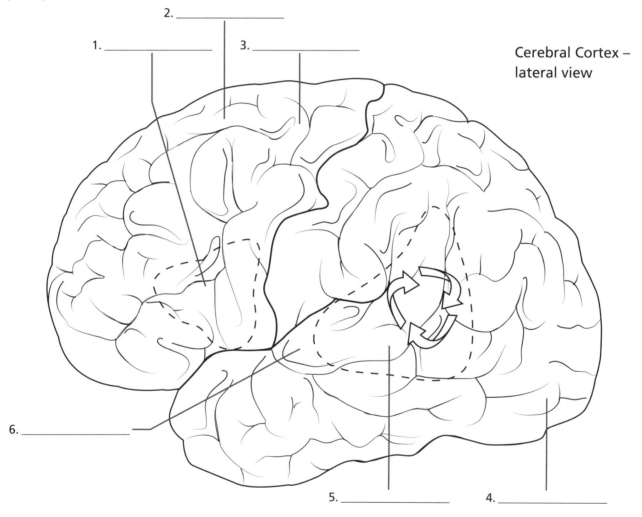

2. _____

1. _____ 3. _____

Cerebral Cortex –
lateral view

6. _____

5. _____ 4. _____

The dominant hemisphere is in charge of most language comprehension, while the less dominant homologous area participates in comprehension of ambiguous words and melodic information.

It has been seen that language processing can be 'shifted' to homologous areas on the less dominant side should the dominant side malfunction or become damaged (e.g. through growth of a tumour). This compensation is enabled by a mechanism of neural plasticity.

Answers

1. Broca's area, 2. frontal lobe, 3. motor cortex, 4. primary visual cortex, 5. Wernicke's area, 6. primary auditory cortex

Electroencephalograph

The electroencephalograph (EEG) is a non-invasive method of recording spontaneous electrical activity of the brain via the surface potentials on the scalp. These surface potentials are from the ionic currents of the neurons of the brain. Neurons of the brain are polarised (electrically charged), with their polarity constantly changing (resting membrane/action potentials). However, the electrical potential of a single neuron is too small to be shown on an EEG. The EEG therefore does not look at individual neurons but instead reflects the summation of the synchronous activity of up to millions of neurons with similar spatial orientation in the brain. For example, the pyramidal neurons of the cortex are well aligned and fire synchronously, giving a clear EEG signal.

The potentials of surface neurons are easier to detect, whereas those from deeper neurons are much more difficult to detect. EEG activity shows as oscillations, the frequencies and spatial distributions of which are associated with different brain functions. The majority of the cerebral signals observed in scalp EEGs are in the range of 1–20 Hz and are classified as follows: delta (<4 Hz), theta (4-7 Hz), alpha (8–15 Hz), and beta (16–31 Hz).

The EEG is used commonly for diagnosis of epilepsy, coma, and sleep disorders; additional applications include brain-computer interfaces, in which the mind is used to control devices such as wheelchairs, robots, computers, etc.

mental state	Normal Adult Brain Waves	type of wave and frequency
awake with mental activity		1. _____ 2. _____
awake and resting		3. _____ 4. _____
sleeping		5. _____ 6. _____
deep sleep		7. _____ 8. _____

1 second

Answers

Brain Metabolism and Blood Flow

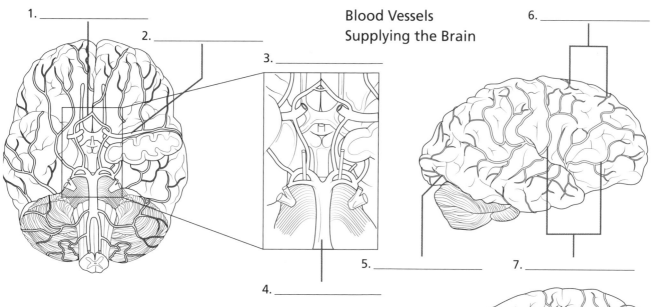

1. _____

2. _____

Blood Vessels
Supplying the Brain

3. _____

6. _____

5. _____

7. _____

4. _____

The human brain's energy consumption is up to 20 per cent of the body's total – more than for all other organs. The major substrate for metabolism in the brain is normally glucose, but during low blood glucose episodes this switches to ketone bodies or lactate. Ketone bodies are created in the liver from the breakdown of long-chain fatty acids. Long-chain fatty acids are unable to cross the blood-brain barrier, whereas medium-chain fatty acids can and are thus utilised by the brain. The brain stores glucose in small amounts in the form of glycogen.

The brain receives 15 per cent of the total cardiac output, and it is responsible for 20 per cent of total body oxygen consumption and 25 per cent of total body glucose utilisation.

Arterial cerebral circulation has anterior and posterior divisions that are interconnected via bilateral posterior communicating arteries, forming part of the circle of Willis. These provide a 'backup' circulation, in case of occlusion to one of the supply arteries. Venous drainage of the cerebrum is also separated into deep and superficial divisions.

The blood-brain barrier protects the central nervous system (CNS) from common bacterial infections and neurotoxins. The barrier is a highly selectively permeable membrane, separating blood circulation from the extracellular fluid of the CNS. It allows water, lipid-soluble molecules, and some gases to diffuse through, along with the selective transport of amino acids and glucose.

8. _____

9. _____

large molecules

glucose/amino acids

10. _____

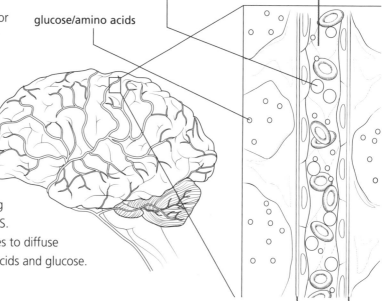

11. _____

Structure of Skeletal Muscle

Skeletal muscle is a collection of muscle cells, or muscle fibres. Each fibre is a long cylindrical cell that has many nuclei. These fibres are grouped together in bundles to form muscle fascicles. Many fascicles, along with nerves and blood vessels, are held together by connective tissue to form the skeletal muscle. Within each muscle fibre are myofibrils, bundles of contractile and elastic proteins that allow for muscle contraction. Each myofibril is composed of thin filaments of the protein actin and thick filaments of the protein myosin. Myosin heads interact with actin molecules to form cross-bridges. Thin and thick filaments are organised into sarcomeres along titin and nebulin, giant accessory proteins. Also within each muscle fibre are transverse tubules, a branching network that is an extension of the sarcolemma (cell membrane of a muscle cell). Transverse tubules abut with the ends (terminal cisternae) of the sarcoplasmic reticulum in what is known as a triad.

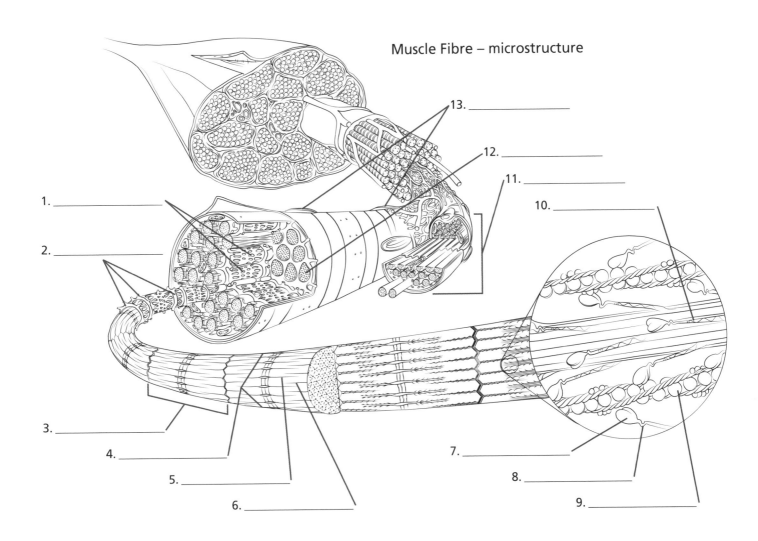

Muscle Fibre – microstructure

1. _____
2. _____
3. _____
4. _____
5. _____
6. _____
7. _____
8. _____
9. _____
10. _____
11. _____
12. _____
13. _____

Structure of Skeletal Muscle

Each myofibril is composed of many sarcomeres, the contractile unit of the myofibril. Sarcomeres contain multiple elements that describe the organisation of the thin and thick filaments. The M line consists of myosin linked with accessory proteins. In the H zone, only myosin is present. The A band is composed of the H zone, with the addition of the remaining portion of myosin filaments that overlaps with actin. Because of this overlap, the outer regions of the A band appear of a darker colour than the central region (H zone). The portion of the thin filaments that does not overlap with the thick filaments is referred to as the I band and is the lightest portion of the sarcomere. Thin filaments are linked together via accessory proteins at the Z discs. Each sarcomere contains two Z discs. The overall length of the sarcomere shortens during contraction as actin and myosin slide past one another. Thus, the A band remains constant during contraction, whereas the H zone and I band both shorten.

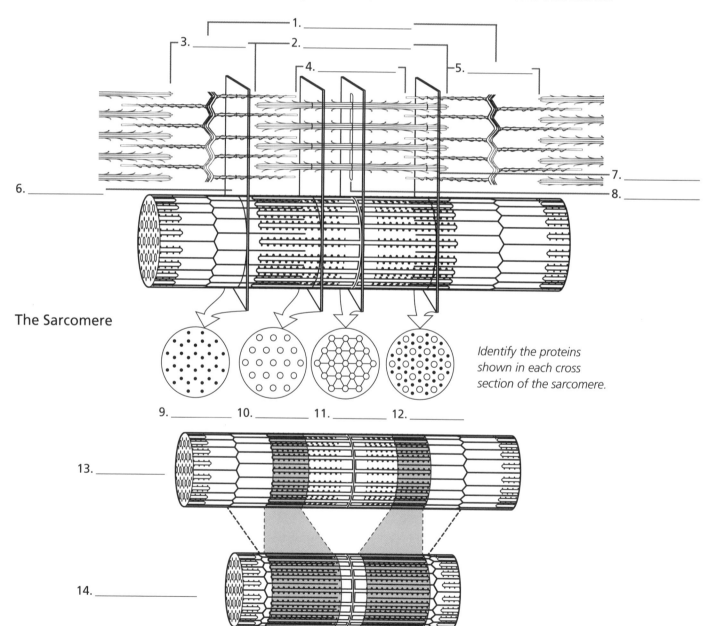

The Sarcomere

1. _____
2. _____
3. _____
4. _____
5. _____
6. _____
7. _____
8. _____

Identify the proteins shown in each cross section of the sarcomere.

9. _____
10. _____
11. _____
12. _____

13. _____
14. _____

Neuromuscular Junction

The neuromuscular junction describes the distal end of a somatic motor neuron and the skeletal muscle fibre it innervates. Specifically, the axon terminal, the motor endplate on the muscle membrane, and Schwann cell sheaths are all contained in this region. The distinctive feature of the motor endplate is the high concentration of nicotinic acetylcholine (ACh) receptors in this area of the sarcolemma. The axon terminal contains vesicles in which ACh is packaged. Upon arrival of an action potential, voltage-gated Ca^{2+} channels open, allowing an influx of calcium ions, which stimulates the vesicles to fuse at the presynaptic membrane. Exocytosis of ACh occurs into the synaptic cleft and ACh binds to nicotinic receptors, depolarising the skeletal muscle cell. Excess ACh is metabolised by acetylcholinesterase present on the postsynaptic membrane into acetyl plus choline for reuptake into the axon terminal and subsequent r-synthesis.

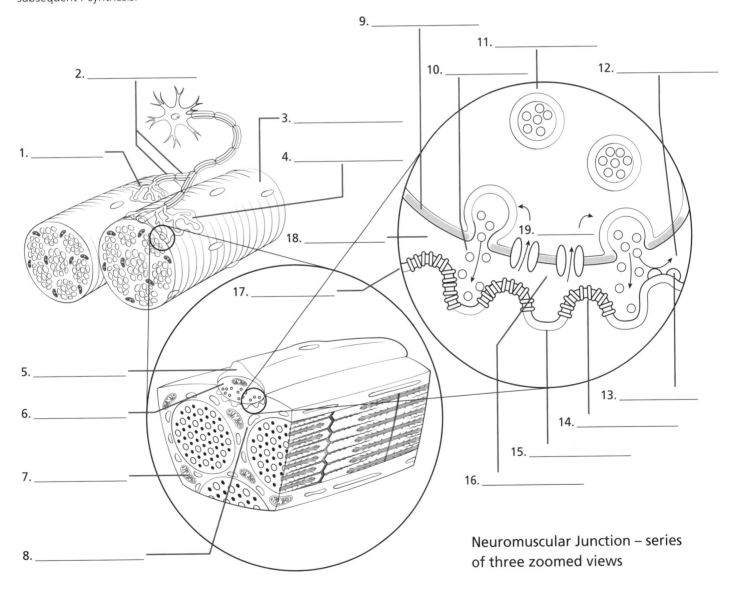

Neuromuscular Junction – series of three zoomed views

Answers

Actin and Myosin

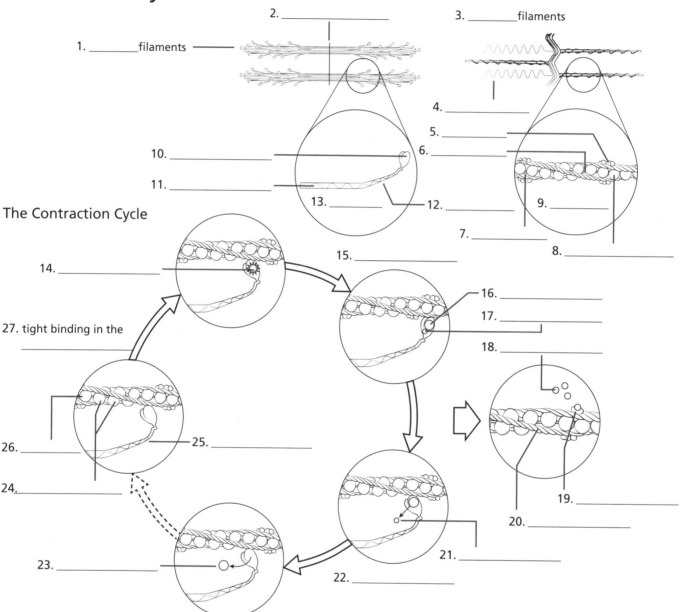

The Contraction Cycle

27. tight binding in the

Actin chains are composed of individual globular G-actin molecules arranged along nebulin strands that help align the actin molecules. In addition, tropomyosin – an elongated protein polymer – wraps around actin filaments, partially covering the actin-myosin binding sites. The position of tropomyosin is regulated by troponin, a three-protein complex that binds calcium ions. Myosin molecules are bundles of myosin tails that end in a hinge region transitioning to the myosin head. The tails are stabilised by titin proteins, which also provide elasticity. In the rigor state, myosin is briefly bound tightly to actin with no nucleotide. As adenosine triphosphate (ATP) binds to the myosin head, it detaches from actin, and energy liberated from ATP hydrolysis is utilised to rotate the myosin head and loosely reattach it to actin in the cocked position, with adenosine diphosphate (ADP) and inorganic phosphate (P_i) remaining bound to the myosin head. Calcium released from the sarcoplasmic reticulum binds to troponin, moving tropomyosin and thus allowing myosin to bind tightly to actin. This tight binding allows for the release of the P_i and swivelling of the myosin head towards the M line (power stroke) that slides the attached actin molecule. Following the power stroke, ADP is released and the myosin and actin are again briefly bound in the rigor state until a new ATP binds.

Answers

1. thick, 2. M line, 3. thin, 4. titin, 5. troponin, 6. nebulin, 7. tropomyosin, 8. G-actin molecule, 9. actin chain, 10. myosin head, 11. myosin tail, 12. hinge region, 13. myosin molecule, 14. adenosine triphosphate (ATP), 15. Ca²⁺ signal, 16. adenosine diphosphate (ADP), 17. inorganic phosphate (P_i), 18. Ca²⁺, 19. troponin, 20. tropomyosin, 21. inorganic phosphate, 22. power stroke, 23. adenosine diphosphate (ADP), 24. myosin binding sites, 25. myosin filament, 26. G-actin molecule, 27. rigor state

Excitation-Contraction Coupling

Excitation-contraction coupling refers to the combination of electrical and mechanical events in a muscle fibre that result in the production of force. Acetylcholine (ACh) is released from the axon terminal of a somatic motor neuron at the neuromuscular junction. When two ACh bind to the nicotinic cholinergic receptors on the sarcolemma, these non-selective monovalent cation channels open, allowing net Na^+ influx and depolarising the muscle fibre. The resulting action potential is carried to the interior of the cell via transverse tubules, where dihydropyridine (DHP) receptors are located and mechanically linked to the nearby sarcoplasmic reticulum. A conformational change in the DHP receptor opens the ryanodine receptors (RyR) of the sarcoplasmic reticulum, allowing Ca^{2+} release into the sarcoplasm. Ca^{2+} then binds to troponin, allowing actin-myosin binding.

Motor Endplate and Calcium Signalling

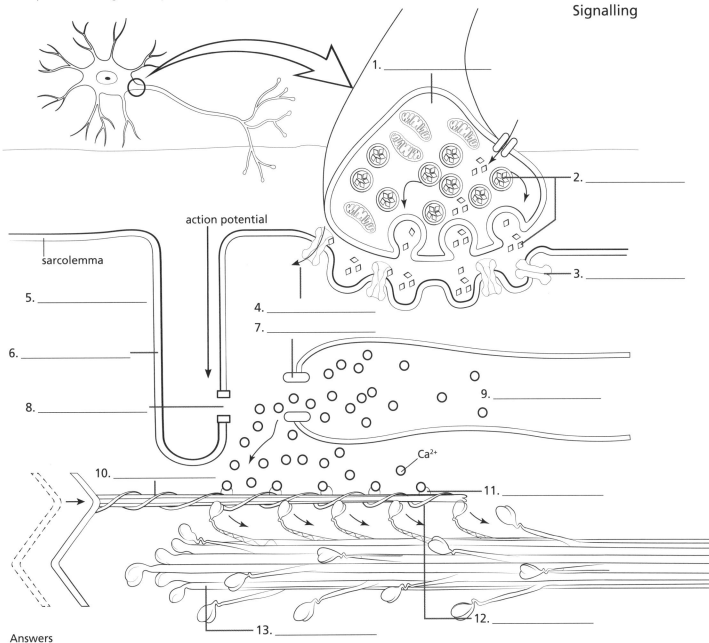

action potential

sarcolemma

1. _____

2. _____

3. _____

4. _____

5. _____

6. _____

7. _____

8. _____

9. _____

10. _____

11. _____

12. _____

13. _____

Ca^{2+}

Answers

1. axon terminal, somatic motor neuron, 2. acetylcholine (ACh), 3. nicotinic receptor, 4. Na^+, 5. muscle fibre, 6. T tubule, 7. ryanodine receptor-channel, 8. dihydropyridine L-type calcium channel, 9. sarcoplasmic reticulum, 10. actin, 11. troponin, 12. tropomyosin, 13. myosin

Muscle Tension and Length

The tension developed during a single muscle twitch is directly related to the number of cross-bridges formed between the thick and thin filaments. Accordingly, if there are too few cross-bridges formed, tension will be decreased. If, during contraction, new cross-bridge binding sites are not available as the sarcomere shortens, tension will also be diminished. The resting length of the muscle fibre thus has a significant effect on the amount of tension that can be produced from a given muscle twitch. At increased resting length, too few cross-bridges form. At decreased resting length, the Z discs provide a barrier to contraction and formation of new cross-bridges as the sarcomere shortens. Thus, there is an optimal resting length that produces optimal tension generation.

Length-Tension Relationships

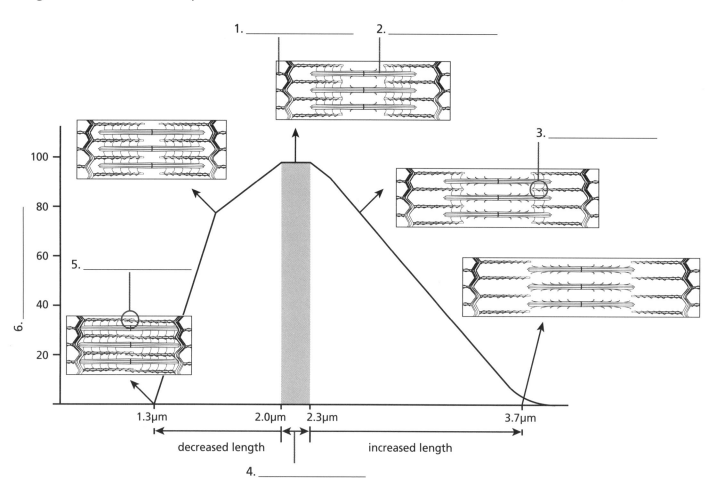

Summation of Contraction

To increase the force generated by the contraction of a single muscle fibre, the frequency of action potentials that stimulate the fibre can be increased. However, it should be noted that this can only be shown in the laboratory. In normal physiology, muscles are always activated with a frequency of action potentials to produce tetani within the muscle fibre. When stimuli occur at a low frequency, there is sufficient time for the muscle to relax fully before the next stimulus for contraction. As frequency increases and stimuli occur more rapidly, there is insufficient time for full relaxation and a more forceful contraction results. This process is known as summation. At consistent high frequencies, muscle twitches will sum, or add together, until tetanus is reached, the state of maximal contraction of a muscle fibre. If there is slight relaxation between stimuli, tetanus is unfused, whereas if stimuli are rapid enough to result in a constant maximal tension, complete tetanus has occurred. Fatigue of a single muscle fibre occurs when the tension decreases despite a continued stimulus.

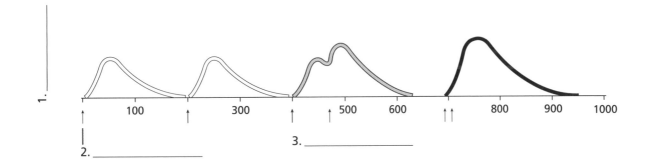

1.

100   300   500   600   800   900   1000

2. _____

3. _____

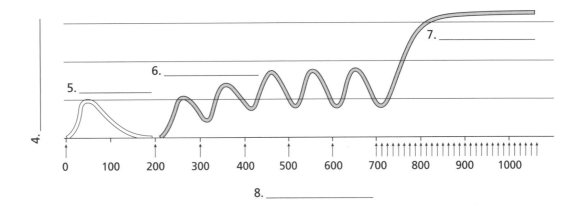

4.

5. _____

6. _____

7. _____

0   100   200   300   400   500   600   700   800   900   1000

8. _____

Motor Unit Recruitment

Multiple Motor Units of Multiple Fiber Types

Whole muscles are made of many fibres that are organised into motor units. All muscle fibres within a single motor unit are of the same type. Slow oxidative (type I) fibres have low myosin ATPase activity and high oxidative capacity. These fibres have small diameters and small motor neurons and motor units, and they produce the least amount of force. Given their high oxidative capacity, they are fatigue-resistant and are recruited initially in force production. Fast oxidative glycolytic fibres (type IIa) combine high myosin ATPase activity with high oxidative capacity and intermediate glycolytic capacity. These fibres have large diameters and intermediate-sized motor neurons and motor units. Recruited secondly, they have some fatigue resistance yet are also capable of producing significant force. Fast glycolytic fibres (type IIb) combine high myosin ATPase activity and high glycolytic capacity. Large fibre size and large motor unit and motor neuron size of IIb fibres result in the greatest capacity to produce tension; however, these fibres fatigue rapidly. Given a low fatigue resistance, IIb fibres are generally recruited last, when large amounts of force are needed over time. In order to resist overall fatigue during sustained contractions, the nervous system utilises asynchronous recruitment of motor units.

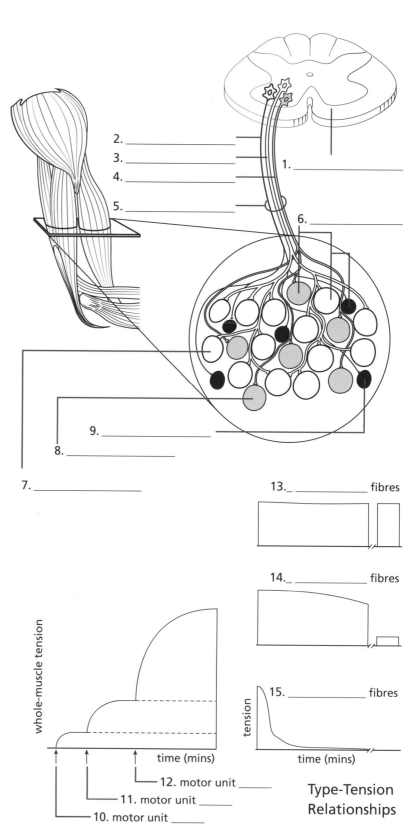

2. _____
3. _____
4. _____
5. _____
1. _____
6. _____
9. _____
8. _____
7. _____

13. _____ fibres
14. _____ fibres
15. _____ fibres

whole-muscle tension

time (mins)

12. motor unit _____
11. motor unit _____
10. motor unit _____

tension

time (mins)

Type-Tension Relationships

Muscle Metabolism

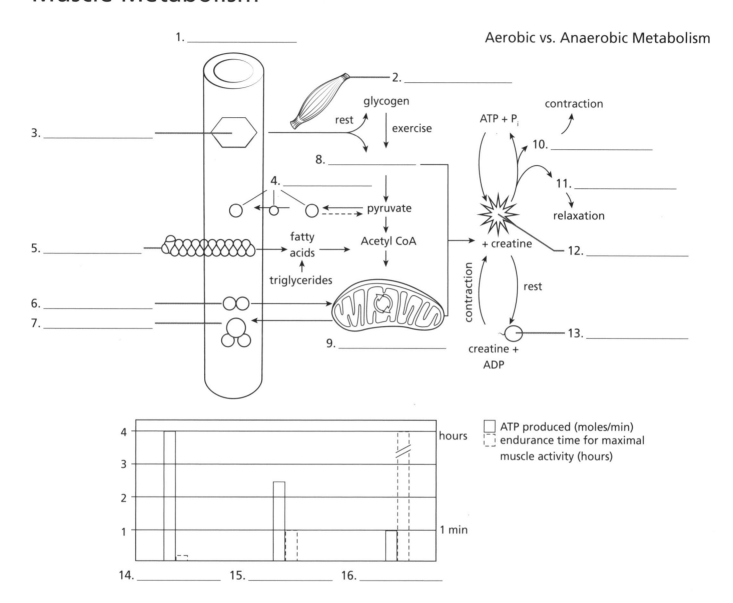

Aerobic vs. Anaerobic Metabolism

In order to provide sufficient adenosine triphosphate (ATP) to fuel muscle contraction, several pathways are involved in muscle metabolism. Glucose from the bloodstream can be stored in skeletal muscle as glycogen. Glycolysis is an anaerobic process that produces two pyruvate molecules from one glucose molecule. In anaerobic conditions, pyruvate is shuttled to lactate. In aerobic conditions, pyruvate is converted to acetyl-CoA and enters the citric acid cycle. In aerobic conditions, fatty acids can undergo beta oxidation, producing acyl units that also enter the citric acid cycle as acetyl-CoA. Within the mitochondria, oxygen is consumed and carbon dioxide is produced during oxidative phosphorylation and ATP is generated. Hydrolysis of ATP to adenosine diphosphate (ADP) and inorganic phosphate (P_i) occurs via myosin ATPase to stimulate contraction through the power stroke. ATP is also utilised by the sarcoplasmic reticulum Ca^{2+}-ATPase in the relaxed state. As an immediate source of ATP, phosphocreatine (PCr) is capable of combining with ADP to form a rapid yet short-lived source of ATP. The speed of ATP production and endurance of each pathway differs; however, PCr, anaerobic metabolism, and aerobic metabolism together provide energy to support muscle contraction in a variety of conditions.

Answers

1. blood, 2. muscle tissue, 3. glucose, 4. lactate, 5. fatty acids, 6. oxygen, 7. carbon dioxide, 8. glycolysis (anaerobic), 9. oxidative phosphorylation and citric acid cycle (aerobic), 10. myosin ATPase, 11. Ca^{2+}-ATPase, 12. adenosine triphosphate (ATP), 13. phosphocreatine (PCr), 14. phosphocreatine, 15. anaerobic metabolism, 16. aerobic metabolism

Overview of the Circulatory System

Circulatory System
– anterior view

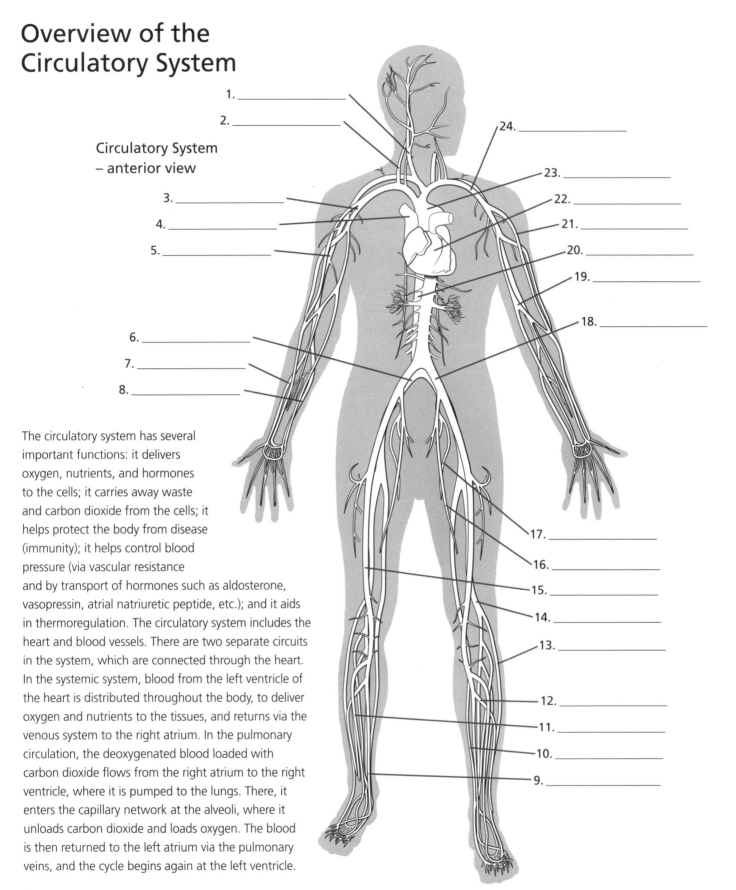

1. _____
2. _____
3. _____
4. _____
5. _____
6. _____
7. _____
8. _____

24. _____
23. _____
22. _____
21. _____
20. _____
19. _____
18. _____
17. _____
16. _____
15. _____
14. _____
13. _____
12. _____
11. _____
10. _____
9. _____

The circulatory system has several important functions: it delivers oxygen, nutrients, and hormones to the cells; it carries away waste and carbon dioxide from the cells; it helps protect the body from disease (immunity); it helps control blood pressure (via vascular resistance and by transport of hormones such as aldosterone, vasopressin, atrial natriuretic peptide, etc.); and it aids in thermoregulation. The circulatory system includes the heart and blood vessels. There are two separate circuits in the system, which are connected through the heart. In the systemic system, blood from the left ventricle of the heart is distributed throughout the body, to deliver oxygen and nutrients to the tissues, and returns via the venous system to the right atrium. In the pulmonary circulation, the deoxygenated blood loaded with carbon dioxide flows from the right atrium to the right ventricle, where it is pumped to the lungs. There, it enters the capillary network at the alveoli, where it unloads carbon dioxide and loads oxygen. The blood is then returned to the left atrium via the pulmonary veins, and the cycle begins again at the left ventricle.

Answers

1. common carotid artery, 2. external jugular vein, 3. axillary vein, 4. superior vena cava, 5. brachial artery, 6. common iliac vein, 7. radial artery, 8. ulnar artery, 9. posterior tibial artery, 10. great saphenous vein, 11. anterior tibial artery, 12. fibular artery, 13. small saphenous vein, 14. popliteal vein, 15. femoral artery, 16. obturator artery, 17. obturator vein, 18. common iliac artery, 19. basilic vein, 20. inferior vena cava, 21. cephalic vein, 22. heart, 23. aortic arch, 24. subclavian vein

Basic Structure of the Heart and Cardiac Muscle

The heart lies in the midline of the thorax, between the lungs, and is surrounded by the double-layered membrane of the pericardium. The right and left atria are located superior, whereas the right and left ventricles are located inferior. A septum divides the right and left atria and the right and left ventricles. Each atrium opens into a ventricle through an atrioventricular orifice, which is guarded by a valve to ensure blood flows in only one direction. The left atrium and ventricle receive oxygenated blood from the lungs via the pulmonary veins and pump it out to the body via the aorta. The right atrium and ventricle receive relatively deoxygenated blood from the body via the vena cavae and pump it to the lungs via the pulmonary arteries. A cross-sectional view of the heart exposes the four chambers and valves. The mitral valve sits between the left atrium and ventricle. Blood exiting from the left ventricle is released through the aortic valve. The tricuspid valve sits between the right atrium and ventricle. Blood leaving the right ventricle passes through the pulmonary valve.

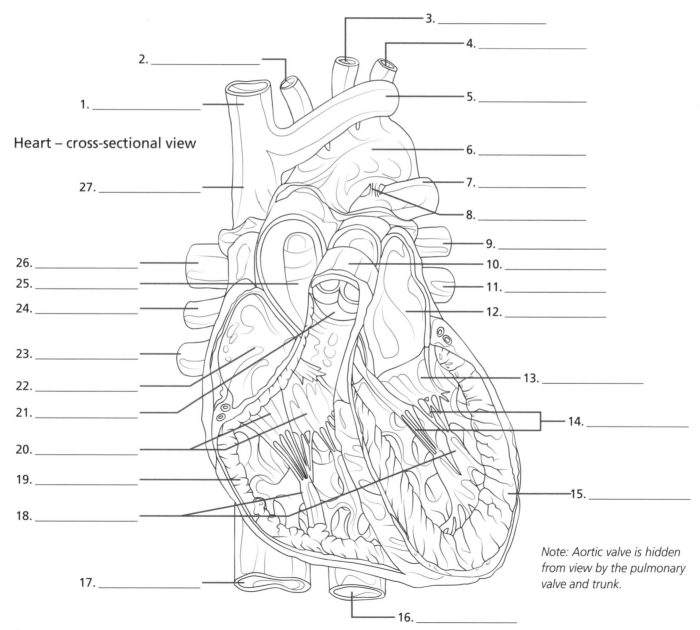

Heart – cross-sectional view

1. _____
2. _____
3. _____
4. _____
5. _____
6. _____
7. _____
8. _____
9. _____
10. _____
11. _____
12. _____
13. _____
14. _____
15. _____
16. _____
17. _____
18. _____
19. _____
20. _____
21. _____
22. _____
23. _____
24. _____
25. _____
26. _____
27. _____

Note: Aortic valve is hidden from view by the pulmonary valve and trunk.

Answers

1. right brachiocephalic vein, 2. brachiocephalic artery, 3. left common carotid artery, 4. left subclavian artery, 5. left brachiocephalic vein, 6. aortic arch, 7. left pulmonary artery, 8. ligamentum arteriosum, 9. left superior pulmonary vein, 10. pulmonary trunk, 11. left inferior pulmonary vein, 12. left atrium, 13. cusp of mitral valve, 14. chordae tendineae, 15. left ventricle, 16. descending thoracic aorta, 17. inferior vena cava, 18. papillary muscles, 19. right ventricle, 20. cusp of tricuspid valve, 21. pulmonary valve, 22. right atrium, 23. right inferior pulmonary vein, 24. right superior pulmonary vein, 25. ascending aorta, 26. right pulmonary artery, 27. superior vena cava

Basic Structure of the Heart and Cardiac Muscle

Cardiac muscle is similar to skeletal muscle in that it is striated – it has a banded appearance due to the overlapping actin and myosin fibres. However, whereas skeletal muscle cells are very elongated and multinucleate, cardiac muscle cells are shorter and branched and have only one nucleus per cell. Cardiac fibres are also orientated spirally in four layers – two groups wind around the outside of both ventricles, a third group beneath winds around both ventricles, and a fourth group winds around the left ventricle. This unique orientation allows the contractions to squeeze the ventricular chambers from the apex to the base and thus pump blood into the pulmonary and aortic arteries. The T tubules of cardiac muscle carry the electrical depolarisation of the cardiac action potential deep into the cell in order to initiate muscle contraction. The definitive feature of cardiac muscle cells is that they are interconnected to other cardiac cells via intercalated discs, which are high-density areas of gap junctions. This allows the cardiac muscle cells to communicate both chemically and electrically via the cytoplasm. Most importantly, it allows the heart muscle to contract as a unit, in a coordinated fashion, to pump blood.

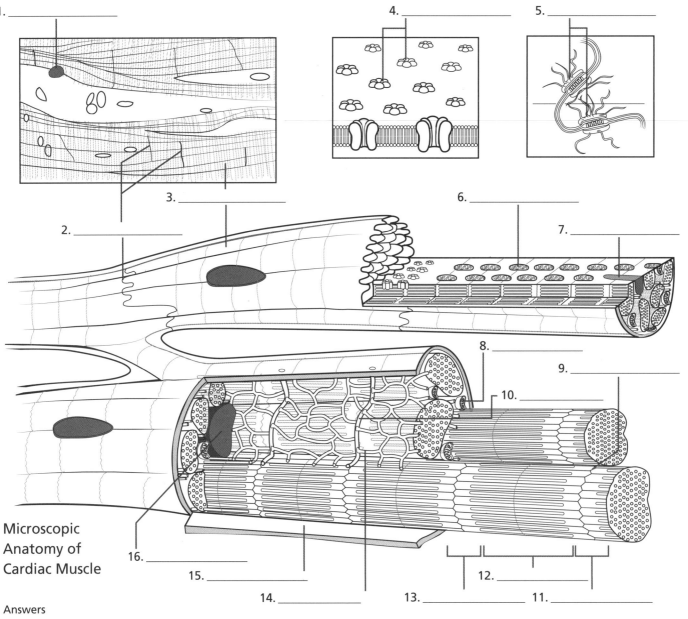

1. _____

2. _____

3. _____

4. _____

5. _____

6. _____

7. _____

8. _____

9. _____

10. _____

11. _____

12. _____

13. _____

14. _____

15. _____

16. _____

Microscopic
Anatomy of
Cardiac Muscle

Answers

1. nucleus, 2. nucleus, 3. intercalated discs, 4. cardiac muscle cell, 5. fasciae adherens, 6. mitochondrion, 7. nucleus, 8. mitochondrion, 9. Z disc, 10. T tubule, 11. I band, 12. I band, 13. A band, 14. sarcoplasmic reticulum, 15. sarcolemma, 16. nucleus

Basic Structure of Blood Vessels:
Structure of Blood Vessels

artery

1. _____

2. _____

3. _____

4. _____

5. _____

7. _____

valve

6. _____

Types of Blood Vessels

layers of
walls of
a vein

8. _____

11. _____

10. _____

9. _____

12. _____

13. _____

16. _____

15. _____

14. _____

18. _____

17. _____

Blood is composed of red blood cells (erythrocytes), various types of white blood cells (leukocytes), and platelets (thrombocytes) in a solution (plasma) of water, electrolytes, and proteins. Red blood cells carry oxygen to the tissues, while plasma carries essential nutrients to the tissues. White blood cells are the agents of the body's immune system. Blood vessels form an intricate system through which the blood circulates. As they conduct oxygenated blood away from the heart to the tissues, arteries branch into arterioles, which become capillaries, allowing oxygen and other nutrients to be exchanged in the surrounding tissues. Then, as the blood vessels conduct deoxygenated blood back to the heart, they increase in diameter; capillaries become venules, which join to become veins. Many veins contain one-way valves. Fenestrated capillaries have openings, or windows, in their walls; continuous capillaries do not.

Answers
1. endothelium, 2. smooth muscle, 3. arteriole, 4. capillary, 5. venule, 6. vein, 7. artery, 8. valves closed, 9. adventitia, 10. muscularis, 11. intima, 12. leukocyte (neutrophil), 13. erythrocytes (red blood cells), 14. leukocytes (white blood cells), 15. platelets, 16. fenestrations, 17. fenestrated capillary, 18. continuous capillary

Basic Structure of Blood Vessels: Arteries, Arterioles, Capillaries, Venules, and Veins

Larger blood vessels (veins and arteries) have a similar tunica externa, or outer protective tissue layer. Immediately internal to this, it is clear that arteries have a much thicker muscular tunica media compared to veins, as well as added external and internal elastic lamina. The increased elasticity of arteries is important in expansion and contraction under pressure (compliance). The endothelial layer is similar in all vessel types, comprising very flat and smooth epithelial cells that reduce the friction of blood flow. For any given region, vein lumen size is much larger than arterial lumen size. In addition, veins have one-way valves to prevent backflow of blood returning to the heart. Arterioles are smaller versions of arteries, having only a tunica media layer and endothelium. They are able to vasodilate and vasoconstrict to control blood flow to the capillaries. Venules are small vessels collecting blood from the capillaries. They have only a tunica externa layer and endothelial layer. Capillaries are essentially endothelial cells, and many have fenestrations that allow plasma to leak into the interstitial fluid. Gas, fluid, nutrient, and waste exchange occur between the capillaries and surrounding tissues.

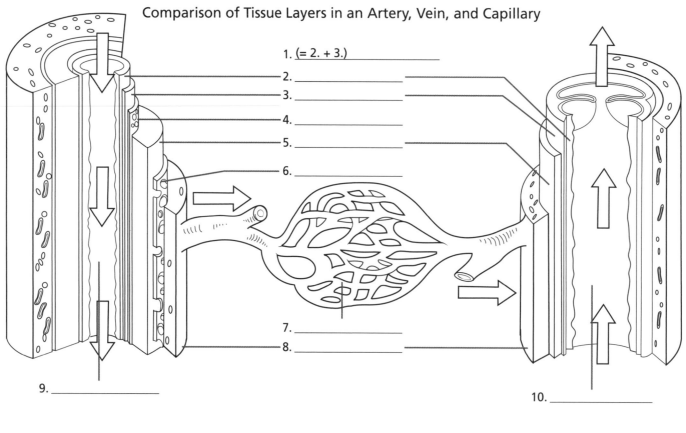

Comparison of Tissue Layers in an Artery, Vein, and Capillary

1. (= 2. + 3.) _____
2. _____
3. _____
4. _____
5. _____
6. _____

7. _____
8. _____

9. _____

10. _____

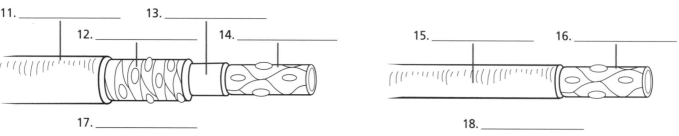

11. _____   13. _____

12. _____   14. _____

15. _____   16. _____

17. _____

18. _____

Answers

Basic Structure of Blood Vessels: Capillary Structure and Function

Capillaries are the vessels that interact with tissues during gas exchange (delivery of oxygenated blood and removal of carbon dioxide), nutrient delivery, and waste removal. Continuous capillaries have tightly connected endothelial cells and, therefore, very little fluid leaks out. Fenestrated capillaries have oval pores in the endothelial cells for fluid movement. Sinusoidal capillaries have fenestrations as well as loosely connected endothelial cells, which allows fluid and larger molecules to pass through them. On the arterial side of the capillary network, hydrostatic pressure is high enough to push blood physically through the capillary but also push plasma through the fenestrations into the interstitial fluid (if). As the blood continues to flow to the venous side of the capillary network, hydrostatic pressure drops and the lower amount of plasma increases the colloid osmotic pressure (oncotic pressure) because of the increased concentration of remaining plasma proteins. As a result, the capillaries (cap) gain interstitial fluid via osmosis. Net filtration pressure (NFP) = $(P_{cap} - P_{if}) - (\pi_{cap} - \pi_{if})$, where P is hydrostatic pressure and π is osmotic pressure. Typically, the net result is fluid loss at the capillaries, which is collected by the lymphatic capillaries and returned to the general circulation via the lymphatic vessels.

Variation in Capillary Structure

1. _____

2. _____

3. _____

4. _____

5. _____

6. _____

7. _____

8. _____

9. _____

10. _____

11. _____

12. _____

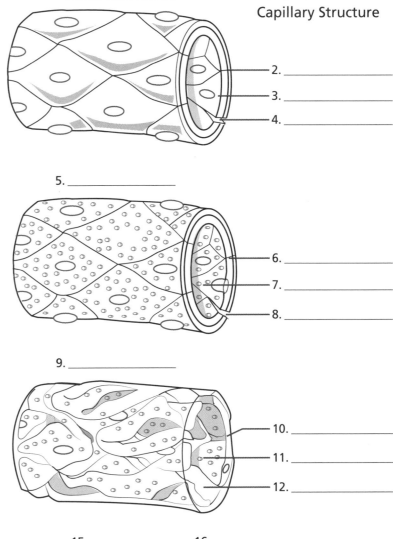

14. _____ 15. _____ 16. _____

For 14-16, supply relationship between P and π.

13. _____

Net Pressure Changes along a Generalised Capillary

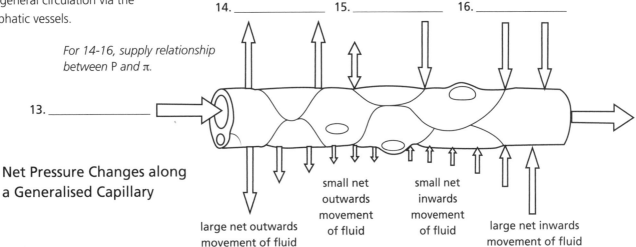

large net outwards movement of fluid

small net outwards movement of fluid

small net inwards movement of fluid

large net inwards movement of fluid

Answers

Action Potential of Cardiac Muscle

The cardiac action potential is the major electrical potential reversal in cardiac muscle that precedes cardiac muscle contraction (the coordinated heartbeat). It is initiated in the pacemaker cells of the sinoatrial (SA) node. Pacemaker cells have an unstable resting membrane potential due to leaky sodium channels. As sodium leaks into the cells, the rising membrane potential eventually activates a critical number of voltage-gated sodium channels to initiate the action potential. In contrast to the extremely fast neural action potential, the cardiac action potential is a much slower event, lasting up to 0.3 seconds. This is because slower voltage-gated calcium channels are opened, which prolongs the depolarisation (creating a plateau). This extends the absolute refractory period and allows the heart muscle to contract without the interruption of another cardiac action potential. Repolarisation begins as voltage-gated potassium channels open and potassium leaves the cell while calcium channels close. The membrane returns to its resting potential until a depolarisation in the SA node starts the process again. Because of the intercalated discs in cardiac muscle cells, this depolarisation spreads to adjacent cardiac muscle cells and throughout the heart.

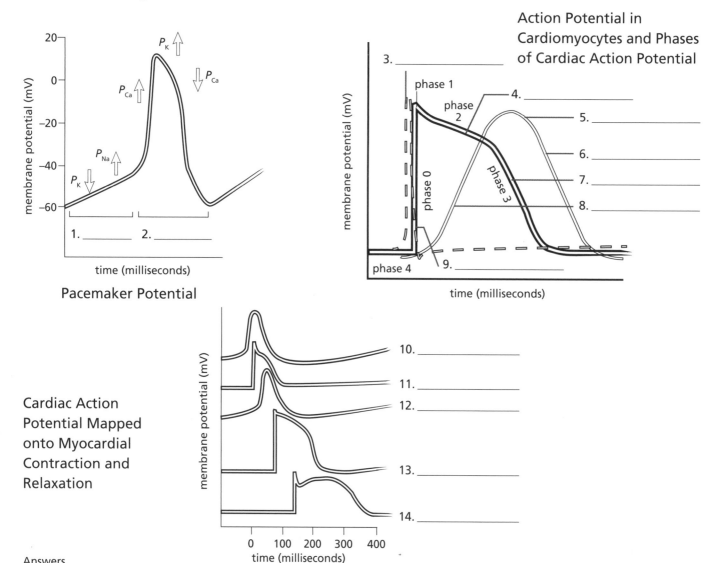

Action Potential in Cardiomyocytes and Phases of Cardiac Action Potential

Pacemaker Potential

Cardiac Action Potential Mapped onto Myocardial Contraction and Relaxation

Excitation-Contraction Coupling in Cardiac Muscle

The cardiac action potential begins in the pacemaker cells within the sinoatrial node. This depolarisation spreads to adjacent cardiac muscle cells via gap junctions within the intercalated discs. It also spreads deep into each cardiac muscle cell via T tubules. Depolarisation opens voltage-gated calcium channels in the plasma membrane of the sarcoplasmic reticulum (SR). Extracellular calcium enters the cell and by a process called calcium-induced calcium release, activates ryanodine receptors on the sarcoplasmic reticulum to release intracellular calcium stores. This calcium moves via diffusion into the vicinity of the actin and myosin fibres. Calcium binds to troponin, changing its conformation, which causes tropomyosin to reveal the myosin-binding sites on the actin molecule. The cross-bridge cycle begins; in other words, muscle fibres contract. The prolonged cardiac action potential (caused by slow voltage-gated calcium channels) causes a sustained depolarisation (up to 200 ms) and, therefore, a prolonged contraction phase. To begin the relaxation phase, calcium is actively pumped back into the sarcoplasmic reticulum. Its removal from troponin causes the tropomyosin molecule to cover the myosin-binding site on actin, ceasing cross-bridge cycling (i.e. muscle relaxation).

Excitation-Contraction Coupling in Cardiac Muscle

❶ Depolarisation wave travels to contractile cell
❷ Action potential spreads over membrane to T tubules
❸ Depolarisation wave causes Ca^{2+} channels on plasma membrane and SR to open, releasing Ca^{2+}
❹ Ca^{2+} induces Ca^{2+} release from SR
❺ Released Ca^{2+} binds to troponin, which changes conformation to reveal myosin-binding sites on actin
❻ Myosin begins ratcheting along actin, leading to muscle contraction
❼ Using ATP, Ca^{2+} is pumped back into the SR and extracellular fluid
❽ Unbinding of Ca^{2+} from troponin causes tropomyosin to cover the myosin-binding site on actin

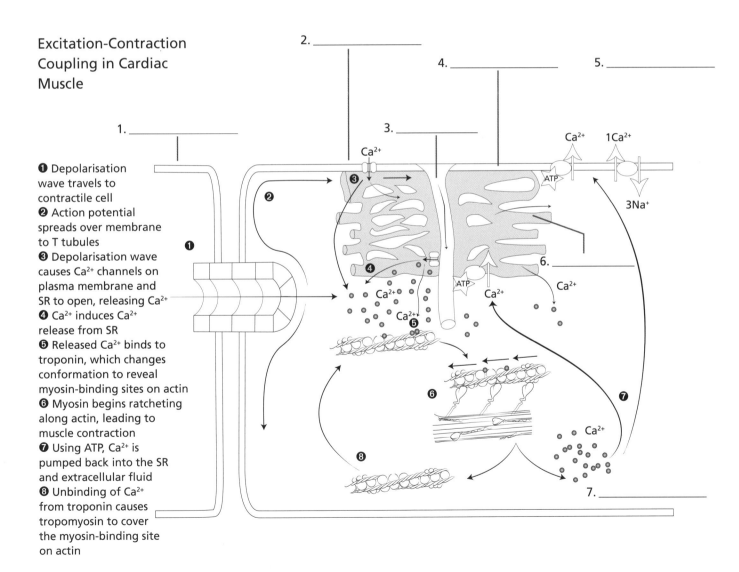

1. _____
2. _____
3. _____
4. _____
5. _____
6. _____
7. _____

Answers

Electrocardiograms and Impulse Conduction in the Heart

ECG and Impulse Conduction in the Heart

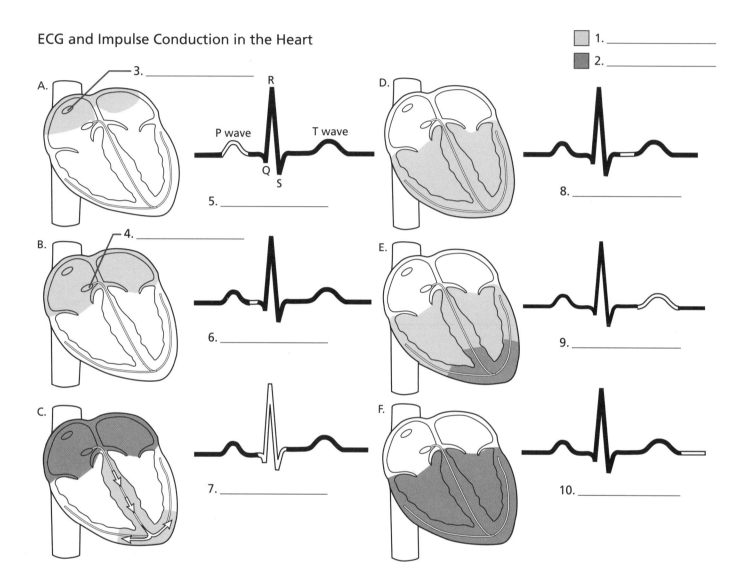

1. _____

2. _____

A.

3. _____

R

P wave   T wave

Q
S

5. _____

B.

4. _____

6. _____

C.

7. _____

D.

8. _____

E.

9. _____

F.

10. _____

The cardiac action potential is a depolarisation event that spontaneously originates in the sinoatrial node of the heart. This depolarisation spreads in a specific manner throughout the entire heart and can be measured and visualised as an electrocardiogram (ECG). As the depolarisation wave travels across the atria, this is visualised in the ECG as the P wave. Once complete, the depolarisation wave is delayed at the atrioventricular (AV) node to allow the atria to complete contraction. Through low-resistance cardiac tissues, such as the bundle of His and Purkinje fibres, the wave travels to the apex of the ventricles towards the atria. This is represented in the ECG by the QRS complex. Atrial repolarisation occurs during this time as well. Ventricular repolarisation begins at the ventricular apex and travels towards the atria. It is represented in the ECG as the T wave. It is important to remember that the ECG represents the electrical activity of the cardiac muscle, not the mechanical contraction. Contraction follows depolarisation, and relaxation follows repolarisation.

Answers

Physics of Blood Flow: Poiseuille's Law

Poiseuille's law describes flow rate in a tube as related to pressure differences and resistance. This relationship assumes that the flow is laminar and that the fluid is incompressible. Flow rate through a vessel is directly related to the pressure difference across the length of the vessel being measured, and inversely proportional to the resistance. Resistance is directly proportional to the viscosity of the fluid and the length of the vessel, whereas it is inversely proportional to the radius of the vessel to the fourth power. This means that vessel radius has by far the greatest effect on resistance, and therefore blood flow. Flow rates in arterioles, for example, can be altered dramatically due to only tiny changes in vessel radius caused by contraction or relaxation of associated smooth muscles. Flow in vessels can be described as laminar (molecules moving in a straight line parallel to the vessel wall) or turbulent (chaotic). The Reynolds number is used to represent the relative value of flow regime. A Reynolds number of less than 2,000 represents laminar flow, whereas a value greater than about 3,000 represents turbulent flow.

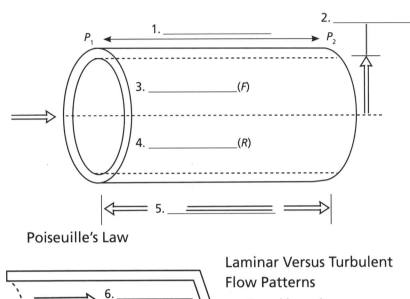

P_1 1. _____ 2. _____

3. _____ (F)

4. _____ (R)

5. _____

Poiseuille's Law

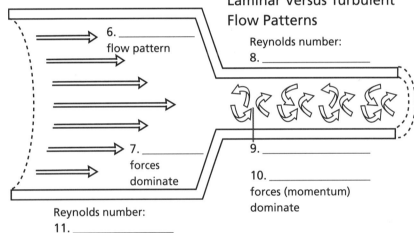

Laminar Versus Turbulent Flow Patterns

6. _____ flow pattern

7. _____ forces dominate

Reynolds number:
11. _____

Reynolds number:
8. _____

9. _____

10. _____ forces (momentum) dominate

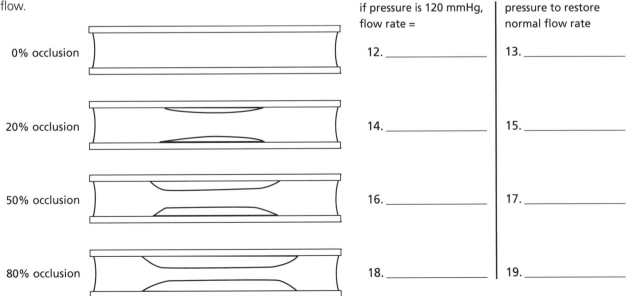

	if pressure is 120 mmHg, flow rate =	pressure to restore normal flow rate
0% occlusion	12. _____	13. _____
20% occlusion	14. _____	15. _____
50% occlusion	16. _____	17. _____
80% occlusion	18. _____	19. _____

Effects of Arterial Occlusion on Flow Rate

Answers

1. pressure drop, 2. radius (r), 3. volume flow rate, 4. resistance to flow, 5. length (L), 6. laminar, 7. viscous, 8. >3,000, 9. turbulent flow, 10. inertial, 11. <2,000, 12. 100 cm³/min, 13. 120 mmHg, 14. 41 cm³/min, 15. 293 mmHg, 16. 6.3 cm³/min, 17. 1,230 mmHg, 18. 0.16 cm³/min, 19. 75,000 mmHg

Arterial Pressure and Its Measurement

Blood pressure is the pressure exerted by the flowing blood on the walls of the vessels through which it travels. Typically, blood pressure refers to arterial pressure, or the pressure of the blood in the arteries. Blood pressure values describe two measurements: systolic pressure is the blood pressure at full ventricular contraction, and diastolic pressure is the blood pressure at full ventricular relaxation. A normotensive value for blood pressure is 120/80 mmHg, which tends to increase with age. Mean arterial pressure is the average pressure over one cardiac cycle and is determined by the cardiac output, the vascular resistance, and the central venous pressure. Pulse pressure is the difference between the systolic and diastolic pressures. The standard method for measuring blood pressure is by using a sphygmomanometer. A cuff is placed on the upper arm and inflated beyond systolic pressure, with the pressure that is created directly squeezing and pinching off the brachial artery. The cuff is then slowly deflated to release the pressure on the artery. As the vessel is still compressed, turbulent flow (see 'Physics of Flow,' p. 91) causes Korotkoff sounds to be heard – the pressure recorded at the moment these are first heard is the systolic pressure. The pressure recorded at the moment the flow becomes silent is the diastolic pressure.

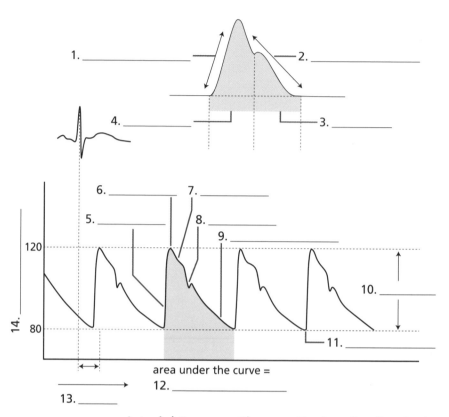

1. _____ 2. _____
4. _____
6. _____ 7. _____
5. _____ 8. _____
9. _____
120
10. _____
14. _____
80
11. _____
area under the curve =
12. _____
13. _____

Arterial Pressure Changes During Cardiac Cycle

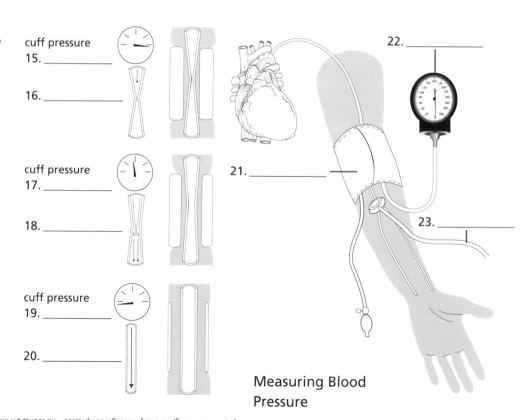

cuff pressure
15. _____
16. _____

cuff pressure
17. _____
18. _____

cuff pressure
19. _____
20. _____

21. _____

22. _____

23. _____

Measuring Blood Pressure

Cardiac Cycle and Function of Heart Valves

The cardiac cycle refers to all the events occurring during the generation of one heartbeat to the next. It includes a complex series of electrical impulses that precede the mechanical contractions that pump the blood. It is the sinoatrial node that initiates a cardiac action potential, which produces a wave of depolarisation that travels across the atria, causing them to contract. The atrioventricular valves (mitral and tricuspid) open as the blood flows to top off the ventricles from the atria. The cusps of the atrioventricular valves have tough fibrous cords, the chordae tendineae, which are attached along the free edge of the valve. The other ends of the chordae tendineae are attached to the papillary muscles. During isovolumetric contraction, the atrioventricular valves close while the ventricle contracts. As ventricular pressure builds, the aortic valve opens, causing rapid blood ejection out of the aorta and pulmonary arteries. During isovolumetric relaxation, the valves are closed. As the mitral valve opens, the ventricles fill rapidly with blood. As the filling slows, the mitral valve closes during the diastasis of the cardiac cycle. At this point, the cycle begins again.

Cardiac Cycle

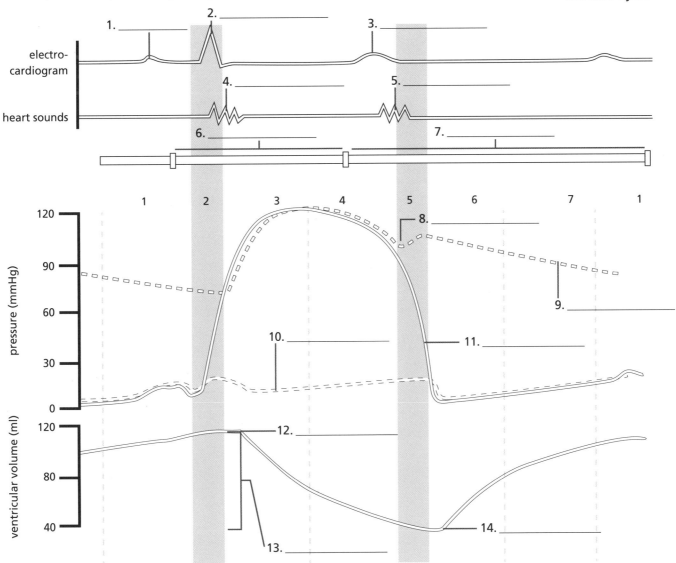

Frank-Starling Law

At the organ level, the Frank-Starling law states that the stroke volume of the heart increases with the end-diastolic volume (assuming all other factors remain constant). The increased filling causes the ventricular wall to contract with more force compared to lower amounts of ventricular filling. This balances cardiac output with increased venous return when it occurs, such as during exercise. At the cellular level, initially increasing the end-diastolic volume physically stretches the sarcomere of the muscle, such that there is maximal overlap between actin and myosin filaments, while concurrently allowing a greater cross-bridge cycling distance. Additionally, the stretching of the sarcomere increases the calcium sensitivity of troponin, causing a greater number of cross-bridges to form. The Frank-Starling mechanism contributes most to increasing stroke volume at rest and at lower exercise levels. However, Frank-Starling curves can change within the individual based on the contractile state of the heart, most commonly when this increases during exercise. The slope of the Frank-Starling curve can decrease substantially during heart failure and even more during cardiogenic shock as the contractile properties decrease.

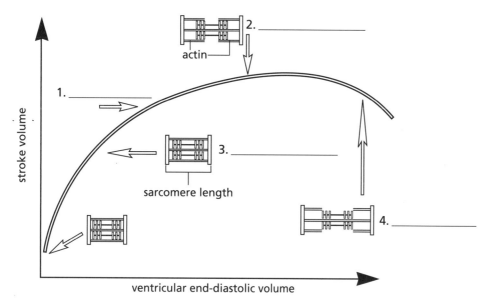

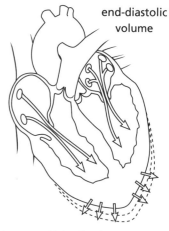

Frank-Starling Law

end-diastolic volume

increased blood volume causes increased stretch of myocardium

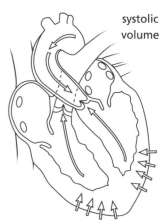

systolic volume

leads to increased force to pump blood out

Relationship Between Ventricular End-Diastolic Volume and Stroke Volume

Answers

Baroreceptors and Baroreflexes

Baroreceptors are a type of mechanoreceptor found in the blood vessels of all vertebrates. As they are stretched, they send excitatory signals via neurons to the brain. The baroreceptors act as part of a negative feedback loop (the baroreflex) that regulates blood pressure on the acute timescale. When blood pressure increases, this stretches the baroreceptors in the carotid arteries and aorta. This causes an increase in the frequency of action potential sent (via cranial nerves IX and X) to the cardiovascular (CV) control centre in the medulla oblongata. The resulting general output from the CV control centre is to increase parasympathetic output and decrease sympathetic output. More specifically, the parasympathetic system increases acetylcholine output on the sinoatrial node, thereby decreasing heart rate, which causes cardiac output to drop and blood pressure to decrease. Concurrently, decreased sympathetic output reduces the amount of noradrenaline (NE) released. In the heart, less NE reduces β_1-receptor activity, causing reduced heart rate and reduced contractile force, both of which decrease cardiac output. In the vasculature, less NE reduces α-receptor activity, which increases vasodilation, causing peripheral resistance to decrease. Decreased peripheral resistance lowers blood pressure.

Anatomical Map of Baroreceptor Reflex

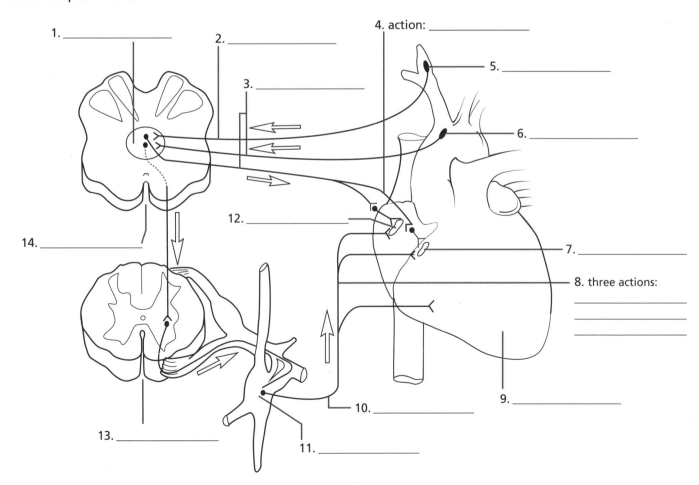

1. _____

2. _____

3. _____

4. action: _____

5. _____

6. _____

7. _____

8. three actions:

_____

_____

_____

9. _____

10. _____

11. _____

12. _____

13. _____

14. _____

Answers

Regulation of Arterial Pressure

On the acute timescale (minute to minute), blood pressure regulation tends to be governed by the baroreflexes (p. 95). On the chronic timescale (day to day), blood pressure homeostasis is maintained by a balance between the renin-angiotensin-aldosterone system and atrial natriuretic peptide. Aside from high blood pressure triggering the baroreflex response, increased pressure in the atria causes the release of atrial natriuretic peptide from the heart muscle cells. This causes significant vasodilation and increases sodium and water loss at the kidneys, thus reducing blood pressure overall. If the body senses low blood pressure (due to low volume or low resistance) via juxtaglomerular cells in the kidneys, the cells release renin into the general circulation. Renin acts as an enzyme, converting angiotensinogen (produced by the liver) to angiotensin I. Angiotensin-converting enzyme produced by the endothelium, which contributes to a large percentage of lung tissue mass, converts angiotensin I to angiotensin II. Angiotensin II causes vasoconstriction, which directly increases blood pressure. Angiotensin II also stimulates the secretion of aldosterone from the adrenal cortex. Aldosterone increases the reabsorption of sodium in the kidney tubules, which causes retention of water, thus maintaining blood volume and therefore blood pressure.

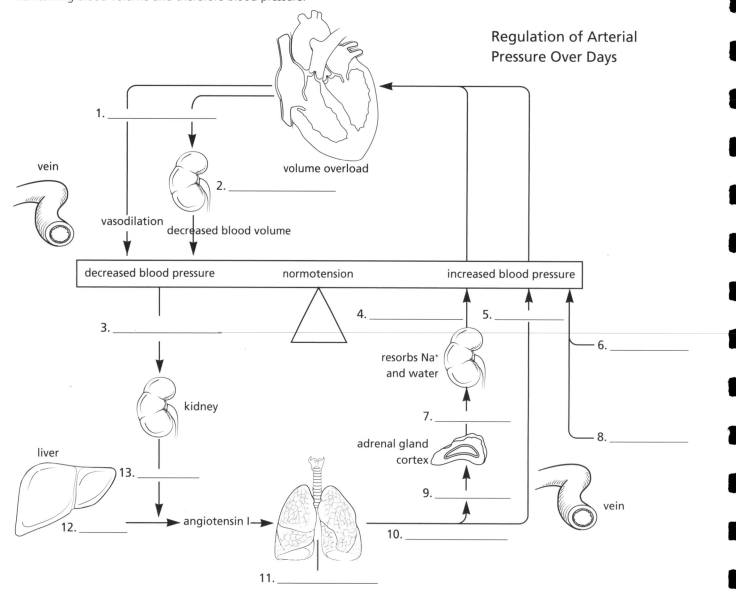

Regulation of Arterial Pressure Over Days

1. _____

vein

volume overload

2. _____

vasodilation   decreased blood volume

| decreased blood pressure | normotension | increased blood pressure |

3. _____

4. _____   5. _____

6. _____

resorbs Na⁺ and water

kidney

7. _____

8. _____

liver

adrenal gland cortex

13. _____

9. _____

12. _____ → angiotensin I →

vein

10. _____

11. _____

Postural Change on Blood Pressure

In addition to the pressure exerted by the heart, hydrostatic pressure from fluid-column effects is also important in blood flow and blood pressure. Any vertical column of continuous fluid will exert a pressure in proportion to the height of the column. Because the blood vessels form a column, fluid-column pressures are present in vertebrate circulatory systems. It is important to remember that while gravity influences pressure differences in arteries, it does not promote blood flow. For example, the blood pressure in the arteries of the legs is much higher than that of the systemic aorta, but blood does not flow from your feet to your heart in the arteries. A simple act of moving from sitting to standing unleashes a series of complex interactions between the autonomic nervous system (which regulates blood pressure) and cerebral autoregulation (which maintains cerebral perfusion) – i.e. ensuring you do not faint when you stand up quickly. Initially, standing causes a decrease in venous return, which reduces stroke volume and mean arterial pressure. This leads to a reduction in the firing rate of baroreceptors, which causes the central nervous system (CNS) to turn down the parasympathetic output. Concurrently, the CNS increases sympathetic output in order to increase venous return, heart contractility, and peripheral resistance. Together, they act to increase mean arterial pressure.

Effects of Gravity on Blood Pressure

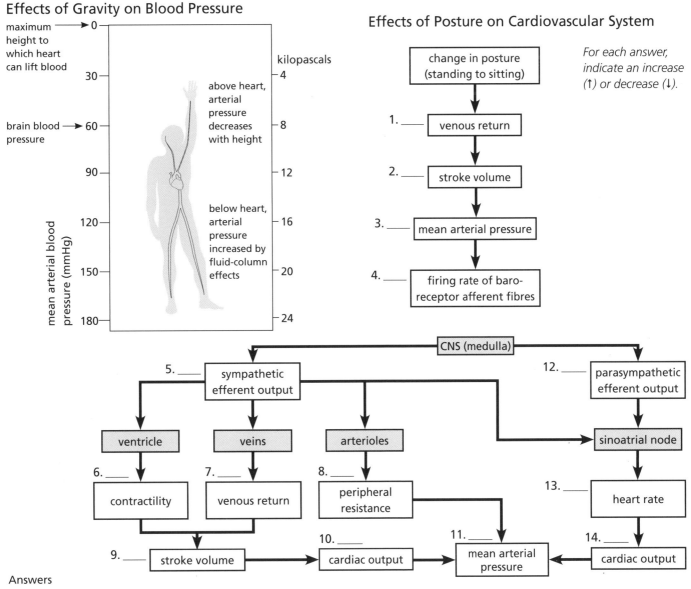

Effects of Posture on Cardiovascular System

For each answer, indicate an increase (↑) or decrease (↓).

Answers

1. decrease, 2. decrease, 3. decrease, 4. decrease, 5. increase, 6. increase, 7. increase, 8. increase, 9. increase, 10. increase, 11. increase, 12. decrease, 13. decrease, 14. increase

Control and Measurement of Cardiac Output

Cardiac output is defined as the amount of blood ejected from the heart per unit time (stroke volume × heart rate). Measurement of cardiac output can be very mathematically complex for non-invasive techniques. Doppler techniques use sound waves to detect changes in flow, whereas pulse pressure methods derive flow from an arterial pressure waveform. Regulation of cardiac output is determined by the factors directly affecting heart rate and stroke volume. Heart rate is primarily controlled by the interaction of the parasympathetic and sympathetic nervous systems. Exercise, for example, increases sympathetic activity, which causes an increase in heart rate. Stroke volume is greatly affected by preload (venous return and filling time), heart muscle contractility, and afterload. During exercise, the contraction of skeletal muscles significantly increases venous return, which increases stroke volume. The increased sympathetic response during exercise also increases the contractile force of the cardiac muscle. Hormones such as adrenaline and thyroxine also play a role in increasing heart rate as well as the contractive force of the cardiac muscle.

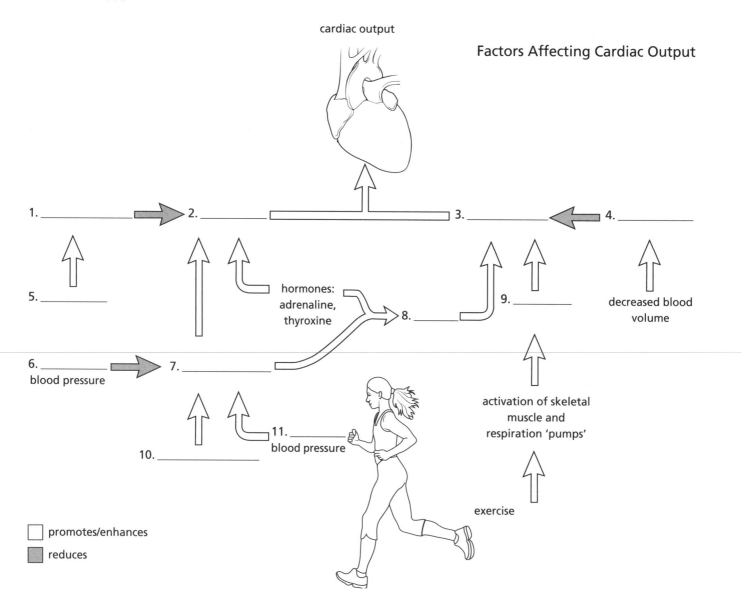

cardiac output

Factors Affecting Cardiac Output

1. _____ 2. _____ 3. _____ 4. _____

5. _____

hormones: adrenaline, thyroxine 8. _____

9. _____

decreased blood volume

6. _____ 7. _____

blood pressure

activation of skeletal muscle and respiration 'pumps'

11. _____ blood pressure

10. _____

exercise

☐ promotes/enhances
▨ reduces

Answers

Starling Forces on the Capillary Bed

Fluid movement in capillaries results from the processes of diffusion, filtration, and pinocytosis. Blood in the capillaries is under hydrostatic pressure caused by the heart and peripheral resistance. Additionally, proteins in the plasma exert a force called colloid osmotic pressure (COP) or oncotic pressure. Starling noted that under normal conditions, the amount of fluid filtering out from the arterial end is almost equal to the fluid being absorbed at the venous end of the capillaries. The small amount not returned at the venous end is returned via the lymphatic system. The Starling equation illustrates the relationship between hydrostatic pressure and COP in the movement of fluid across capillary membranes. Throughout the length of the capillary, the net COP remains constant. Therefore, it is the drop in hydrostatic pressure across the length of the capillary that affects the net filtration pressure. At the arterial end of the capillary, the hydrostatic pressure is much higher than the COP, which causes fluid to leak out. On the venous side of the capillary, the hydrostatic pressure is smaller than the COP, which causes fluid to leak into the capillary.

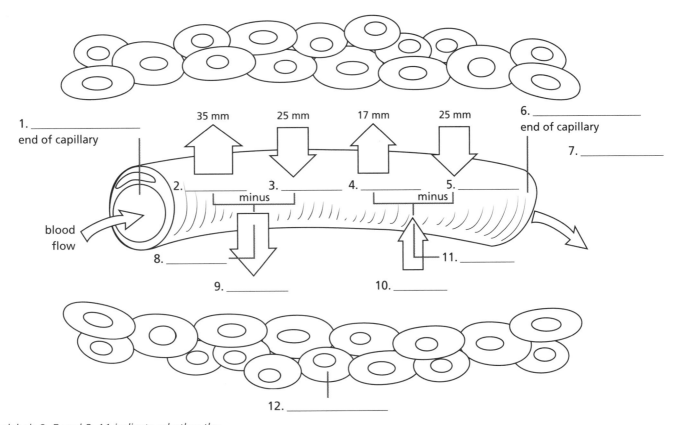

Starling Law of the Capillaries

For labels 2–5 and 8–11 indicate whether the label should be net hydrostatic pressure (HP), net osmotic pressure (OP), net filtration pressure (FP), or simply net pressure, and indicate its magnitude or direction.

Answers

Venous Storage and Return of Blood to Heart

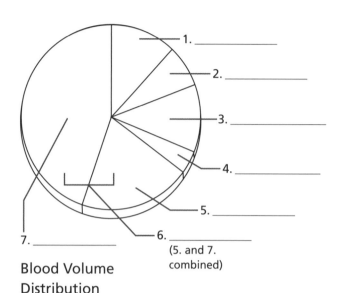

8. _____ 9. _____ 10. _____

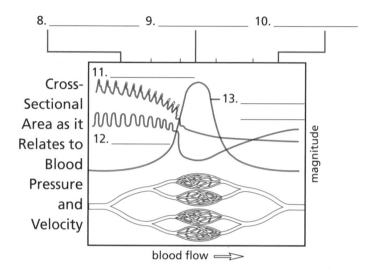

Cross-Sectional Area as it Relates to Blood Pressure and Velocity

11. _____
13. _____
12. _____

magnitude

blood flow ⟹

1. _____
2. _____
3. _____
4. _____
5. _____
6. _____
(5. and 7. combined)
7. _____

Blood Volume Distribution

Blood flows to the heart from capillary beds in the systemic tissues through a series of venules and veins. At any given time, the volume of blood in the venous system can be 60–70 per cent of the body's total blood volume. The capacitive properties of the veins (easily distended) allow them to accommodate blood volume that cannot be retained elsewhere in the circulatory system. While blood pressure declines significantly on entering the venous system, there is still enough pressure to aid in blood flow to the heart, although this is not the only factor contributing to venous return. The contraction of skeletal muscles (musculovenous pump) squeezes blood in nearby veins. With the aid of many one-way valves to prevent backflow, skeletal muscle contraction moves blood towards the heart. The act of inspiration (respiratory pump) creates a pressure difference between the thoracic and abdominal cavities, which essentially 'pulls' the blood towards the right atrium. Because there is no valve between the vena cavae and the right atrium, the diastolic cycle of the heart aids in venous return. Venous capacitance, venous compression, respiratory pressure changes, and gravity are all factors affecting venous return.

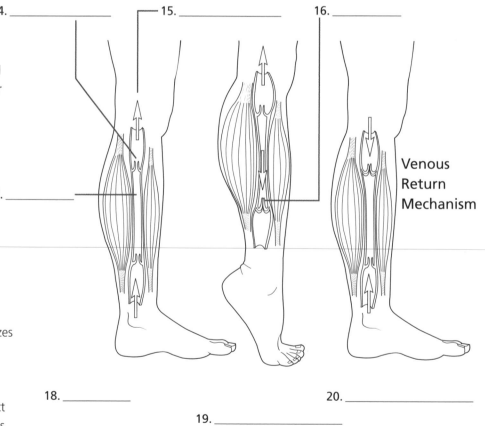

14. _____   15. _____   16. _____

17. _____

Venous Return Mechanism

18. _____   20. _____
19. _____

Answers

Lymphatic System

Lymph Vessel

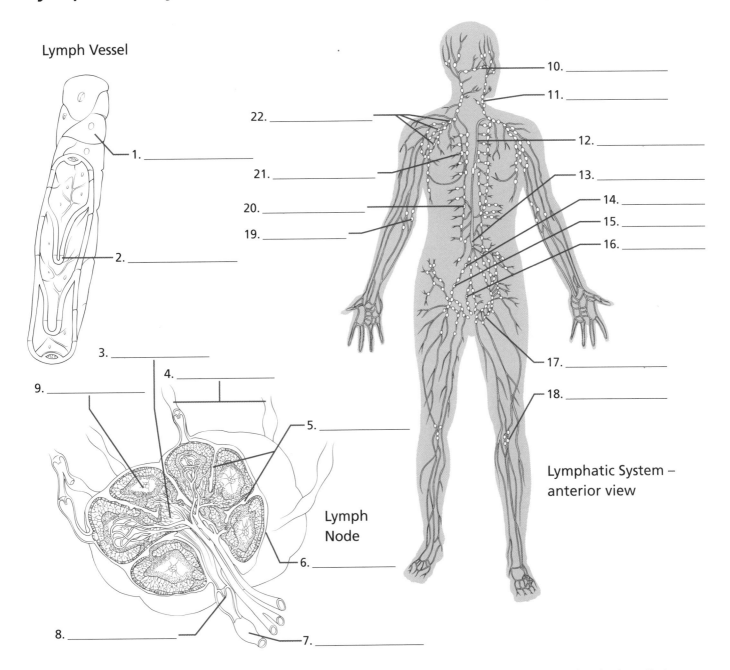

1. _____

2. _____

3. _____

4. _____

9. _____

5. _____

Lymph Node

6. _____

8. _____

7. _____

10. _____

11. _____

22. _____

21. _____

20. _____

19. _____

12. _____

13. _____

14. _____

15. _____

16. _____

17. _____

18. _____

Lymphatic System – anterior view

The lymphatic system is a one-way system that begins with blind-ended vessels similar to capillaries. These lymphatic capillaries collect large molecules and interstitial fluid and converge to form gradually larger lymphatic vessels that carry lymph back to the circulatory system. Lymph vessels have one-way valves to ensure one-way flow. Collections of lymph nodes are found in series along the lymph vessels. Lymph nodes contain white blood cells, filter the lymph, and are involved in immune function. Filtered lymph travels through efferent lymphatic vessels and collects in two large ducts in the thoracic region: the right lymphatic duct and the thoracic duct (left side of the body). Each of these ducts drains lymph into the circulatory system at the junction of the internal jugular vein and the subclavian vein on its own side of the body. Any mismatch in fluid flow between the circulatory capillaries, the interstitial fluid, and the lymphatic capillaries can result in fluid accumulation in the tissues called oedema. Similar fluid accumulation in the lungs is termed pulmonary oedema.

Answers

1. lymphatic endothelial cell, 2. closed valve, 3. medullary sinus, 4. afferent lymphatic vessels, 5. trabeculae, 6. capsule, 7. efferent lymphatic vessel, 8. valve, 9. follicle of cortex, 10. buccal nodes, 11. cervical nodes, 12. thoracic duct, 13. cisterna chyli, 14. common iliac nodes, 15. external iliac nodes, 16. internal iliac nodes, 17. inguinal and femoral nodes, 18. popliteal nodes (posterior side of knee), 19. cubital nodes, 20. posterior intercostal nodes, 21. parasternal nodes, 22. axillary nodes

Structure of the Respiratory Tract

The major function of the respiratory system is to load the blood with oxygen and remove the accumulated carbon dioxide from the blood. Air that is inhaled flows into the airways via the nose, pharynx, larynx, trachea, and bronchi. Contraction of the diaphragm and external intercostal muscles is responsible for creating the negative pressure that moves air into the lungs. However, it is not until the respiratory gas reaches the respiratory bronchioles and alveoli that gas exchange occurs. The right ventricle pumps deoxygenated blood to the alveolar capillaries, where oxygen loading and carbon dioxide unloading occur. The oxygenated blood flows to the left atrium via the pulmonary veins, where the left ventricle then pumps the blood to the tissues of the body.

Passive exhalation of the respiratory gas in the lungs is accomplished by relaxation of the diaphragm and the external intercostal muscles. The lungs also play a role in immune function (defence against inhaled substances).

Respiratory System – anterior view

1. _____
2. _____
3. _____
4. _____
5. _____
6. _____
7. _____

9. _____
8. _____

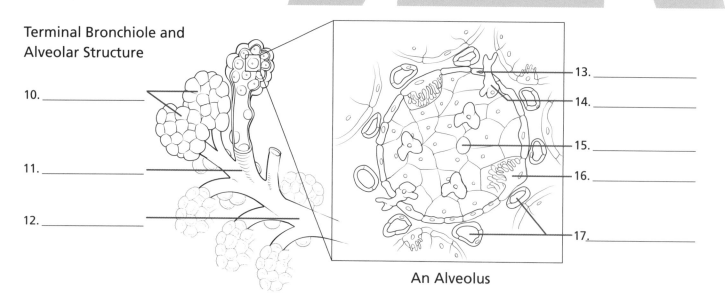

Terminal Bronchiole and Alveolar Structure

10. _____
11. _____
12. _____

13. _____
14. _____
15. _____
16. _____
17. _____

An Alveolus

Answers

Biomechanics of Lung Ventilation

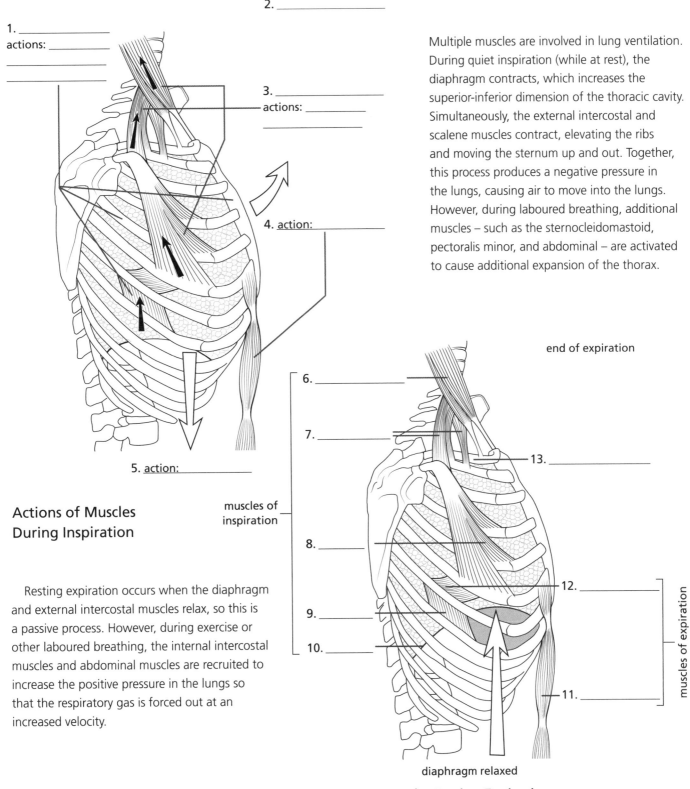

1. _____
actions: _____
_____
_____

2. _____

3. _____
actions: _____
_____

4. action: _____

5. action: _____

Actions of Muscles During Inspiration

Multiple muscles are involved in lung ventilation. During quiet inspiration (while at rest), the diaphragm contracts, which increases the superior-inferior dimension of the thoracic cavity. Simultaneously, the external intercostal and scalene muscles contract, elevating the ribs and moving the sternum up and out. Together, this process produces a negative pressure in the lungs, causing air to move into the lungs. However, during laboured breathing, additional muscles – such as the sternocleidomastoid, pectoralis minor, and abdominal – are activated to cause additional expansion of the thorax.

Resting expiration occurs when the diaphragm and external intercostal muscles relax, so this is a passive process. However, during exercise or other laboured breathing, the internal intercostal muscles and abdominal muscles are recruited to increase the positive pressure in the lungs so that the respiratory gas is forced out at an increased velocity.

end of expiration

6. _____

7. _____

13. _____

muscles of inspiration

8. _____

12. _____

9. _____

10. _____

11. _____

muscles of expiration

diaphragm relaxed

Muscles During Expiration

Answers

1. quiet breathing: external intercostal muscles contract, ribs elevate, sternum moves, 2. end of inspiration, 3. laboured breathing: additional muscles contract, causing additional expansion of thorax, 4. abdominal muscles relax, 5. diaphragm contracts, 6. sternocleidomastoid, 7. scalenes, 8. pectoralis minor, 9. external intercostals, 10. diaphragm, 11. abdominal muscles, 12. internal intercostals, 13. clavicle

Pulmonary Surfactants, Surface Tension, and Lung Compliance

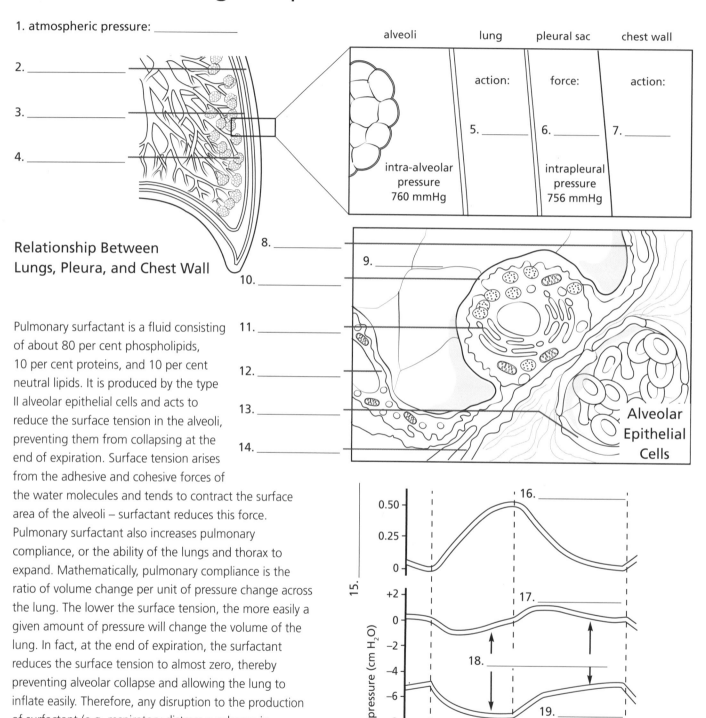

1. atmospheric pressure: _____

2. _____

3. _____

4. _____

Relationship Between Lungs, Pleura, and Chest Wall

alveoli | lung | pleural sac | chest wall

action:

force:

action:

5. _____

6. _____

7. _____

intra-alveolar pressure 760 mmHg

intrapleural pressure 756 mmHg

8. _____

9. _____

10. _____

11. _____

12. _____

13. _____

14. _____

Alveolar Epithelial Cells

Pulmonary surfactant is a fluid consisting of about 80 per cent phospholipids, 10 per cent proteins, and 10 per cent neutral lipids. It is produced by the type II alveolar epithelial cells and acts to reduce the surface tension in the alveoli, preventing them from collapsing at the end of expiration. Surface tension arises from the adhesive and cohesive forces of the water molecules and tends to contract the surface area of the alveoli – surfactant reduces this force. Pulmonary surfactant also increases pulmonary compliance, or the ability of the lungs and thorax to expand. Mathematically, pulmonary compliance is the ratio of volume change per unit of pressure change across the lung. The lower the surface tension, the more easily a given amount of pressure will change the volume of the lung. In fact, at the end of expiration, the surfactant reduces the surface tension to almost zero, thereby preventing alveolar collapse and allowing the lung to inflate easily. Therefore, any disruption to the production of surfactant (e.g. respiratory distress syndrome in neonates) will increase the pressure required to ventilate the alveoli and compromise gas exchange.

15. _____

16. _____

17. _____

18. _____

19. _____

20. _____

21. _____

pressure (cm H_2O)

0.50
0.25
0
+2
0
-2
-4
-6
-8

Changes in Lung Volume, Alveolar Pressure, Pleural Pressure, and Transpulmonary Pressure During Normal Breathing

Answers

1. 760 mmHg, 2. chest wall, 3. pleural sac, 4. alveoli, 5. elastic recoil of chest wall, 6. force due to negative intrapleural pressure, 7. elastic recoil of lung, 8. basal lamina, 9. alveolus, 10. surfactant, 11. type II alveolar cell, 12. macrophage, 13. capillary endothelium, 14. type I alveolar cell, 15. volume change (litres), 16. lung volume, 17. alveolar pressure, 18. transpulmonary pressure, 19. pleural pressure, 20. inspiration, 21. expiration

Lung Volumes and Ventilation

Lung ventilation volumes can and do vary, from very small volumes under resting conditions to very large volumes during exercise. A spirometer is a piece of equipment used to measure ventilatory volumes. Tidal volume is the amount of air inhaled and exhaled per breath and is typically around 500 millilitres in a young healthy male during quiet breathing. Following a tidal inspiration, the additional amount of air inhaled to maximum is called the inspiratory reserve volume. Conversely, the amount of maximal expiration following a tidal expiration is termed the expiratory reserve volume. While the total lung capacity is the entire volume of the lung and respiratory pathways, there is a residual volume that remains after a full forced expiration (i.e. one cannot fully void all the gas in the lungs without collapsing them). Therefore, the vital capacity is the total amount of gas that can be moved (inspiratory reserve volume + tidal volume + expiratory reserve volume). Vital capacity is an important measurement of respiratory health. It can be increased with physical training but tends to decrease with age and with some diseases.

A spirometer is used to measure and record volumes of inspired and expired air. The graph produced is called a spirogram.

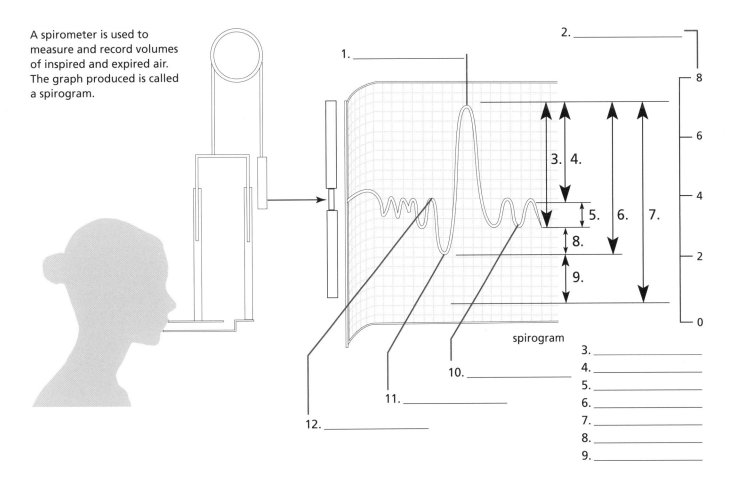

spirogram

1. _____

2. _____

3. _____
4. _____
5. _____
6. _____
7. _____
8. _____
9. _____

10. _____

11. _____

12. _____

Regulation of Lung Ventilation

Ventilation is a physiological process that can be under involuntary or voluntary control. Voluntary control of ventilation originates from the cerebral cortex of the brain. Although the involuntary mechanism of ventilatory control is not completely understood, it involves the integration of neural signals in respiratory centres located in the medulla and pons. In the medulla, the dorsal respiratory group (DRG) controls inspiratory movement and timing, while the ventral respiratory group (VRG) controls forced exhalation as well as ventilatory rhythm. In the pons, the pontine respiratory group (PRG, comprising the pneumotaxic centre and apneustic centre) coordinates the speed of inhalation and exhalation and overall fine-tunes the ventilation rate. This area has the ability to send excitatory or inhibitory signals to the respiratory centres of the pons and medulla to either prolong or end inspiration, respectively. The respiratory centres are also affected by high carbon dioxide and low pH. Outside of the brainstem, there are peripheral chemoreceptors that sense low oxygen, high carbon dioxide, and low pH levels of the blood and react to increased ventilation. Stretch receptors in the muscle and lung can increase ventilation but also prevent overinflation (i.e. the Hering-Breuer reflex).

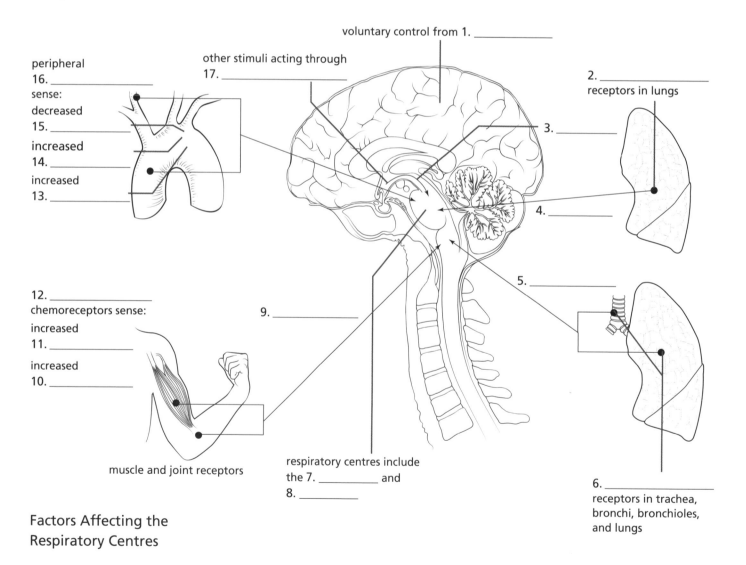

voluntary control from 1. _____

other stimuli acting through
17. _____

peripheral
16. _____
sense:
decreased
15. _____
increased
14. _____
increased
13. _____

2. _____
receptors in lungs

3. _____

4. _____

5. _____

12. _____
chemoreceptors sense:
increased
11. _____
increased
10. _____

9. _____

muscle and joint receptors

respiratory centres include
the 7. _____ and
8. _____

6. _____
receptors in trachea,
bronchi, bronchioles,
and lungs

Factors Affecting the
Respiratory Centres

Diffusion of Gases Across the Alveolar Wall

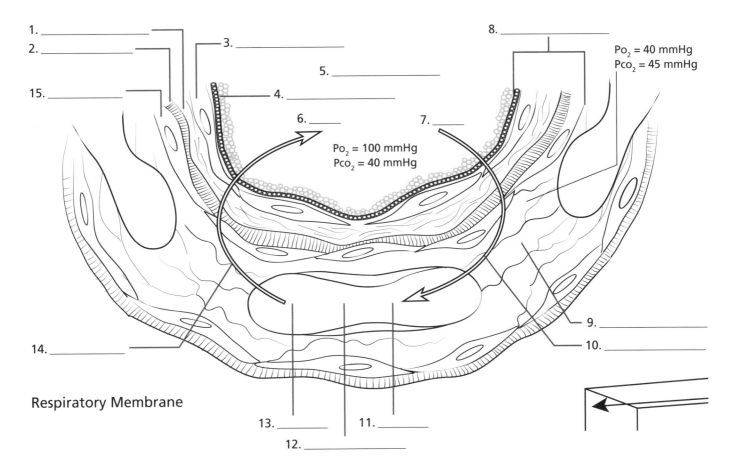

1. _____
2. _____
3. _____
5. _____
4. _____
6. _____
7. _____
8. _____

Po_2 = 40 mmHg
Pco_2 = 45 mmHg

Po_2 = 100 mmHg
Pco_2 = 40 mmHg

15. _____

9. _____
10. _____

14. _____

Respiratory Membrane

13. _____
11. _____
12. _____

The entire process of respiration involves convective movement of gases (ventilation), the diffusion of oxygen and carbon dioxide across the alveolar wall, the convective movement of respiratory gases via the blood (circulation), and finally the diffusion of respiratory gases into and out of the cells of the body. Diffusion is a passive process by which molecules move (via natural molecular agitation) from regions of high concentration to regions of low concentration. The Fick equation shows the factors that affect the rate of diffusion across a membrane such as the alveolar wall. The rate of diffusion will be greater when the diffusion distances are shorter and the partial pressure differences are larger. The partial pressure differences across the alveolar wall are approximately 60 mmHg for oxygen and about 5 mmHg for carbon dioxide (this discrepancy for the two respiratory gases will be explained in later pages). Diffusion rate is maximised in the alveoli by having an extremely thin alveolar membrane (from 2 μm down to 0.4 μm in some areas) and having an extremely large surface area for diffusion (approximately 30–100 m²).

Fick's Law of Diffusion

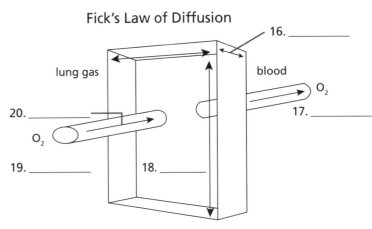

16. _____

lung gas

blood

O_2

17. _____

20. _____

O_2

19. _____

18. _____

Haemoglobin and Oxygen Transport

Haemoglobin is the respiratory pigment that binds to oxygen after it diffuses across the alveolar wall into the capillaries. It is necessary for oxygen transport because oxygen is so poorly soluble in plasma. Haemoglobin shows cooperativity in that once one oxygen molecule binds, three additional oxygen molecules bind much more easily. Cooperativity can be visualised by the sigmoid shape of the oxygen dissociation curve. During oxygen loading at the lungs, a partial pressure of 100 mmHg is enough to saturate the haemoglobin with oxygen completely. At rest, even though the partial pressure of oxygen (Po_2) in the tissue is about 40 mmHg, only 25 per cent of the oxygen is removed from the haemoglobin. During exercise, the Po_2 of the tissues drops only about 20 mmHg, yet about 50 per cent of the oxygen can be removed in that small change in Po_2. Furthermore, the oxygen dissociation curve is actually dynamic – oxygen loading and unloading can be affected by the environment surrounding the haemoglobin. Low pH, high CO_2 concentration, and increased temperature all reduce the affinity (increase the P_{50} – the Po_2 at which 50 per cent of the haemoglobin is bound with O_2) of haemoglobin for oxygen. This is advantageous for oxygen delivery at the tissues.

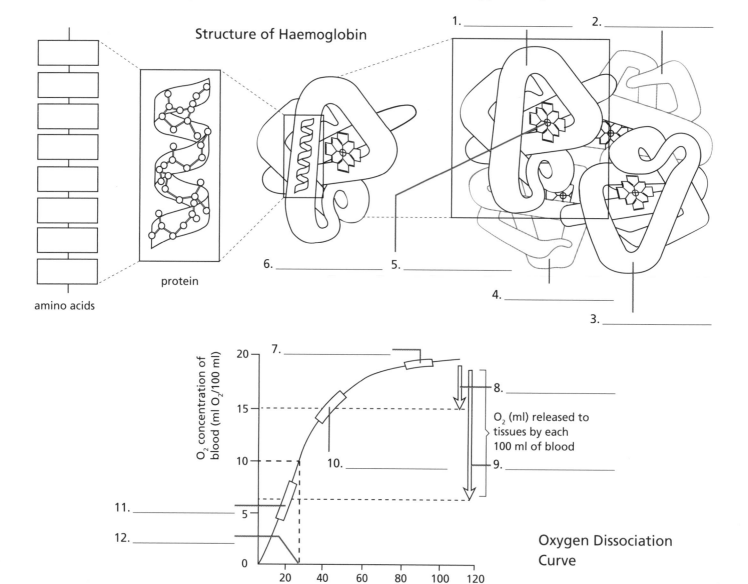

Structure of Haemoglobin

1. _____ 2. _____

6. _____ 5. _____

4. _____

3. _____

protein

amino acids

7. _____

O_2 concentration of blood (ml O_2/100 ml)

8. _____

O_2 (ml) released to tissues by each 100 ml of blood

10. _____

9. _____

11. _____

12. _____

Oxygen Dissociation Curve

partial pressure of O_2 in blood (mmHg)

Answers

Transport of Carbon Dioxide and Hydrogen Ions by the Blood

Carbon dioxide is much more soluble in plasma compared to oxygen, so it doesn't require a large partial pressure difference to move from tissues to plasma. Given its high solubility, only about 7 per cent of CO_2 is transported in the plasma. About 23 per cent of CO_2 is transported attached to haemoglobin, and the majority (about 70 per cent) is transported as bicarbonate (HCO_3^-). Carbon dioxide must first diffuse into the erythrocyte, where it undergoes a chemical reaction catalysed by carbonic anhydrase. Carbon dioxide reacts with water to form HCO_3^- and H^+. Imidazole groups on the haemoglobin molecule attach to H^+ (their affinity increases when haemoglobin is deoxygenated), acting as a buffer. Although some of the HCO_3^- remains buffered inside the erythrocyte, most of it diffuses out into the plasma via rapid ion-exchange proteins in exchange for chloride (a process called the chloride shift). At the alveolar capillaries, the processes are reversed in order to produce gaseous CO_2 so that it can diffuse into the alveoli in preparation for exhalation.

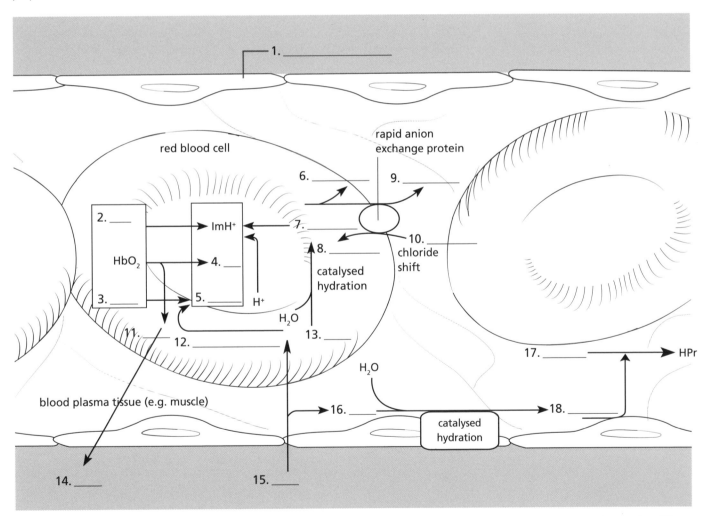

Red Blood Cell in a Systemic Tissue Capillary

Answers

Acid-Base Balance

Responses to Changes in Blood pH

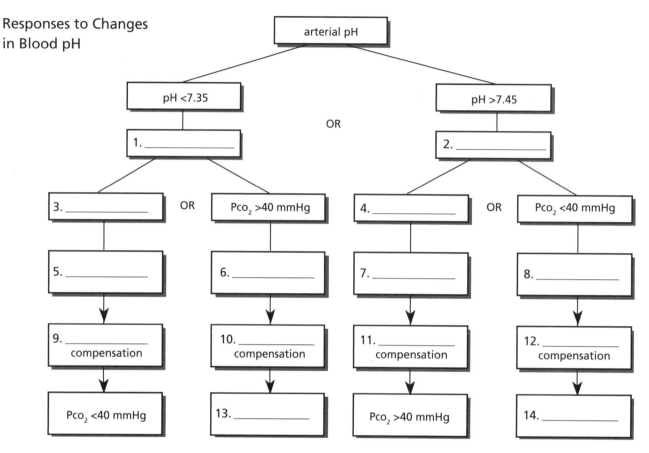

```
                        arterial pH
                    /               \
            pH <7.35        OR        pH >7.45
               |                         |
            1. _____               2. _____
            /      \                 /       \
    3. _____  OR  Pco₂ >40 mmHg  4. _____  OR  Pco₂ <40 mmHg
        |            |              |              |
    5. _____    6. _____      7. _____      8. _____
        ↓            ↓              ↓              ↓
    9. _____    10. _____     11. _____     12. _____
    compensation  compensation   compensation   compensation
        ↓            ↓              ↓              ↓
    Pco₂ <40 mmHg 13. _____    Pco₂ >40 mmHg  14. _____
```

Normal cellular function relies on chemical reactions, which are invariably controlled by enzymes. pH ($-\log_{10}[H^+]$) has a major effect on the activity of enzymes and thus cellular function. A small change in either factor can have lethal consequences. In endotherms such as humans, temperature is highly regulated via a balance of metabolic rate and heat retention/loss. The normal pH range is tightly regulated between 7.35 and 7.45 by a combination of buffering, and respiratory and renal compensations. Acidosis (pH <7.35) is the prevailing condition and can have a respiratory or metabolic origin. A slight respiratory acidosis occurs every time we hold our breath. In fact, the urge to breathe is essentially brought about by the partial pressure of carbon dioxide (P_{CO_2}) in the blood. Metabolic acidosis is commonly produced by excessive lactic acid resulting from anaerobic activity. It can also occur during excessive loss of HCO_3^- in gastrointestinal fluids. Compensation for acidosis involves increased ventilation and increased reabsorption of HCO_3^-. Alkalosis (pH >7.45) is less common and occurs mainly due to hyperventilation. This is called respiratory alkalosis. Compensation occurs by reducing the ventilation rate and excreting more HCO_3^- at the kidneys. Metabolic alkalosis is not very common and is often a result of excessive fluid loss (vomiting or diarrhoea) voiding significant amounts of H^+.

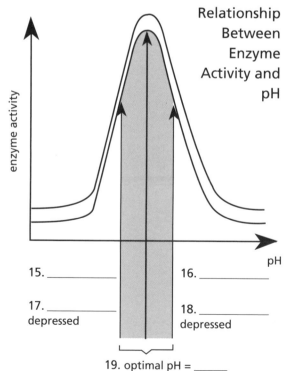

Relationship Between Enzyme Activity and pH

enzyme activity

pH

15. _____   16. _____

17. _____   18. _____
depressed   depressed

19. optimal pH = _____

Answers

Overview of the Digestive System

The gastrointestinal (GI) tract is essentially a long tube open at both ends, starting at the mouth and ending at the anus, made up of distinct parts including the mouth, oesophagus, stomach, and small and large intestines. Organs including the salivary glands, liver, gallbladder, and pancreas are distinct from the GI tract yet are involved in the process of digestion through the secretion of enzymes. Different regions of the tract have different functions, including motility, digestion, absorption, and elimination of waste. These functions are controlled by different means, such as hormonal and neuronal mechanisms. Digestion starts when food enters the mouth and is broken down mechanically and chemically. As the food passes through the GI tract, further breakdown occurs in the stomach through the presence of gastric acid, mucus, and enzymes, producing chyme. The chyme moves subsequently into the small intestine, where absorption of nutrients occurs. Here, enzymes and hormones released from the pancreas aid in fat digestion. The chyme moves through the small intestine and into the large intestine, where water is absorbed. This absorption leads to the formation of solid faecal masses, which are moved by peristalsis to the rectum and eliminated via the anus.

Components of the Digestive System

1. _____
2. _____
3. _____
4. _____
5. _____
6. _____
7. _____
8. _____
9. _____
10. _____
11. _____
12. _____
13. _____
14. _____
15. _____
16. _____

Answers

Salivary Gland Function

1. _____

2. _____

8. _____

7. _____

6. _____

Parotid Gland – cellular level

5. _____

4. _____

3. _____

Saliva is secreted by three pairs of major salivary glands: the parotid glands located in the cheeks, the sublingual glands located under the tongue, and the submandibular glands located under the lower jaw. There are also minor glands that are found underneath the epithelial layer of the oral mucosa. Salivary glands contain acinar exocrine glands, with the acini being either serous or mucous types. The serous acini secrete watery saliva, as found in the parotid glands, and mucous acini secrete a viscous fluid containing mucins, as found in the sublingual glands. The submandibular glands have both serous and mucous acini. Through the course of a day, 1.5 litres of saliva is secreted, controlled largely by the release of acetylcholine from parasympathetic neurons.

Serous saliva contains the digestive enzyme ptyalin, an amylase, which breaks down starches to maltose. Another salivary enzyme, lysozyme, acts as an antibacterial agent, protecting the mouth and teeth. The mucous saliva aids mastication and lubricates the food bolus in preparation for swallowing. Other constituents of saliva include sodium, potassium, calcium, bicarbonate (which creates a bicarbonate-buffered fluid to maintain suitable pH levels in the mouth), hormones, and antibodies (IgA).

9. _____

10. _____

14. _____

Submandibular Gland – cellular level

11. _____

12. _____

13. _____

15. _____

16. _____

17. _____

Sublingual Gland – cellular level

18. _____

20. _____

19. _____

Physiology of Swallowing

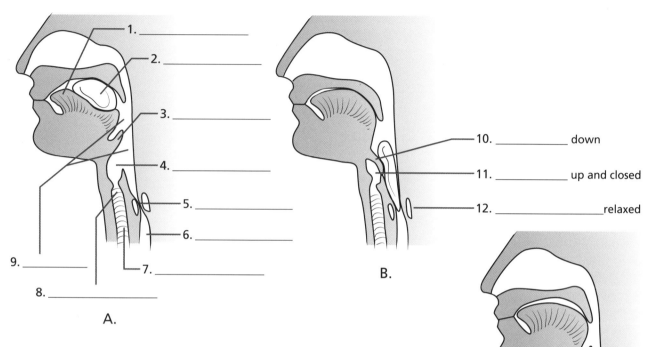

1. _____
2. _____
3. _____
4. _____
5. _____
6. _____
9. _____
7. _____
8. _____

A.

10. _____ down
11. _____ up and closed
12. _____ relaxed

B.

Stages in Swallowing a Food Bolus (A-C)

Swallowing takes place over a number of different phases. The first of these is a voluntary phase that involves the formation of a food bolus via chewing and tongue movements, after which the bolus is moved back towards the pharynx. The phases from this point on are no longer voluntary but are reflex responses, or swallowing reflexes, which are regulated by neural centres in the medulla. Once the bolus reaches the pharynx, the soft palate closes the nasal passage, and the epiglottis moves over the glottis to close the larynx and trachea to prevent the bolus from entering either the upper or lower respiratory tracts. Once the bolus reaches the back of the pharynx, the upper oesophageal sphincter relaxes, allowing the bolus to enter the oesophagus. The muscular wall of the oesophagus is made up of layers of both circular and longitudinal smooth muscle. To move the bolus down the oesophagus, the muscle layers undergo coordinated waves of relaxation in front of the bolus and contraction behind it, which propel it into the stomach. This process is known as peristalsis and is controlled by activity in the vagus nerve and the enteric nervous system.

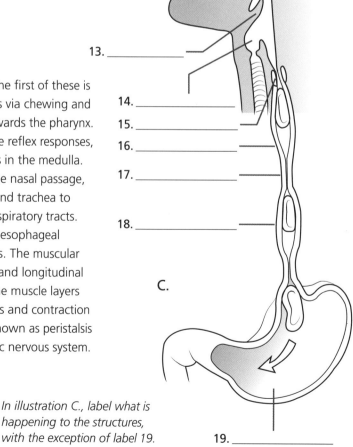

13. _____
14. _____
15. _____
16. _____
17. _____
18. _____

C.

In illustration C., label what is happening to the structures, with the exception of label 19.

19. _____

Answers

1. tongue, 2. food bolus, 3. epiglottis up, 4. glottis, 5. oesophageal sphincter contracted, 6. oesophagus, 7. trachea, 8. larynx, 9. pharynx, 10. epiglottis, 11. glottis, 12. oesophageal sphincter, 13. epiglottis up, 14. glottis down and open, 15. oesophageal sphincter contracted, 16. relaxed muscles, 17. contracted muscles, 18. relaxed muscles, 19. stomach

Structure and Function of the Stomach

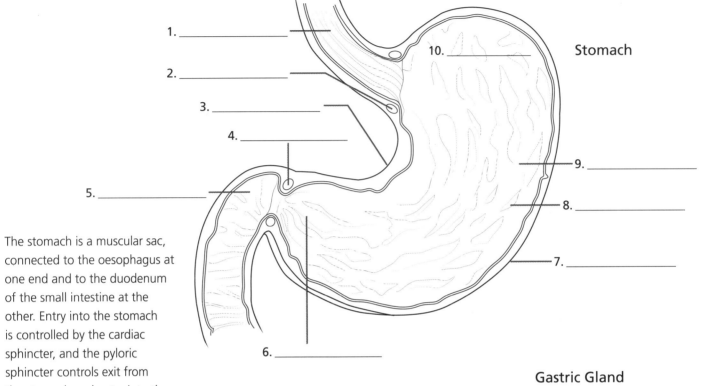

1. _____

2. _____

3. _____

4. _____

5. _____

6. _____

10. _____

Stomach

9. _____

8. _____

7. _____

The stomach is a muscular sac, connected to the oesophagus at one end and to the duodenum of the small intestine at the other. Entry into the stomach is controlled by the cardiac sphincter, and the pyloric sphincter controls exit from the stomach and entry into the duodenum of the small intestine. Once the bolus of food has entered the stomach, it becomes mixed with gastric juices to form chyme. Gastric juice is a mixture of enzymes, mucus, and acid secreted by the stomach mucosa. The stomach mucosa is lined with gastric glands that contain different cell types, including mucous cells, parietal cells, chief cells, enterochromaffin-like (ECL) cells, and G cells. G cells are stimulated by gastrin-releasing peptide, causing gastrin to enter the bloodstream. Gastrin acts upon ECL cells, causing production of histamine, which, along with gastrin, stimulates the release of acid from parietal cells. The acid environment allows the conversion of inactive pepsinogens, secreted by the chief cells, into active pepsins, which aid in the breakdown of protein. Acid secretion is regulated by the release of somatostatin from D cells in the antrum of the stomach, which can act directly on parietal cells, and also ECL and G cells to inhibit the production of gastrin and histamine.

Gastric Gland and Pit

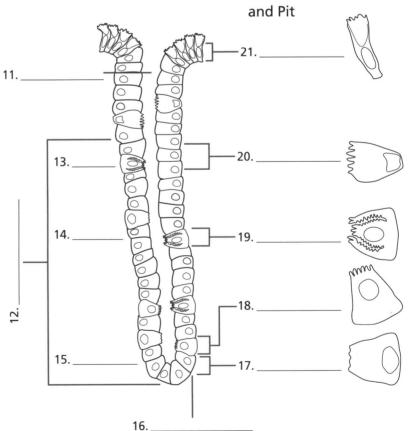

11. _____

12. _____

13. _____

14. _____

15. _____

21. _____

20. _____

19. _____

18. _____

17. _____

16. _____

Neural Control of Gut Function

Neural regulation of digestion is controlled by both the sympathetic and parasympathetic divisions of the autonomic nervous system, with the parasympathetic fibres generally being responsible for the increase in secretion and motility in the gastrointestinal (GI) tract and the sympathetic fibres inhibiting these functions. Digestive activity can be split into three phases that occur consecutively: cephalic, gastric, and intestinal. The cephalic phase is brought about by the sight, taste, smell, and mastication of food. These stimulations cause vagal stimulation of the enteric nervous system, leading to release of acetylcholine (ACh) from postganglionic parasympathetic fibres, which in turn stimulate the release of gastrin from G cells. The gastric phase occurs once food has entered the stomach, with mechanoreceptors sensing increased bulk and chemoreceptors detecting the presence of peptides in the food. These stimuli cause myenteric and longer vagovagal reflexes; subsequent ACh secretion; and secretion of histamine, gastrin, acid, mucus, and enzymes. The intestinal phase starts once chyme enters the duodenum. Controlled by the autonomic nervous system, gastric motility and secretion are increased at first to promote further digestion and emptying. As chyme fills the small intestine, hormonal signals act in an inhibitory fashion to decrease gastric secretion and motility, allowing intestinal digestion to take place.

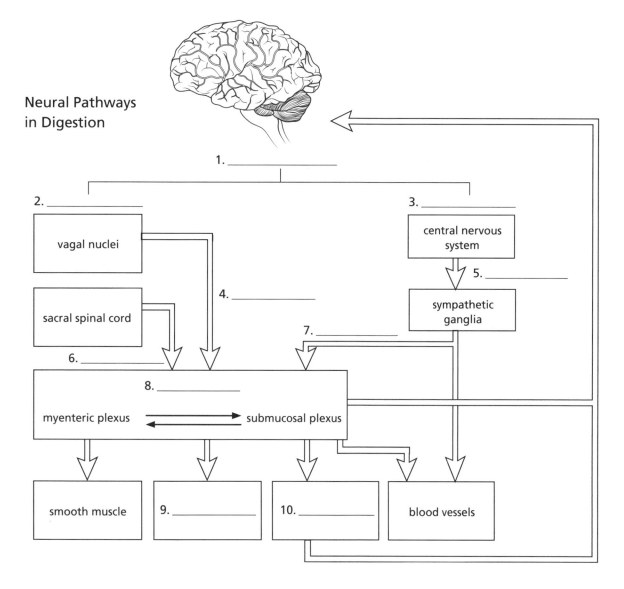

Neural Pathways in Digestion

1. _____

2. _____

vagal nuclei

3. _____

central nervous system

5. _____

sympathetic ganglia

sacral spinal cord

4. _____

7. _____

6. _____

8. _____

myenteric plexus → submucosal plexus

smooth muscle

9. _____

10. _____

blood vessels

Answers

Enteric Nervous System

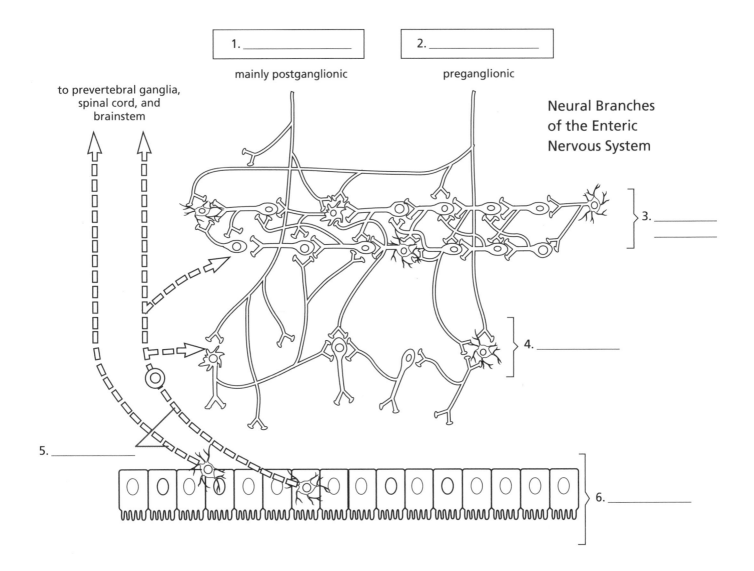

1. _____
mainly postganglionic

2. _____
preganglionic

to prevertebral ganglia, spinal cord, and brainstem

Neural Branches of the Enteric Nervous System

3. _____

4. _____

5. _____

6. _____

The wall of the gut has a large number of short axons and interneurons that make up the enteric nervous system (ENS). The ENS consists of two sets of ganglia: the submucosal plexus (Meissner's plexus) and the myenteric plexus (Auerbach's plexus). The submucosal plexus is mainly responsible for regulating the digestive glands, while the myenteric plexus is primarily responsible for regulating gut motility owing to its location deeper within the muscle layers. Sensory neurons found in the ENS are connected to chemo- and stretch receptors in the gut, while efferent neurons increase gastric gland activity and induce smooth muscle contraction; the act of peristalsis is completely controlled via the ENS. The neurons of the ENS are also able to secrete a variety of neurotransmitters, including acetylcholine (ACh), noradrenaline, nitric oxide, substance-P, and vasoactive intestinal peptide. These neurotransmitters can control both muscle contraction in the gut wall and glandular secretion.

Answers

1. sympathetic, 2. parasympathetic, 3. myenteric plexus, 4. submucosal plexus, 5. sensory neurons, 6. epithelium

Hormonal Control of Gut Function

Along with neural regulation of gut function, hormones also have an important role to play. The hormone gastrin stimulates both acid secretion and motility in the stomach. It is released from G cells upon stimulation of the enteric nervous system as food enters the stomach. The food then mixes with the gastric juices, forming chyme. As the chyme enters the small intestine, another set of hormones is released from endocrine cells located in the duodenum. The acidic and fatty chyme stimulates chemoreceptors in the duodenal wall, causing the release of somatostatin, secretin, and cholecystokinin (CCK). Somatostatin and secretin inhibit acid secretion in the stomach, which helps to protect the duodenum from excessive acid. In the pancreas, secretin stimulates the secretion of pancreatic juices, which help to neutralise the acidic chyme and provide an optimum environment for digestive enzymes, while CCK acts on the pancreas to stimulate secretion enzymes such as lipase. Another site of action for CCK is the gallbladder. When stimulated by CCK, particularly after a fatty meal, the gallbladder contracts, causing the release of bile into the small intestine to aid in the emulsification of fat.

liver

bile

gallbladder

bile

1. _____

stomach

acid chyme

2. _____

3. _____

4. _____

pancreas

pancreatic juices

duodenum

5. _____

—— stimulation

- - - inhibition

**Gut Hormones, Sites of
Release and Action**

*Label the gut hormones
released where shown.*

Answers

1. gastrin, 2. somatostatin, 3. cholecystokinin, 4. secretin, CCK, 5. secretin

Structure and Function of the Small Intestine

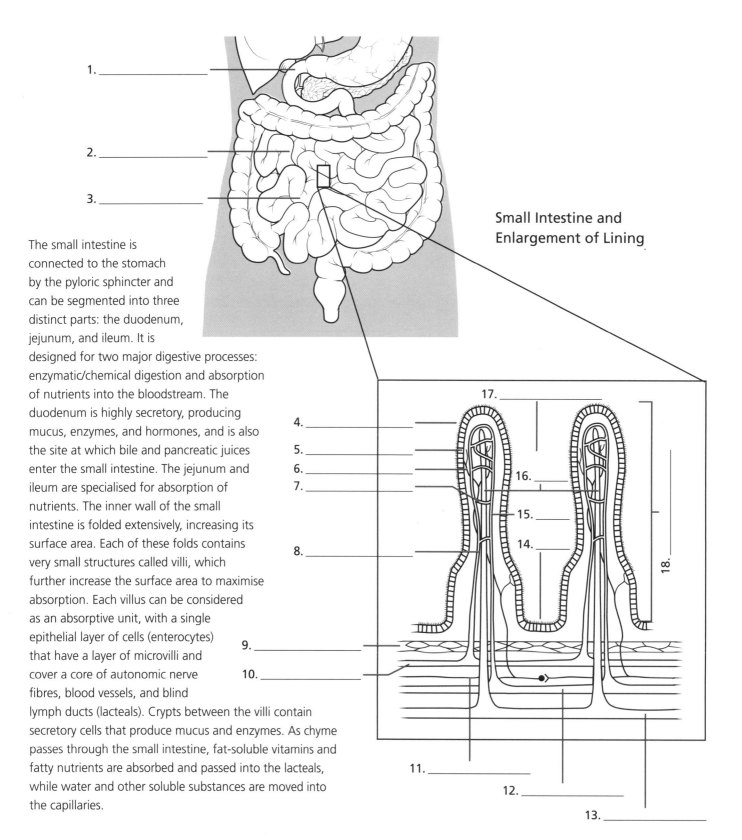

1._____

2._____

3._____

Small Intestine and Enlargement of Lining

The small intestine is connected to the stomach by the pyloric sphincter and can be segmented into three distinct parts: the duodenum, jejunum, and ileum. It is designed for two major digestive processes: enzymatic/chemical digestion and absorption of nutrients into the bloodstream. The duodenum is highly secretory, producing mucus, enzymes, and hormones, and is also the site at which bile and pancreatic juices enter the small intestine. The jejunum and ileum are specialised for absorption of nutrients. The inner wall of the small intestine is folded extensively, increasing its surface area. Each of these folds contains very small structures called villi, which further increase the surface area to maximise absorption. Each villus can be considered as an absorptive unit, with a single epithelial layer of cells (enterocytes) that have a layer of microvilli and cover a core of autonomic nerve fibres, blood vessels, and blind lymph ducts (lacteals). Crypts between the villi contain secretory cells that produce mucus and enzymes. As chyme passes through the small intestine, fat-soluble vitamins and fatty nutrients are absorbed and passed into the lacteals, while water and other soluble substances are moved into the capillaries.

4._____
5._____
6._____
7._____
8._____
9._____
10._____
11._____
12._____
13._____
14._____
15._____
16._____
17._____
18._____

Answers

1. duodenum, 2. jejunum, 3. ileum, 4. microvilli, 5. epithelial cells, 6. nerve fibre, 7. capillaries, 8. arteriole, 9. muscularis mucosae, 10. artery, 11. nerve, 12. vein, 13. lymph duct, 14. crypt, 15. venule, 16. lacteal, 17. lumen, 18. villus

Liver, Gallbladder, and Bile in Digestion

The liver is well known for its role in detoxification of drugs and toxins. However, due to its exocrine function – primarily the production of bile – it also has a role in digestion. Bile is made up of water (97 per cent), bile acid, and bile pigments. Hepatocytes synthesise bile acid from cholesterol and produce approximately 0.5 litres of bile per day. The bile is secreted from hepatocytes into the bile canaliculi and the common bile duct; this leads to the gallbladder, where bile can be stored and concentrated. As fat enters the duodenum, the hormone cholecystokinin (CCK) is released and acts on the gallbladder, causing it to contract and the sphincter of Oddi to relax, thereby allowing bile to be delivered into the duodenum. Once in the duodenum, the bile acids act as a fat-solubilising agent. Bile acids emulsify large fat droplets, allowing further digestion by lipase. The breakdown products from lipase digestion combine with bile acids to form lipid micelles, which can then be absorbed by the intestinal mucosa. Bile acids are recycled through enterohepatic circulation, in which they are reabsorbed in the terminal ileum (95 per cent); the remaining approximately 5 per cent is lost through the faeces.

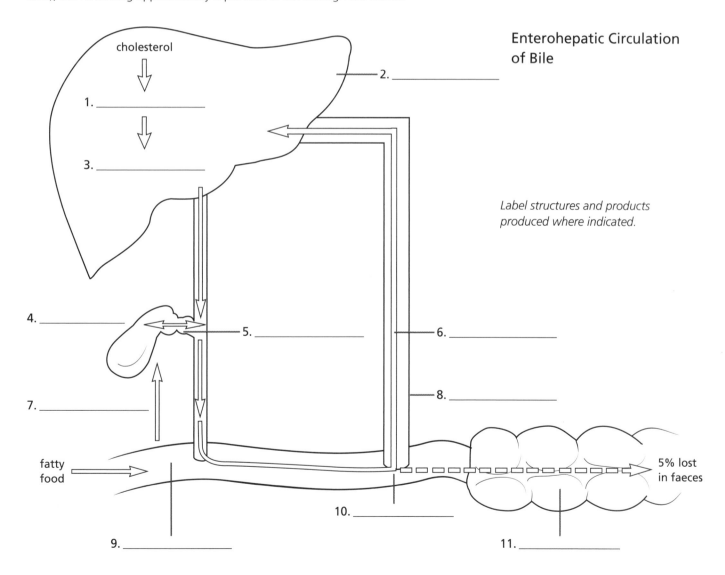

Enterohepatic Circulation of Bile

cholesterol

1. _____

2. _____

3. _____

Label structures and products produced where indicated.

4. _____

5. _____

6. _____

7. _____

8. _____

fatty food

5% lost in faeces

10. _____

9. _____

11. _____

Answers

Exocrine Pancreas in Digestion

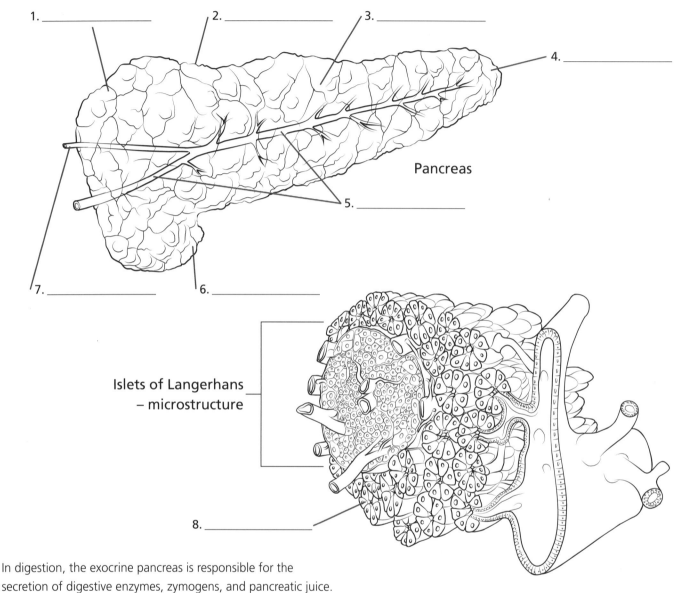

1. _____
2. _____
3. _____
4. _____

Pancreas

5. _____

7. _____
6. _____

Islets of Langerhans
– microstructure

8. _____

In digestion, the exocrine pancreas is responsible for the secretion of digestive enzymes, zymogens, and pancreatic juice.

Pancreatic juice is a bicarbonate-rich alkaline fluid secreted from pancreatic ductal cells in response to the hormone secretin, with approximately 1.5 litres per day being produced. The alkaline solution helps to neutralise stomach acid that has entered the duodenum and also provides an optimal environment for intestinal digestion.

Digestive enzymes and their precursors (zymogens) are secreted by the pancreatic acinar cells. The enzymes are packaged into zymogen granules within the acinar cells and are released by regulated exocytosis resulting from increases in intracellular calcium concentrations in response to the hormone cholecystokinin (CCK) and the neurotransmitter acetylcholine (ACh). These exocrine secretions pass along the pancreatic ducts and enter the duodenum, where they can aid with the digestion of dietary fats, proteins, and polysaccharides. Examples of pancreatic enzymes include pancreatic lipase and a-amylase, both of which are secreted in active forms and are responsible for the digestion of fat and starch. Proteases such as trypsin and chymotrypsin are secreted as their inactive precursor forms (trypsinogen and chymotrypsinogen) and are activated in the intestine; they subsequently aid in the digestion of protein.

Answers

1. head (of pancreas), 2. neck (of pancreas), 3. body (of pancreas), 4. tail (of pancreas), 5. main pancreatic duct, 6. uncinate process, 7. accessory pancreatic duct, 8. pancreatic acinar cell

Absorption in the Small Intestine

As chyme passes through the small intestine, absorption of water, electrolytes, fats, minerals, carbohydrates, amino acids, and vitamins takes place. Nutrients may move between the gastrointestinal tract and blood by a variety of mechanisms, passing through or around the epithelial cells. Water is absorbed by osmosis, following an osmotic gradient set up by the transport of ions, in particular the involvement of the sodium-potassium pump. Carbohydrates are usually absorbed in monosaccharide form, which can be transported across the epithelium and into the bloodstream via cotransporter molecules. Proteins broken down into their constituent amino acids can be absorbed by either cotransporter methods or active transport linked to the movement of sodium. The absorption of dietary calcium and iron requires the involvement of binding proteins. Iron binds to transferrin, allowing movement from the intestinal lumen, through the mucosa, and into the plasma. Calcium transporters found in the microvilli brush border actively take up calcium, which is then transported across the cell via calcium-binding proteins. Fatty acids can either pass across the intestinal mucosa by diffusion or as micelles at the brush border.

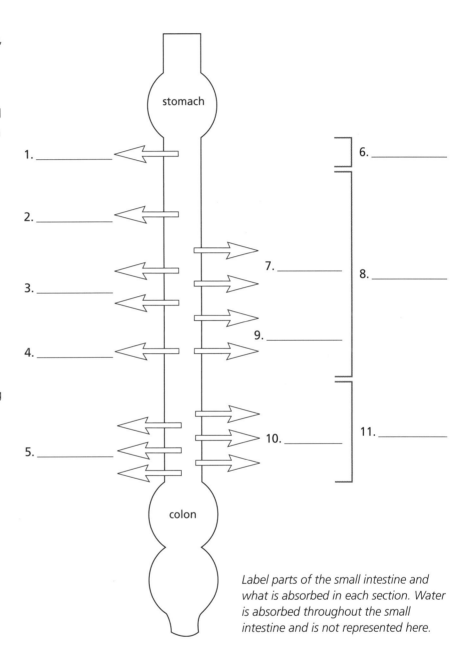

Label parts of the small intestine and what is absorbed in each section. Water is absorbed throughout the small intestine and is not represented here.

Intestine – schematic representation

Structure and Function of the Large Intestine

The large intestine comprises the caecum; ascending, transverse, descending, and sigmoid colon; rectum; and anal canal. The surface of the large intestine has a single layer of epithelial cells that have microvilli facing into the lumen. The main function of the large intestine is absorption of water and electrolytes. Chyme enters the caecum from the ileum via the ileocecal sphincter and undergoes mixing known as haustration, which takes place in sac-like compartments called haustrae. This mixing allows the exposure of chyme to the mucosal surface, where absorption takes place. Motility in the large intestine is slow – chyme can remain there for up to 20 hours. As in the small intestine, water is absorbed via osmosis against a concentration gradient controlled by sodium-potassium pumps located on the lateral and basolateral membranes of the epithelial cells. There is also movement of potassium and bicarbonate ions from the blood into the large intestine due to absorption of sodium and chloride ions across the cell wall. Absorption of water causes dehydration of chyme, which in turn helps to produce solid faecal matter.

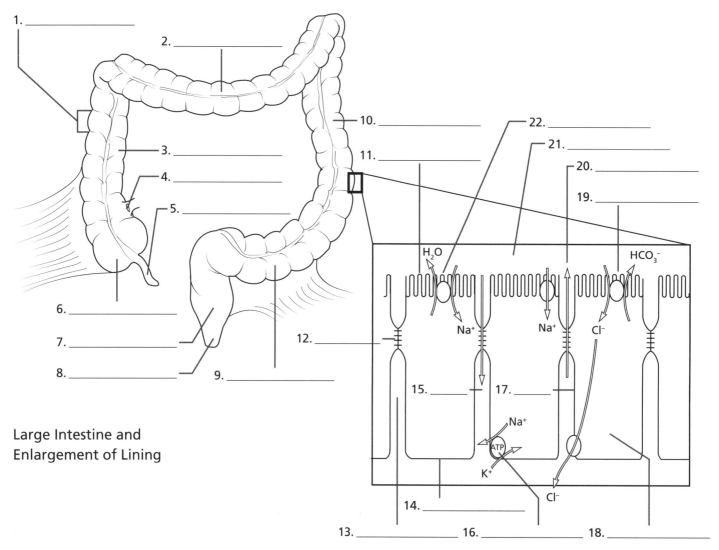

1. _____
2. _____
3. _____
4. _____
5. _____
6. _____
7. _____
8. _____
9. _____
10. _____
11. _____
12. _____
13. _____
14. _____
15. _____
16. _____
17. _____
18. _____
19. _____
20. _____
21. _____
22. _____

Large Intestine and
Enlargement of Lining

Answers

Metabolism of Carbohydrates

A six-carbon molecule of glucose ($C_6H_{12}O_6$) can combine with oxygen molecules (O_2), adenosine diphosphate (ADP), and inorganic phosphate (P_i) to form carbon dioxide (CO_2), water (H_2O), and adenosine triphosphate (ATP), the energy currency of the cell. In the first portion of this conversion, glycolysis, a molecule of glucose is converted into two pyruvate molecules by a series of enzymatically catalysed reactions. A minimal amount of energy is provided by this reaction, which does not require oxygen. Given adequate oxygen availability, pyruvate will be transported into the mitochondria and react with coenzyme A (CoA) to produce acetyl-CoA, one nicotinamide adenine dinucleotide (NADH), and one CO_2 molecule. In anaerobic conditions, pyruvate will be converted to lactate. The two-carbon acyl unit of acetyl-CoA will then enter the citric acid cycle, another multistep metabolic pathway. Several high-energy electron carriers are produced (three NADH and one flavin adenine dinucleotide, or $FADH_2$) from each pyruvate.

Electrons passing along mitochondrial proteins known as the electron transport system create a hydrogen (H^+) concentration gradient in the intermembrane space. The flow of H^+ through the ATP synthase protein transfers energy to the phosphate bond of ATP. Given that O_2 is required as the final acceptor of electrons and H^+, this process is also known as oxidative phosphorylation.

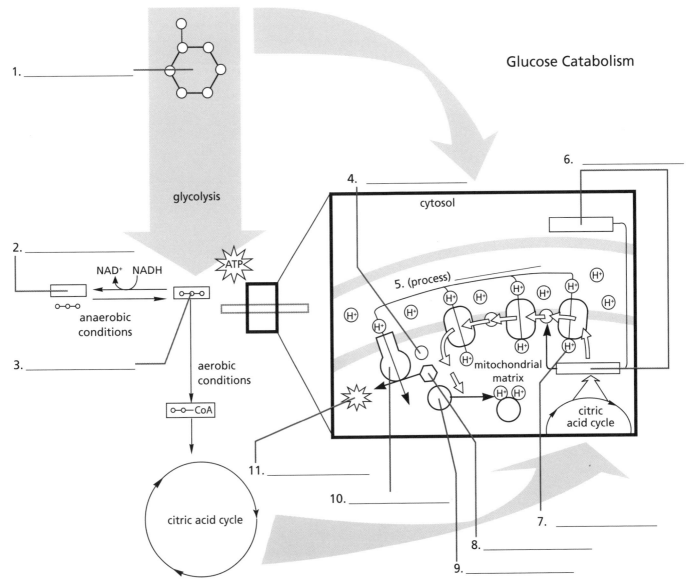

Glucose Catabolism

1. _____

glycolysis

2. _____

NAD⁺ NADH

anaerobic conditions

3. _____

aerobic conditions

o—o—CoA

citric acid cycle

4. _____

cytosol

6. _____

5. (process) _____

mitochondrial matrix

citric acid cycle

11. _____

10. _____

7. _____

8. _____

9. _____

Answers

Neural Regulation of Blood Glucose Levels

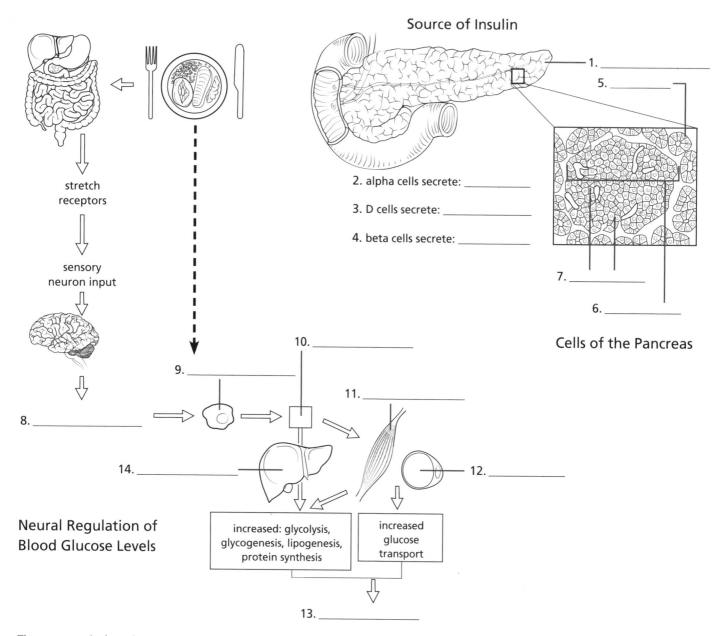

Source of Insulin

1. _____

5. _____

2. alpha cells secrete: _____

3. D cells secrete: _____

4. beta cells secrete: _____

7. _____

6. _____

Cells of the Pancreas

stretch receptors

sensory neuron input

8. _____

9. _____

10. _____

11. _____

14. _____

12. _____

Neural Regulation of Blood Glucose Levels

increased: glycolysis, glycogenesis, lipogenesis, protein synthesis

increased glucose transport

13. _____

The pancreas is the primary organ responsible for the regulation of blood glucose levels. The endocrine pancreas is made up of islets of Langerhans containing three main cell types. About 20 per cent are alpha cells, which secrete glucagon. The majority of the islet cells are beta cells, producing insulin and amylin. The remaining cells are somatostatin-secreting D cells. A fourth cell type, PP cells (or F cells), can also be found in very small numbers, and are thought to modestly alter insulin and glucagon secretion. Upon eating, distention of the gastrointestinal tract wall activates stretch receptors that stimulate increased sensory neuronal input to the central nervous system. The resulting action is a direct increase in parasympathetic output to the beta cells of the pancreas. Insulin secretion is stimulated, which acts upon the liver to increase glycolysis, glycogenesis, lipogenesis, and protein synthesis. Insulin also acts upon the muscle, adipose, and other cells to facilitate glucose transport into these cells. Together, these effects cause a decrease in plasma glucose concentrations.

Answers

1. pancreas, 2. glucagon, 3. somatostatin, 4. insulin, 5. exocrine cells, 6. islet of Langerhans, 7. endocrine cells, 8. increased parasympathetic output, 9. beta cell, 10. increased insulin, 11. skeletal muscle, 12. adipose tissue, 13. decreased blood glucose, 14. liver

Hormonal Regulation of Blood Glucose Levels

Blood glucose concentrations are primarily regulated by two important hormones: insulin and glucagon. Depending on whether the body is in a fed (postprandial) or fasted state, the ratio of insulin to glucagon differs. In the fed state, insulin predominates, increasing glucose oxidation, glycogen synthesis, fat synthesis, and protein synthesis. Overall, metabolism is anabolic, storing the energy consumed. In the fasting state, glucagon predominates, increasing glycogenolysis, gluconeogenesis, and ketogenesis. Overall, metabolism is catabolic, mobilising stored energy for use by the tissues. Prior to a meal, plasma glucagon concentrations are high and plasma insulin concentrations are low. Upon eating, a rapid increase in plasma glucose occurs, increasing insulin and decreasing glucagon. Over a period of a few hours, plasma glucose levels will gradually return to fasting levels, as insulin decreases and glucagon begins to increase.

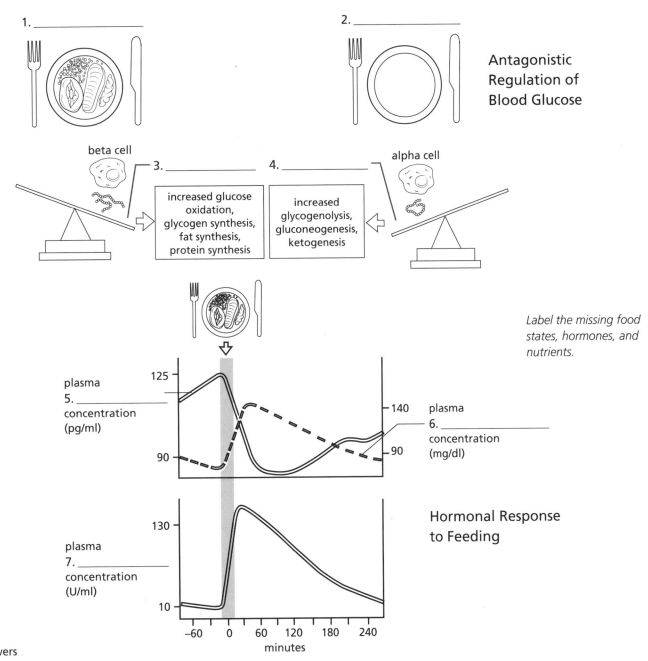

1. _____

2. _____

Antagonistic Regulation of Blood Glucose

beta cell

3. _____   4. _____

alpha cell

increased glucose oxidation, glycogen synthesis, fat synthesis, protein synthesis

increased glycogenolysis, gluconeogenesis, ketogenesis

Label the missing food states, hormones, and nutrients.

plasma
5. _____
concentration
(pg/ml)

125

90

140

90

plasma
6. _____
concentration
(mg/dl)

Hormonal Response to Feeding

130

plasma
7. _____
concentration
(U/ml)

10

−60 0   60 120 180 240

minutes

Answers

Metabolism and Regulation of Fats

Body Fat Stores and Utilisation

In addition to carbohydrates, fats are an important source of energy for the body. Carbohydrates that are broken down to glucose contribute to the overall glucose pool, and any excess glucose is then converted into fats via lipogenesis. Ingested fats are absorbed as fatty acids and monoglycerides. Free fatty acids are stored as adipose tissue, also by lipogenesis, a nutrient pool that excess glucose also contributes to. Stored fats can be converted, via lipolysis, to yield fatty acids that can then be metabolised for adenosine triphosphate (ATP) production. Intracellular lipases digest the triglycerides into glycerol and three fatty acids. Glycerol is then a substrate for metabolism via glycolysis.

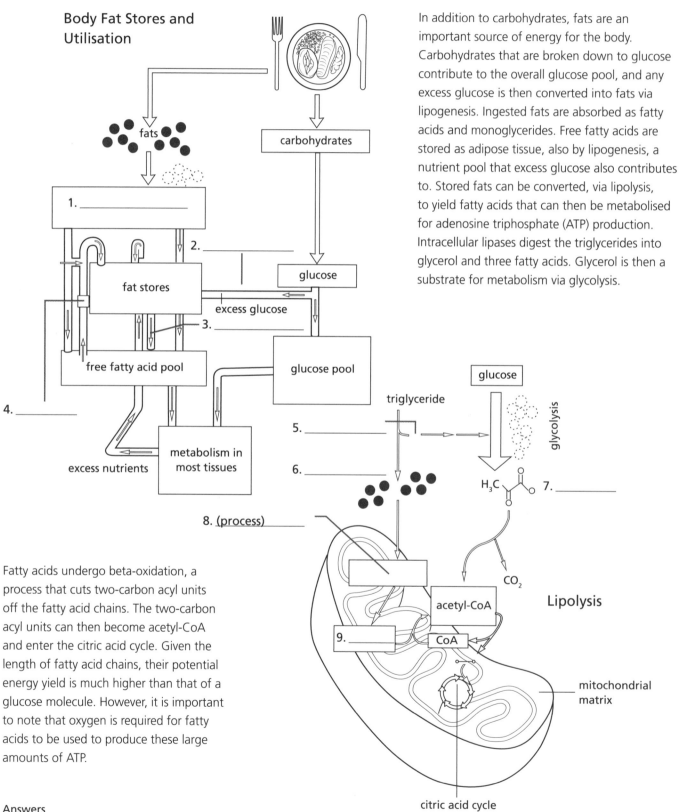

Fatty acids undergo beta-oxidation, a process that cuts two-carbon acyl units off the fatty acid chains. The two-carbon acyl units can then become acetyl-CoA and enter the citric acid cycle. Given the length of fatty acid chains, their potential energy yield is much higher than that of a glucose molecule. However, it is important to note that oxygen is required for fatty acids to be used to produce these large amounts of ATP.

Answers

Cholesterol and Lipoproteins

Transport and Fate of Ingested Fats

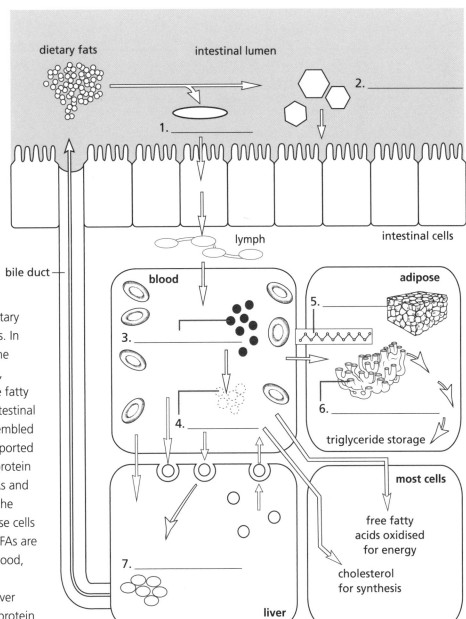

dietary fats intestinal lumen

2. _____

1. _____

lymph

intestinal cells

bile duct

blood

adipose

5. _____

3. _____

4. _____

6. _____

triglyceride storage

most cells

free fatty
acids oxidised
for energy

cholesterol
for synthesis

7. _____

liver

In addition to being used for energy, dietary fats are also used in cholesterol synthesis. In the intestinal lumen, bile salts assist in the breakdown of dietary fats to cholesterol, monoglycerides, phospholipids, and free fatty acids (FFA) for absorption. Within the intestinal cells, the absorbed components are assembled into chylomicrons (CM), which are transported to the blood via lymphatic vessels. Lipoprotein lipase (lpl) converts triglycerides into FFAs and glycerol, which are reassembled within the smooth endoplasmic reticulum of adipose cells into triglyceride storage. In other cells, FFAs are used for energy production. From the blood, chylomicron remnants and high-density lipoprotein (HDL) cholesterol enter the liver for further processing, where other lipoprotein complexes such as low-density (LDL) and very-low-density lipoproteins (VLDL) are created. In addition, some cholesterol is recycled in new bile salts. LDL is then transported back to the blood for distribution to most tissues for use in synthesis.

Answers

1. cholesterol, 2. phospholipids, 3. fatty acids, 4. glycerol, 5. lipolysis, 6. smooth endoplasmic reticulum, 7. bile salts

Metabolism of Amino Acids and Proteins

Unlike carbohydrates and lipids, ingested proteins are normally not used for the purpose of energy. Amino acids in the bloodstream are taken to the liver, where they undergo a process known as deamination, in which an amino group is removed and an organic acid remains. Ammonia (NH_3) is a relatively toxic by-product of this process and must be removed from the body. The nitrogenous waste is converted to urea within the liver and is then transported to the kidney to be excreted in urine. During periods of significant fasting, amino acids can be used as a precursor of glucose via gluconeogenesis. Additionally, some amino acids can serve as a precursor to pyruvate and subsequently enter the citric acid cycle for energy production.

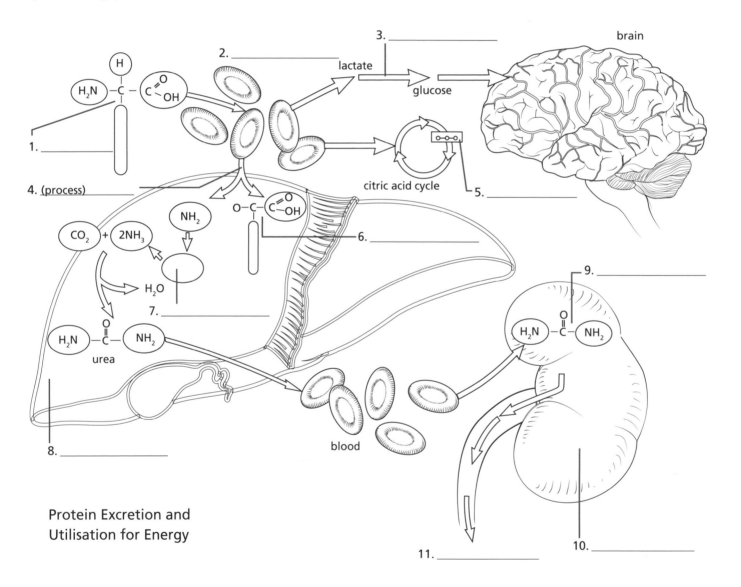

Protein Excretion and Utilisation for Energy

Body Temperature – Heat Production Versus Heat Loss

Body temperature is regulated by a number of homeostatic responses. Heat balance in the body is a dynamic equilibrium between heat gain and loss. The two components of heat input are internal heat production and external heat input. Radiation describes the radiant energy given off by objects. The human body absorbs radiant heat from the sun or other warm sources such as a heater. Conductive heat is a transfer of heat between two touching objects, like a heating pad on the skin. Internal heat production is the result of normal metabolism as well as the heat released during muscle contraction. The body has four ways in which heat can be lost. Conductive heat loss requires contact with an object that is cooler than the body, such as an ice pack. The majority of heat loss from the body is due to radiant heat loss. Both radiant and conductive heat loss are enhanced by convection heat loss, the process by which heat rises and thus carries away additional heat. Lastly, evaporative heat loss occurs on the skin in the form of sweating and in the respiratory tract by humidifying air. In both cases, the conversion of water from liquid to gas requires heat energy and thus removes heat.

1. _____

2. _____

3. _____

4. _____

5. _____

6. _____

7. _____

8. _____

9. _____

Mechanism of Heat
Gain and Loss

Answers

Thermoregulation

In response to changes in body temperature, a number of homeostatic reflexes occur that aim to maintain a relatively constant internal temperature. Environmental changes are detected by peripheral thermoreceptors, while central thermoreceptors in the anterior hypothalamus respond directly to changes in core body temperature. Signals from these sensory inputs are integrated within the hypothalamus, which coordinates the autonomic response to increased and decreased temperature. In the face of increased temperature, sympathetic cholinergic neurons stimulate sweat secretion from sweat glands and vasodilation of cutaneous blood vessels. Both processes increase heat loss to the environment. In response to decreased body temperature, sympathetic adrenergic neurons vasoconstrict cutaneous blood vessels to limit heat loss to the environment, and in adults they may also stimulate brown fat and non-shivering thermogenesis, a source of metabolic heat production. Brown fat responses are slow and the result of prolonged exposure to cold. In addition to the adrenergic response, somatic motor neurons stimulate muscle contraction. These rhythmic tremors are known as shivering thermogenesis, a response that can increase the heat production of resting muscle five-fold or six-fold.

Homeostatic Regulation of Body Temperature

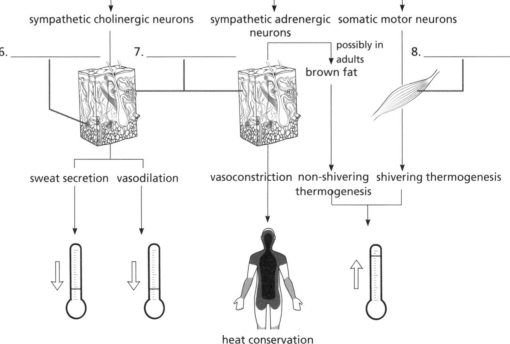

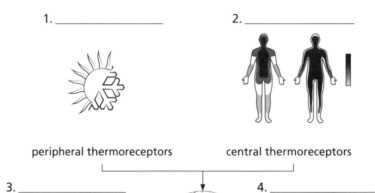

1. environmental change, 2. change in body temperature, 3. increased temperature, 4. decreased temperature, 5. hypothalamus, 6. sweat glands, 7. cutaneous blood vessels, 8. skeletal muscle

Control of Metabolic Rate

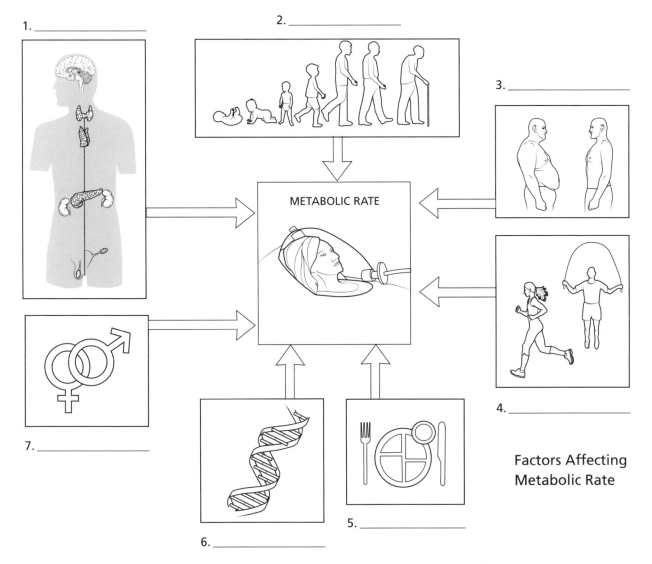

1. _____

2. _____

3. _____

METABOLIC RATE

4. _____

Factors Affecting
Metabolic Rate

7. _____

6. _____

5. _____

Resting metabolic rate (RMR) of humans is commonly measured via indirect calorimetry, through the measurement of oxygen consumption, and is highly variable between people and within a given person from day to day. The amount of lean mass in general impacts RMR, as muscle has a higher resting oxygen consumption than adipose tissue. In general, men have a greater percentage of lean muscle mass and thus tend to have a greater RMR than females. Along these lines, as lean muscle mass declines with age, older men and women have a lower RMR than their younger counterparts. When muscle is active, such as during physical activity, metabolic rate is increased both during and, to a much lesser extent, after exercise. Given the energetic costs of digestion, eating a meal increases metabolic rate. Some claims suggest that different macronutrient compositions of isocaloric diets could have different impacts on RMR; however, this is still debated. Several hormones, including the thyroid hormones and catecholamines (adrenaline and noradrenaline), influence metabolic rate, and so imbalances in these hormones can lead to weight gain or loss. Lastly, a non-modifiable contribution to the control of metabolic rate is genetics. There is a wide variation in the efficiency of the metabolisms of individuals.

Answers

1. hormones, 2. age, 3. lean mass, 4. activity level, 5. diet, 6. genetics, 7. sex

Regulation of Food Intake and Weight Control

The brain is the primary regulator of food intake by regulating appetite. Neuropeptide Y is a hypothalamic neurotransmitter that stimulates appetite. In addition, the hypothalamus is affected by leptin, a peptide hormone synthesised by adipocytes in proportion to the amount of fat they contain. A number of other factors are thought to alter the brain's signalling of hunger, some of them suppressing hunger and others stimulating hunger. Conditioned responses, increased palatability of food, increased plasma ghrelin (a hormone primarily released in the stomach that can increase the release of growth hormone and increase neuropeptide Y), and in some cases stress can all increase hunger. At the same time, stress and conditioned responses can also decrease hunger. Other hunger suppressors include increased plasma glucose, insulin, glucagon, leptin, and gastrointestinal hormones. In addition, increased body temperature and activation of stretch and chemoreceptors in the stomach and duodenum suppress hunger. Over time, if food intake exceeds caloric expenditure (via metabolism and voluntary activity), the body will be in positive energy balance and body weight will increase. If negative energy balance occurs through altered energy intake or expenditure, body weight will decrease.

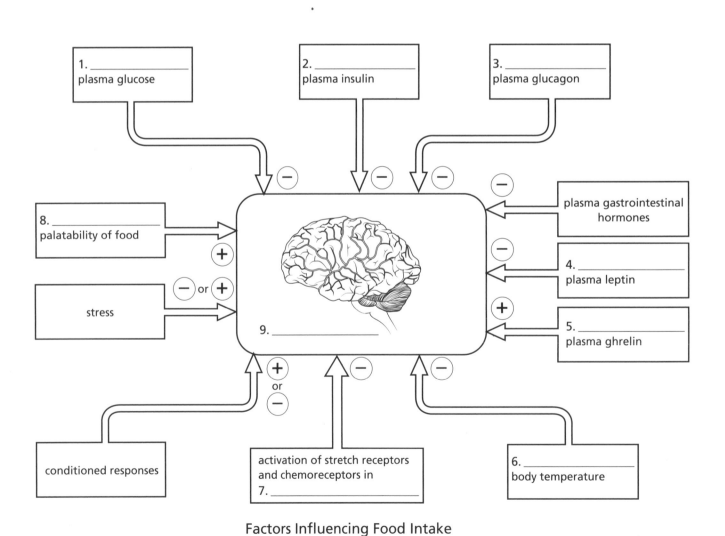

Factors Influencing Food Intake

Overview of Kidney Structure: Macroscopic Structure

Kidneys – anterior view

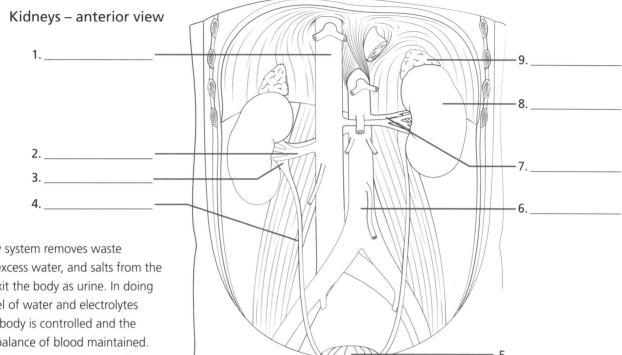

1. _____
2. _____
3. _____
4. _____

9. _____
8. _____
7. _____
6. _____
5. _____

The urinary system removes waste products, excess water, and salts from the blood to exit the body as urine. In doing so, the level of water and electrolytes within the body is controlled and the acid-base balance of blood maintained. Comprising the urinary system are the kidneys, ureters, bladder, and urethra. The kidneys are retroperitoneal organs located on the posterior abdominal wall. On the medial margin of each kidney is a vertical slit called the renal hilum, which is where vessels, nerves, and the renal pelvis enter/leave the kidney. The kidneys receive blood directly from the abdominal aorta (via renal arteries) and venous blood empties into the inferior vena cava (IVC; via renal veins). Innervation of the kidney is from sympathetic, parasympathetic, and visceral afferent fibres (via the renal plexus). Each kidney contains an outer cortex and an inner medulla. The medulla is composed of renal pyramids that have an apex and a base. The renal cortex extends to the base of the pyramids and between them to form the renal columns. The cortex and medulla are composed of nephrons, which form the functional units of the kidney.

Kidney – coronal view of right kidney

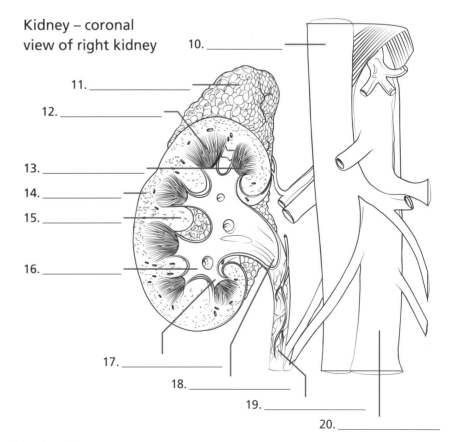

10. _____
11. _____
12. _____
13. _____
14. _____
15. _____
16. _____
17. _____
18. _____
19. _____
20. _____

Answers

Overview of Kidney Structure: Glomerular and Tubular Structure

The kidney contains 2–4 million nephrons. Each nephron has a glomerulus (situated in the cortex) and a long tubule that extends into the medulla of the kidney, before uniting with a collecting tubule. Blood plasma is filtered at the glomerulus, after which the filtrate enters the convoluted proximal tubule. The filtrate continues to flow into the descending proximal tubule and the loop of Henle, and then into the distal convoluted tubule. Fluid enters the collecting duct before passing into larger ducts that empty into the renal calyces. Modification of the plasma filtrate occurs by reabsorption and secretion as it passes along the proximal and distal nephron tubule segments. Eliminated waste products pass from the calyces into the renal pelvis and then through the ureters to the bladder. The urine remains in the bladder before it is excreted during the process of micturition.

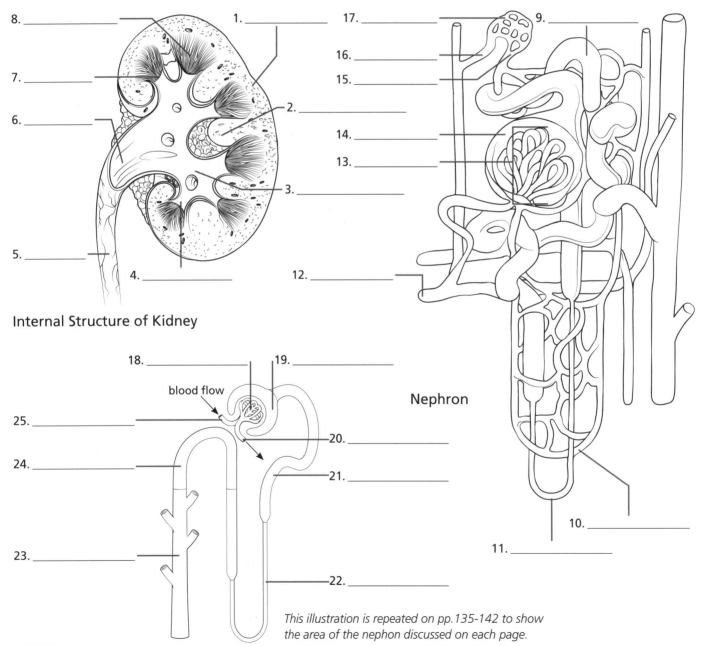

Internal Structure of Kidney

blood flow

Nephron

This illustration is repeated on pp.135-142 to show the area of the nephon discussed on each page.

Answers

The Glomerulus and Ultrafiltration

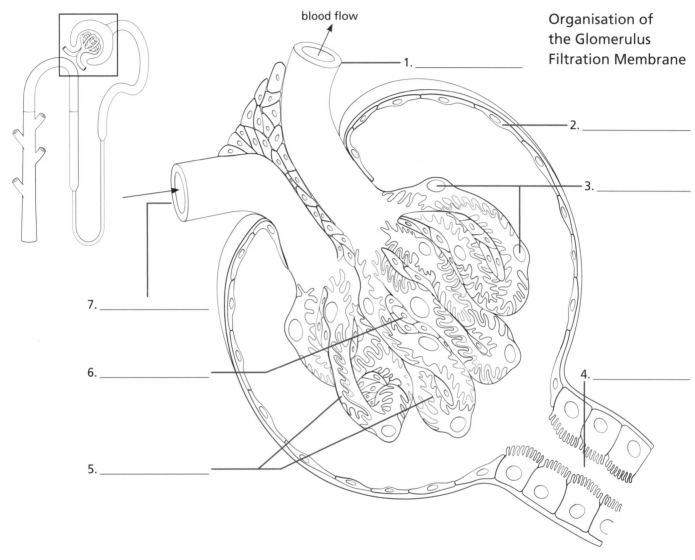

blood flow

Organisation of the Glomerulus Filtration Membrane

1. _____

2. _____

3. _____

4. _____

5. _____

6. _____

7. _____

The glomerulus comprises a bundle of capillaries encased within the glomerular capsule. The walls of the glomerular capillaries consist of a single layer of flattened endothelial cells aligned next to each other to form fenestrae, or 'windows'. With the exception of plasma proteins, blood cells, and platelets, the fenestrae permit most plasma components – including water – to cross the wall of the glomerular capillaries. The filtrate passes across a negatively charged basement membrane, a repellent for any small plasma proteins that 'leak' through the fenestrae. Once passing through the wall of the glomerulus, the filtrate is in the glomerular capsule, which has an inner wall made up of a layer of epithelial cells called podocytes. The podocytes are negatively charged, regulate the total surface area available for filtration, and provide further restrictions to filtration of plasma proteins. This process of filtering plasma components from blood into the glomerulus is known as ultrafiltration. Ultrafiltration occurs as a result of glomerular capillary blood pressure generated from the difference in diameter of the wide afferent arteriole supplying blood into the glomerulus and the narrow efferent arteriole carrying filtered blood away from the glomerulus. This difference in arteriole diameter creates a high pressure that pushes fluid out of the glomerulus, through the basement membrane, and into the glomerular capsule.

Answers

1. efferent arteriole, 2. glomerular capsule, 3. podocytes, 4. proximal convoluted tubule, 5. glomerular capillaries, 6. mesangial cells, 7. afferent arteriole

Tubular Reabsorption and Secretion

Through active transport or passive diffusion, filtered plasma components are selectively reabsorbed back into the bloodstream, with organic acids or bases undergoing tubular secretion back into the lumen. Active transport requiring energy involves movement of ions and molecules against a concentration gradient, a process facilitated by carrier proteins. Carrier proteins exist as symporters (movement of two or more ions or molecules in the same direction) or antiporters (movement of two or more ions or molecules in opposing directions). Passive diffusion is energy deficient and occurs down a concentration gradient. Commencing at the proximal convoluted tubule, all glucose and amino acids, the majority of ions, water, and a small proportion of urea are reabsorbed back into the bloodstream. Within the loop of Henle, the thin descending limb is permeable to water while the thick ascending limb is permeable to sodium and chloride. The early distal convoluted tubule is also involved in reabsorption of ions but is virtually impermeable to water and urea. The late distal convoluted tubule is the site where secretion actively takes place to maintain homeostasis through regulation of hydrogen and potassium, as well as excretion of toxins and drugs in the urine.

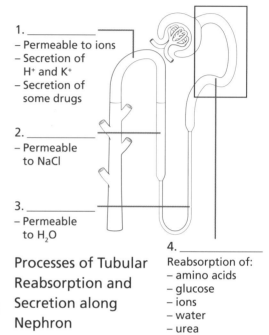

1. _____
– Permeable to ions
– Secretion of H⁺ and K⁺
– Secretion of some drugs

2. _____
– Permeable to NaCl

3. _____
– Permeable to H₂O

4. _____
Reabsorption of:
– amino acids
– glucose
– ions
– water
– urea

Processes of Tubular Reabsorption and Secretion along Nephron

Reabsorption and Secretion Transport Mechanisms in Proximal Convoluted Tubule

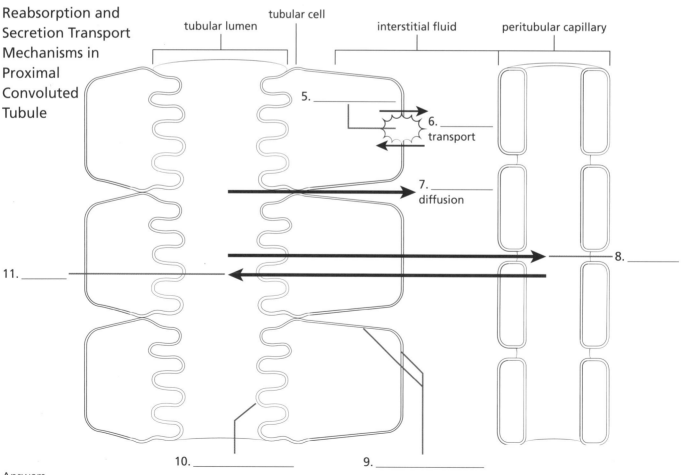

tubular lumen   tubular cell   interstitial fluid   peritubular capillary

5. _____

6. _____ transport

7. _____ diffusion

8. _____

11. _____

10. _____

9. _____

Answers

Regulation of the Glomerular Filtration Rate

Glomerular filtration rate (GFR; measured in ml/min) is defined as the amount of filtrate that is produced by the kidneys per unit of time. Factors influencing GFR include changes in arterial blood pressure impacting resistance of the arterioles, tubuloglomerular feedback mechanisms, the sympathetic nervous system, and hormonal regulation. An increase in arterial blood pressure causes the afferent and efferent arterioles to constrict and dilate, respectively, resulting in a decrease in blood flow. The net result is a decrease in glomerular capillary pressure, and thus a decrease in GFR. The converse is observed following a decrease in arterial blood pressure. GFR regulation by the tubuloglomerular feedback mechanism requires the detection of changes in sodium and chloride concentrations in the filtrate by macula densa cells. Increased or decreased sodium and chloride releases vasoconstrictor or vasodilator chemicals, respectively, altering the diameter of the arterioles to influence GFR. In situations of low arterial blood pressure, such as following severe blood loss, activation of the sympathetic nervous system causes vasoconstriction of the afferent arteriole, leading to a reduction in GFR. This regulatory mechanism is important in mobilising blood to critical areas within the body. Furthermore, hormones with vasoactive properties on the arterioles are also important in regulating GFR.

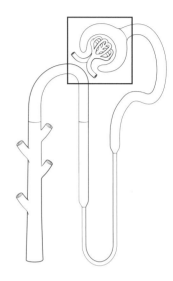

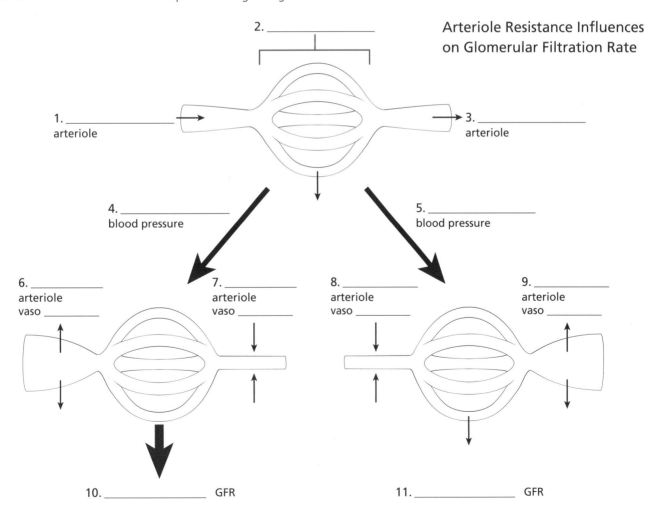

Arteriole Resistance Influences on Glomerular Filtration Rate

2. _____

1. _____
arteriole

3. _____
arteriole

4. _____
blood pressure

5. _____
blood pressure

6. _____
arteriole
vaso _____

7. _____
arteriole
vaso _____

8. _____
arteriole
vaso _____

9. _____
arteriole
vaso _____

10. _____ GFR

11. _____ GFR

Answers

Regulation of Potassium

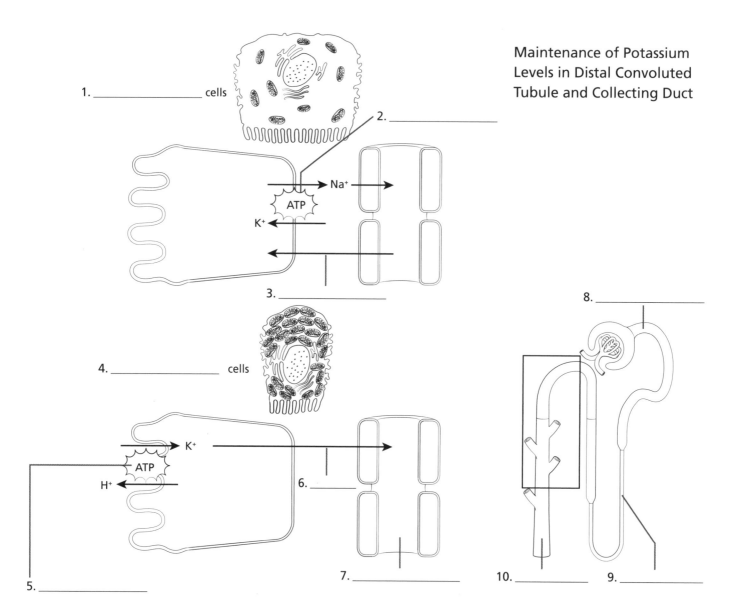

1. _____ cells

2. _____

3. _____

4. _____ cells

5. _____

6. _____

7. _____

8. _____

9. _____

10. _____

Maintenance of Potassium Levels in Distal Convoluted Tubule and Collecting Duct

As potassium ions are integral to numerous physiological and chemical processes, an increase (hyperkalemia) or decrease (hypokalemia) of potassium ions from normal levels can have unfavourable consequences. The kidney is therefore essential in maintaining a balance of potassium ions in the body. Active reabsorption and secretion of potassium ions via carrier proteins from the filtrate commences in the proximal convoluted tubule, with further reabsorption and secretion taking place in the distal convoluted tubule and collecting duct. The distal convoluted tubule and collecting ducts are of interest in regulating potassium ions owing to the presence of intercalated (I) and principal (P) cells. The I cells, which possess abundant mitochondria, reabsorb potassium ions through hydrogen-potassium ATPase carrier proteins, implicating potassium ions in acid-base balance. The P cells, which possess few mitochondria, secrete potassium ions, a process facilitated by the sodium-potassium ATPase carrier protein, which reabsorbs sodium chloride and water at the expense of potassium ions. In a situation of low blood pressure, activation of the renin-angiotensin system promotes an increase in potassium secretion in the distal convoluted tubule and collecting duct through the insertion of sodium-potassium ATPase carrier proteins, which favour sodium reabsorption, but at the expense of potassium ions.

Answers

1. principal (P), 2. sodium-potassium ATPase carrier protein, 3. secretion, 4. intercalated (I), 5. hydrogen-potassium ATPase carrier protein, 6. reabsorption, 7. blood capillary, 8. proximal convoluted tubule, 9. loop of Henle, 10. collecting tubule

Renal Regulation of the Acid-Base Balance

The body's sensitivity to changes in acidity and alkalinity necessitates the maintenance of an optimal environment for normal chemical and physiological processes. In conjunction with the respiratory system, the renal system is integral to maintaining this acid-base balance. An elevation of hydrogen ions within the body stimulates renal buffering systems, one of which is driven by bicarbonate ions. Within the proximal and distal tubules, bicarbonate ions buffer excess hydrogen ions through a chemical reaction that forms the intermediary carbonic acid, followed by its dissociation to carbon dioxide and water. The formed carbon dioxide is subsequently eliminated through ventilatory processes. An absence of bicarbonate ions stimulates their formation in the reverse reaction. The enzyme carbonic anhydrase accelerates the hydration of carbon dioxide, generating bicarbonate and hydrogen ions, which are reabsorbed and secreted, respectively. In addition to the bicarbonate buffering system are the phosphate and ammonia buffering systems. In acidic conditions requiring excess hydrogen ion elimination, water reabsorption concentrates the filtrate with phosphate ions, which buffer the hydrogen ions. With ammonia as a buffer in acidic conditions, a reaction with hydrogen to form ammonium eventually leads to the formation of ammonium chloride, a product that is excreted in urine.

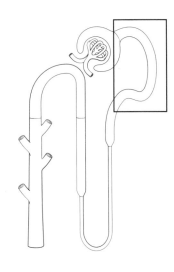

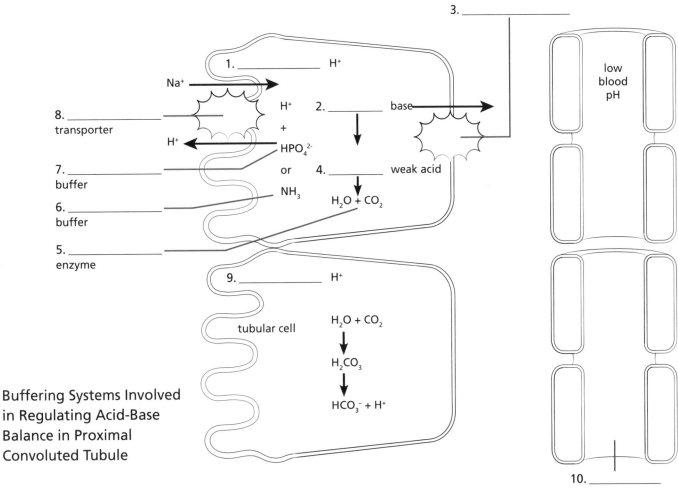

3. _____

1. _____ H^+

Na^+

8. _____
transporter

H^+

H^+
+
HPO_4^{2-}

2. _____ base

low
blood
pH

7. _____
buffer

or

4. _____ weak acid

6. _____
buffer

NH_3

$H_2O + CO_2$

5. _____
enzyme

9. _____ H^+

tubular cell

$H_2O + CO_2$

H_2CO_3

**Buffering Systems Involved
in Regulating Acid-Base
Balance in Proximal
Convoluted Tubule**

$HCO_3^- + H^+$

10. _____

Answers

Water Conservation and Antidiuretic Hormone

Antidiuretic hormone (ADH; also called vasopressin) is synthesised in cells in the hypothalamus, and from there it is transported via axonal transport to the nerve terminals in the pituitary gland for release when required. The association of ADH with water conservation is from its regulation of the osmolality and volume of urine. A deficit in the osmolality and blood volume stimulates the release into the bloodstream of ADH from the pituitary gland. ADH enters the collecting duct of the nephron, where it binds to the G-protein coupled vasopressin (V2) receptor. The binding of ADH to its receptor initiates a procession of signalling, commencing with activation of the enzyme adenylyl cyclase to increase cyclic adenosine monophosphate (cAMP). This increase in cAMP activates protein kinase A (PKA), which phosphorylates and causes inactive water channels within the intracellular vesicles to fuse with the cell membrane. Insertion of aquaporin-2 channels (AQP2) in the fused water channels permits increased reabsorption of water to rectify the decrease in osmolality and blood volume, and thus excretion of concentrated urine. With elevated osmolality and blood volume, the hypothalamus sends a message to the pituitary gland to slow down or stop ADH release. The decrease in ADH stimuli results in a more dilute urine output.

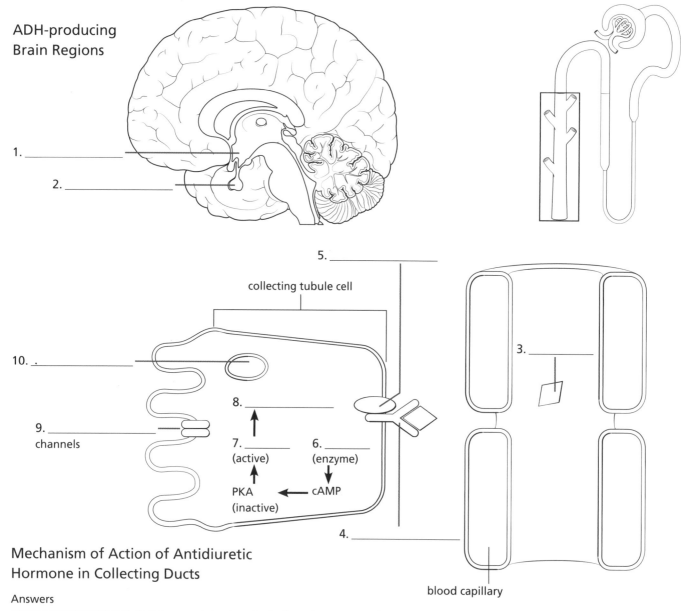

ADH-producing
Brain Regions

1. _____

2. _____

5. _____

collecting tubule cell

10. _____

3. _____

8. _____

9. _____
channels

7. _____ (active)   6. _____ (enzyme)

PKA (inactive) ← cAMP

4. _____

blood capillary

Mechanism of Action of Antidiuretic Hormone in Collecting Ducts

Answers

1. hypothalamus, 2. pituitary gland, 3. antidiuretic hormone, 4. vasopressin (V2) receptor, 5. G-protein, 6. adenylyl cyclase, 7. protein kinase A, 8. protein phosphorylation, 9. aquaporin-2-channel, 10. vesicle (with inactive water channel)

Countercurrent Systems in the Renal Medulla

The flow of solutes and water in and out of the nephron results in countercurrent, a phenomenon of 'running in the opposite direction'. The sole purpose of the countercurrent system is to maintain a high osmolality within the renal medulla, and it is thus a mechanism for water conservation by the kidney. The loop of Henle is a major contributor to this phenomenon through its regional permeability to sodium, chloride, and water. Upon arrival of the filtrate at the ascending limb of the loop of Henle, active transport via sodium-potassium ATPase carrier proteins and chloride channels promotes the exit of sodium and chloride into the renal medulla interstitial fluid. The increase in osmolality within the renal medulla causes the net passive diffusion of water from the thin descending limb of the loop of Henle. As the filtrate flows through the nephron, this countercurrent mechanism results in a progressive increase in solute concentration in the descending limb.and a progressive decrease in solute concentration in the ascending limb. The overall outcome is a concentrated interstitial fluid within the renal medulla – a necessity for water conservation.

Bidirectional Flow of Solutes and Water in Loop of Henle

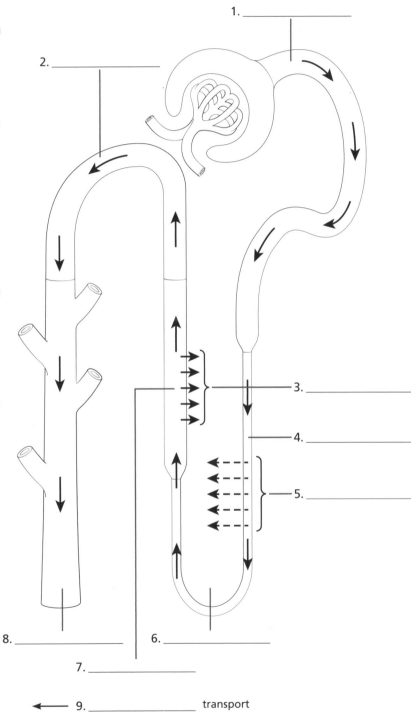

1. _____

2. _____

3. _____

4. _____

5. _____

6. _____

7. _____

8. _____

9. _____ transport

10. _____ transport

Answers

Renin-Angiotensin System

The renin-angiotensin system tightly controls blood volume and sodium balance. Low blood pressure and low sodium levels are sensed in the macula densa cells of the juxtaglomerular apparatus of the kidney, which respond by releasing renin. This proteolytic enzyme cleaves circulating angiotensinogen (a glycoprotein synthesised and released from the liver) to produce the peptide angiotensin I. Angiotensin I is activated by angiotensin converting enzyme (ACE) to form angiotensin II. Angiotensin II has multiple actions including initiating the sensation of thirst and stimulating the release of the steroid hormone aldosterone from the adrenal cortex. Aldosterone increases sodium ion absorption in distal tubular cells and collecting tubules, allowing chloride ions and water to follow via passive reabsorption. The system alleviates low body fluid osmolality, low blood volume, and low blood pressure.

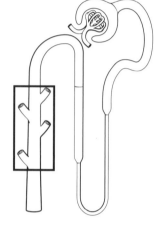

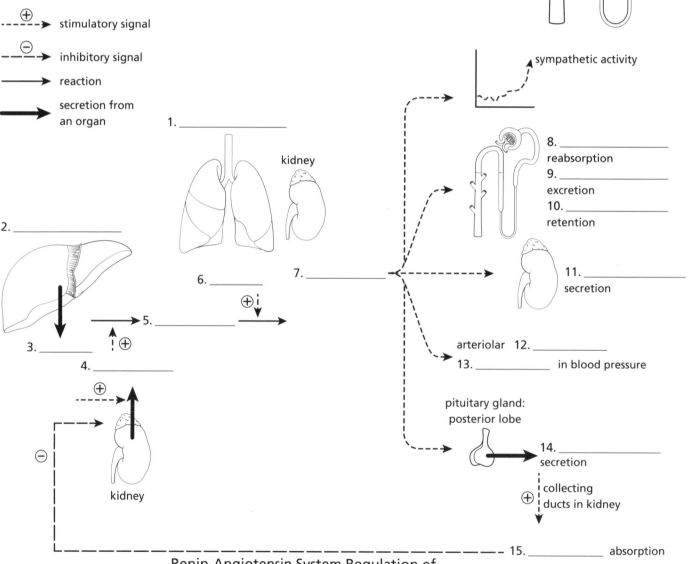

Renin-Angiotensin System Regulation of
Blood Pressure and Fluid Balance

Physiology of Micturition

Urine from the kidneys passes through the ureters to the bladder where it is stored before being expelled from the body via the urethra in a physiological process called micturition. Storage and excretion of urine involves the coordinated interactions between the bladder, urethra, and urethral sphincters, which are under the control of the sympathetic, parasympathetic, and somatic nervous systems. Sympathetic postganglionic neurons activate β-adrenergic receptors (relaxing the detrusor smooth muscle of the bladder) and α-adrenergic receptors (contracting urethral smooth muscle) allowing the bladder to fill. Parasympathetic postganglionic axons release acetylcholine (ACh), which stimulates the detrusor muscle to contract by activation of M2 and M3 muscarinic receptors. These parasympathetic postganglionic nerves also release ATP (exciting detrusor muscle) and nitric oxide (relaxing urethral smooth muscle). This results in the neck of the bladder opening, allowing urine to be expelled through the urethra by the force of bladder contraction. Voluntary overriding of the micturition reflex is learned in early childhood so that the bladder is emptied at an individual's convenience. Here, somatic axons of the pudendal nerve release ACh, which causes the external urethral (striated muscle) sphincter to contract by activation of nicotinic cholinergic receptors.

CNS micturition centres

6. _____

Innervation of the Lower Urinary Tract

1. _____

2. _____

3. _____

4. _____
innervation

5. _____

lumbar 1

lumbar 5

sacral 1

12. _____

11. _____

10. _____

sacral 4

9. _____

8. _____
nerve

7. _____
innervation

Answers

Overview of Endocrine System

The endocrine system functions together with the nervous system to regulate and coordinate body activities by means of chemical messengers, called hormones. These are released directly into the bloodstream from specialised endocrine (ductless) glands and cells throughout the body. Hormones may travel some distance in the bloodstream to a target tissue, may have a localised effect on surrounding tissues (paracrine), or may influence the activity of the same cell type from which they were released (autocrine). The hypothalamus is a critical area of the brain responsible for many functions, including regulating secretions from the pituitary gland, which in turn releases hormones that act on other organs such as the adrenal gland, thyroid, kidney, and uterus. Hormone secretion from glands is regulated by both neural and hormonal stimuli and by mediators circulating in the blood. It is often controlled by negative-feedback mechanisms, in which raised levels of a hormone inhibit further secretion of the same hormone. Other hormone-producing tissues include adipose tissue, the digestive tract, the ovaries, the placenta, and the testes.

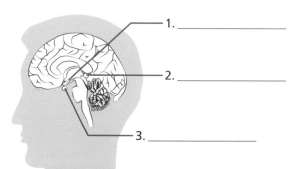

1. _____

2. _____

3. _____

4. _____

5. _____

6. _____

7. _____

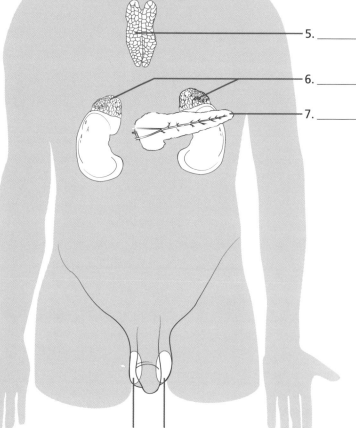

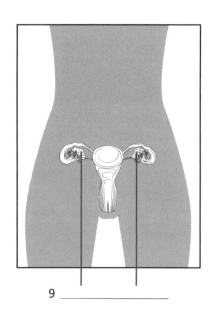

9 _____

Major Endocrine Glands and Tissues

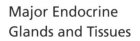

8. _____

Answers

1. hypothalamus, 2. pineal gland, 3. pituitary, 4. thyroid, 5. thymus, 6. adrenal glands, 7. pancreas, 8. testes (male), 9. ovaries (female)

Cellular Action of Hormones

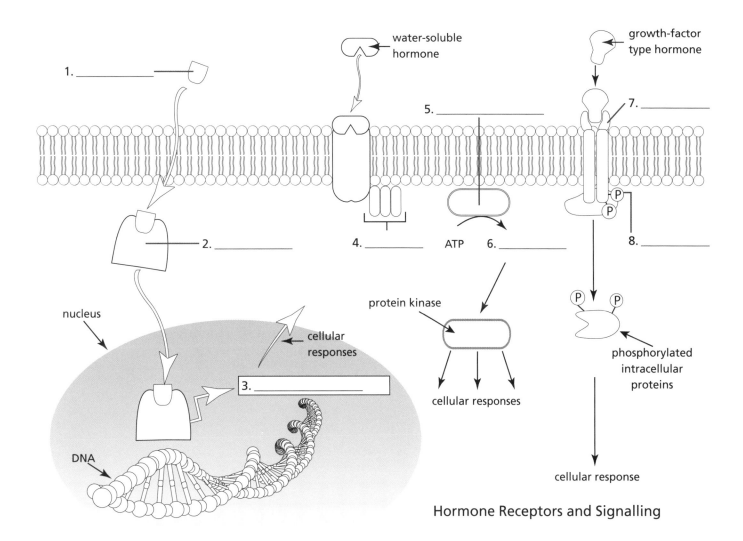

1. _____

water-soluble hormone

growth-factor type hormone

5. _____

7. _____

2. _____

nucleus

4. _____   ATP   6. _____

8. _____

protein kinase

cellular responses

3. _____

cellular responses

P P

phosphorylated intracellular proteins

DNA

cellular response

Hormone Receptors and Signalling

Hormones are delivered to all parts of the body by the bloodstream, but it is only the cells with specific receptors that can respond. There are lipid-soluble hormones (e.g. testosterone and the thyroid hormone, thyroxine), which are carried in the blood, bound to binding proteins, and water-soluble hormones (e.g. adrenaline, glucagon, and growth hormone), with each category acting on cellular receptors in its own way. Lipid-soluble hormones diffuse into the cell and bind to nuclear receptors located in the cytoplasm or nucleus. The hormone-receptor complex binds to regulatory sequences on genes and activates, or represses, gene transcription and protein synthesis that is associated with the cell's response. Many water-soluble hormones bind to integral membrane receptors belonging to the G-protein coupled receptor (GPCR) family. Hormone binding activates the G-protein, which alters the activity of membrane-bound intracellular enzymes such as adenylate cyclase. This leads to the production of cyclic adenosine monophosphate (cAMP), which binds to protein kinases and activates them, in turn leading to many different cellular responses depending on the cell type. The receptors for several protein hormones (e.g. insulin) are integral membrane receptor-type kinases. Once the receptor is activated by the bound hormone, it causes specific proteins to become phosphorylated and results in a subsequent series of cellular events. The original hormonal signal is often amplified via a cascade of events, the timescale of which may range from milliseconds to days.

Answers

1. lipid-soluble hormone, 2. nuclear receptor, 3. gene transcription, 4. G-protein complex, 5. adenylate cyclase, 6. cyclic adenosine monophosphate, 7. tyrosine kinase, 8. phosphorylated intracellular protein

Anterior Pituitary Gland and its Hormones, and the Hypothalamus

The pituitary gland is located at the base of the brain below the hypothalamus, to which it is connected via a funnel-shaped stalk called the infundibulum. The pituitary is about the size of a pea and has two major lobes, one glandular (the anterior lobe) and the other neuronal (the posterior lobe). The anterior pituitary manufactures and releases a number of hormones that in turn regulate the activity of other endocrine glands. Secretions from the anterior pituitary are controlled by the hypothalamus (named for its position below the thalamus in the brain), which is also vital in controlling the autonomic nervous system, physical response to emotions, body temperature, food intake, water balance, and sleep-wake cycles.

When hypothalamic neurons that regulate the anterior pituitary are stimulated, they secrete releasing or inhibiting hormones into the hypophyseal portal system, a branching network of capillary beds connected by veins that link the hypothalamus with the anterior pituitary. These neurohormones are growth hormone-releasing hormone (GHRH), growth hormone-inhibiting hormone (GHIH), thyrotropin-releasing hormone (TRH), corticotropin-releasing hormone (CRH), gonadotropin-releasing hormone (GnRH), prolactin-inhibiting hormone (PIH), and prolactin-releasing hormone (PRH). The hypothalamic hormones travel through the portal system to the anterior pituitary, where they stimulate or inhibit the release of hormones made there. The anterior pituitary secretes hormones into a second capillary network that merges with the general circulation, and this then carries the hormones to their target tissues. The six anterior pituitary hormones secreted are growth hormone (GH), thyroid-stimulating hormone (TSH), adrenocorticotropic hormone (ACTH), follicle-stimulating hormone (FSH), luteinizing hormone (LH), and prolactin (PRL).

TSH, ACTH, FSH, and LH regulate the secretion of hormones from other endocrine glands. These include the thyroid, which produces thyroid hormones in response to TSH; the adrenal cortex of the adrenal gland, which produces the glucocorticoid cortisol and androgens in response to ACTH; and the gonads (ovaries in females and testes in males), which produce oestrogen and progesterone in females and testosterone in males in response to FSH and LH. Multiple levels of inhibitory feedback are exerted either at the level of the anterior pituitary or hypothalamus to ensure tight regulation of secretion and to maintain homeostasis.

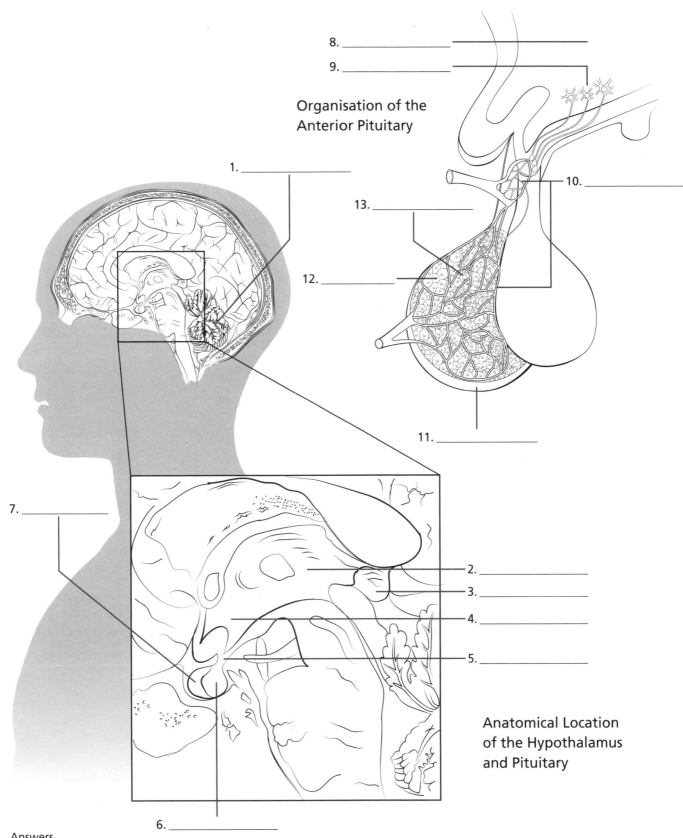

Organisation of the Anterior Pituitary

8. _____

9. _____

1. _____

13. _____

12. _____

10. _____

11. _____

7. _____

2. _____

3. _____

4. _____

5. _____

6. _____

Anatomical Location of the Hypothalamus and Pituitary

Answers

1. cerebellum, 2. thalamus, 3. pineal gland, 4. hypothalamus, 5. infundibulum, 6. posterior pituitary, 7. anterior pituitary, 8. hypothalamus, 9. hypothalamic neurons, 10. hypophyseal portal system, 11. anterior pituitary, 12. endocrine cells, 13. capillary beds

Posterior Pituitary Gland and its Hormones, and the Hypothalamus

The posterior lobe of the pituitary gland is composed of neuronal tissue, and its secretions – antidiuretic hormone (ADH; also called vasopressin) and oxytocin – are called neurohormones, or neuropeptides. Unlike the anterior pituitary (see pp. 146–147), there is no portal system to carry hypothalamic hormones to the posterior pituitary. Instead, the neurohormones are produced by neurons that have cell bodies in the supraoptic nuclei (predominantly ADH-producing neurons) or paraventricular nuclei (predominantly oxytocin-producing neurons) of the hypothalamus. The hormones are then transported from the cell bodies down the interior of axons that pass through the infundibulum to the posterior pituitary, where they are stored in axon terminals. Stimulation of hypothalamic neurons causes conduction of an action potential to the axon terminal, and consequently the release of the neurohormone into the circulatory system of the posterior pituitary, from where it travels in the bloodstream to influence the activity of the target tissues. ADH is released in response to changes in blood osmolality and blood pressure detected by osmoreceptors and baroreceptors, respectively, which stimulate the hypothalamic neurons. It acts on kidney tubules to increase water reabsorption, leading to reduced urine output, increased blood volume and consequently decreased blood osmolality. ADH also constricts blood vessels leading to an increase in blood pressure. Oxytocin increases contractions of the uterus and regulates the release of breast milk during lactation.

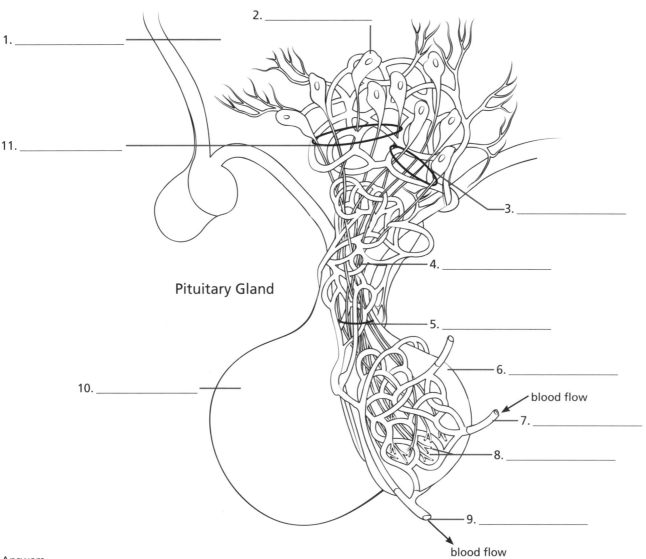

1. _____

2. _____

11. _____

3. _____

4. _____

Pituitary Gland

5. _____

6. _____

blood flow

7. _____

8. _____

10. _____

9. _____

blood flow

Answers

Pineal Gland

The pineal gland is a small reddish-grey endocrine gland about the size of a small pea (approximately 5–8 mm in diameter). It is shaped like a tiny pine cone and is located in a groove where the two halves of the thalamus join in the centre of the brain between the two hemispheres, behind the third cerebral ventricle. Pinealocytes, the predominant cells of the pineal gland, manufacture and secrete melatonin, which is derived from the neurotransmitter serotonin, which is itself derived from the amino acid tryptophan. Melatonin, whose production is stimulated by darkness and inhibited by light, influences the 24-hour sleep-wake cycle (circadian rhythm) and sexual development. Low levels of light lead to high levels of melatonin and result in sleepiness and a delay in the onset of puberty. High levels of light result in wakefulness and increased reproductive cycle events, including puberty and the release of gonadotropins (luteinizing hormone and follicle-stimulating hormone) from the anterior pituitary gland.

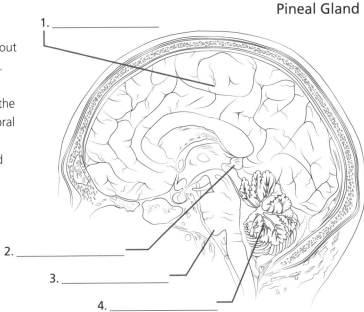

Pineal Gland

1. _____
2. _____
3. _____
4. _____

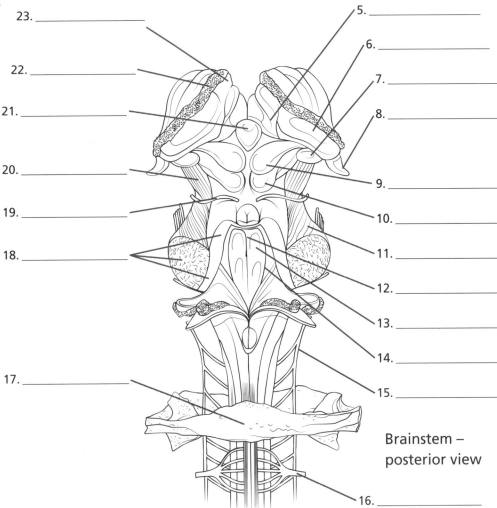

Brainstem – posterior view

5. _____
6. _____
7. _____
8. _____
9. _____
10. _____
11. _____
12. _____
13. _____
14. _____
15. _____
16. _____
17. _____
18. _____
19. _____
20. _____
21. _____
22. _____
23. _____

Answers

1. cerebrum, 2. pineal gland, 3. brainstem, 4. cerebellum, 5. habenula, 6. pulvinar, 7. medial geniculate nucleus, 8. lateral geniculate nucleus, 9. superior colliculus, 10. inferior colliculus, 11. pons, 12. dorsal median sulcus, 13. facial colliculus, 14. sulcus limitans, 15. spinal accessory nerve (XI), 16. first cervical nerve, 17. atlas (C1), 18. cerebellar peduncles, 19. trochlear nerve (IV), 20. cerebral peduncle, 21. pineal body, 22. choroid plexus of lateral ventricle, 23. thalamus

Thyroid Gland

Thyroid hormone synthesis and secretion is stimulated by thyroid-stimulating hormone, released from the anterior pituitary. The thyroid gland is located in the neck just inferior to the larynx. It is a butterfly-shaped gland with two lobes that straddle the trachea. It is one of the largest endocrine glands and secretes two iodine-containing hormones, triiodothyronine (T_3) and thyroxine (T_4), which contain three and four iodine molecules, respectively. T_3 is generally considered to be the main thyroid hormone and has diverse effects throughout the body, in particular on metabolism, growth, and development, and through potentiating the action of catecholamines. The thyroid gland is composed of numerous follicles, which are formed by a single layer of follicular epithelial cells in a spherical formation surrounding a core of protein-rich material called colloid. Colloid is made up of large amounts of thyroglobulin, a precursor of thyroid hormones, secreted by the follicular cells. Between the follicles are loose connective tissue and scattered parafollicular cells, which secrete the hormone calcitonin. The parathyroid glands are located in the posterior part of the thyroid and are composed of densely packed cells of two types: chief cells and oxyphils. The chief cells secrete parathyroid hormone, while the function of oxyphils is unknown.

**Thyroid Gland
– anterior view**

1. _____

3. _____

Thyroid Follicles

4. _____

2. _____

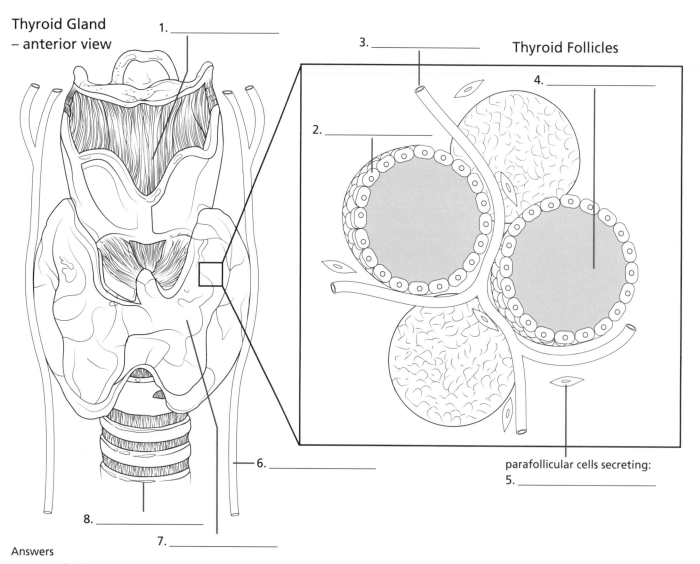

6. _____

parafollicular cells secreting:
5. _____

8. _____

7. _____

Regulation of Calcium

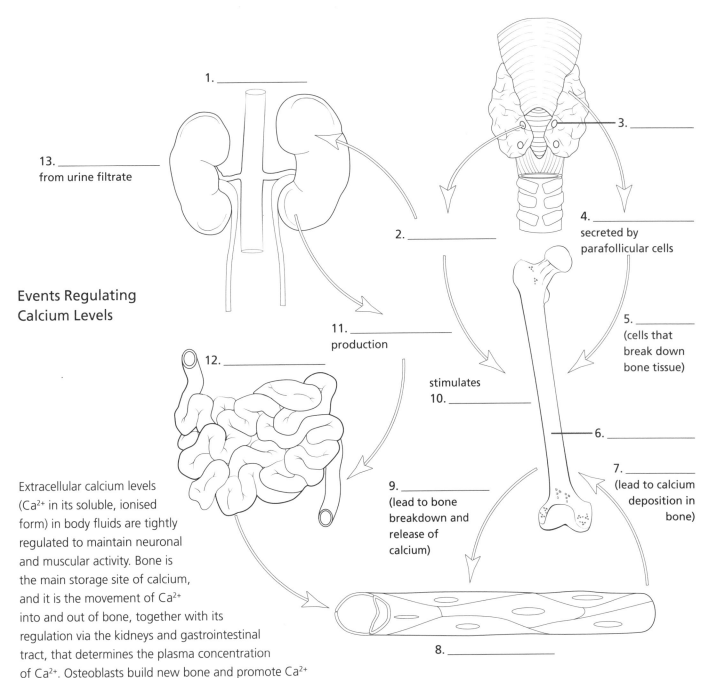

1. _____

13. _____
from urine filtrate

3. _____

4. _____
secreted by
parafollicular cells

2. _____

5. _____
(cells that
break down
bone tissue)

Events Regulating Calcium Levels

11. _____
production

12. _____

stimulates
10. _____

6. _____

7. _____
(lead to calcium
deposition in
bone)

9. _____
(lead to bone
breakdown and
release of
calcium)

8. _____

Extracellular calcium levels (Ca^{2+} in its soluble, ionised form) in body fluids are tightly regulated to maintain neuronal and muscular activity. Bone is the main storage site of calcium, and it is the movement of Ca^{2+} into and out of bone, together with its regulation via the kidneys and gastrointestinal tract, that determines the plasma concentration of Ca^{2+}. Osteoblasts build new bone and promote Ca^{2+} deposition, leading to a decrease in blood Ca^{2+} levels; in contrast, osteoclasts are cells that break down bone tissue. When blood Ca^{2+} levels are too low, osteoclast activity is increased in response to parathyroid hormone (PTH), which is released from the parathyroid gland, leading to the release of Ca^{2+} ions into the blood. PTH also acts on the kidneys to increase reabsorption of Ca^{2+} from urine, and it stimulates vitamin D formation, which in turn increases Ca^{2+} uptake from the small intestine. On the other hand, an increase in blood Ca^{2+} stimulates release of calcitonin from the thyroid, which inhibits osteoclast activity and, together with ongoing osteoblast activity, leads to a net reduction in blood Ca^{2+} levels. In the adult, calcitonin plays a minimal role in regulating calcium homeostasis.

Answers

1. kidney, 2. parathyroid hormone, 3. parathyroid gland, 4. calcitonin, 5. inhibits osteoclasts, 6. bone, 7. osteoblasts (calcium deposition in bone), 8. blood vessel, 9. osteoclasts (bone breakdown, release of calcium), 10. stimulates osteoclasts, 11. vitamin D, 12. small intestine, 13. calcium reabsorption

Bone Growth and Metabolic Regulation

During development, the long bones form by a process known as endochondral ossification, which means bone formation within cartilage. Mesenchymal cells, which are the precursors of connective tissue cells, condense and then differentiate as chondrocytes, which form cartilage through the secretion of cartilage matrix. Normal bone metabolism is a complex sequence of bone turnover (osteoclastogenesis) and bone formation (osteoblastogenesis). Bones contain approximately 99 per cent of the calcium and 86 per cent of the phosphate in the body. Several factors regulate bone growth. Parathyroid hormone (PTH) enhances calcium absorption in the intestines and causes the activation of osteoclasts to increase reabsorption of bone. Vitamin D increases the amount of dietary calcium absorbed by the intestines and decreases the release of PTH to protect against osteoporosis, or bone loss. Calcitonin and oestrogen also act to decrease osteoclastic bone loss, whereas growth, thyroid, and glucocorticosteroid hormone activities result in a decrease in bone formation. Ossification (development of bone) continues until approximately age 20, at which point bone loss occurs at 0.3–0.5 per cent per year. It further decreases by 2–3 per cent per year in untreated women during 6–10 years post-menopause. Bone loss can be mitigated by structural and metabolic factors.

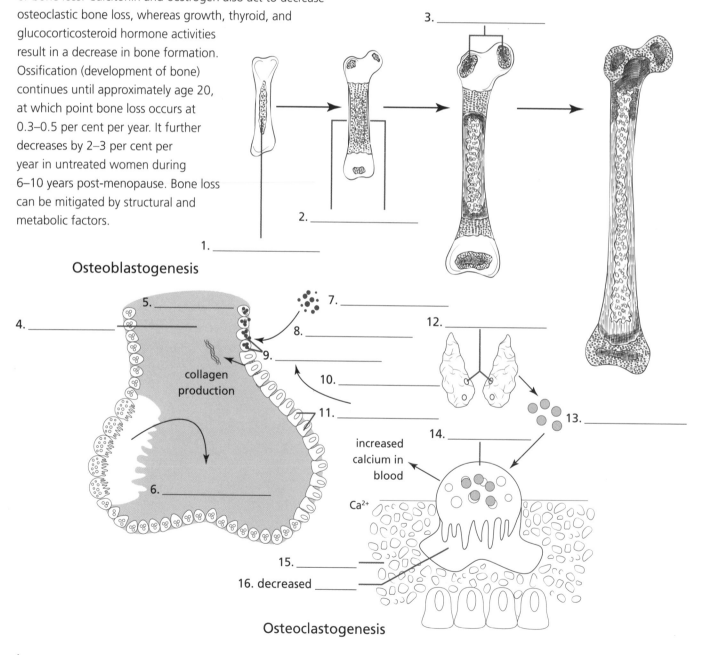

Osteoblastogenesis

Osteoclastogenesis

collagen production

increased calcium in blood

Ca^{2+}

1. _____

2. _____

3. _____

4. _____

5. _____

6. _____

7. _____

8. _____

9. _____

10. _____

11. _____

12. _____

13. _____

14. _____

15. _____

16. decreased _____

Answers

Prostaglandins

Prostaglandin Functions

1. _____ participation in memory and other functions by some prostaglandins

2. _____ that transmit pain signals to spinal cord and brain sensitised by some prostaglandins

muscles in 3. _____ relaxed by two prostaglandins; another contracts them

blood flow in 4. _____ increased by two prostaglandins

lining of 5. _____ protected by two prostaglandins

muscles of 6. _____ caused to contract by two prostaglandins; another relaxes them

small 7. _____ dilated by some prostaglandins; leads to redness and feeling of heat associated with inflammation

Prostaglandins are a group of physiologically active lipid compounds with hormone-like effects. They provide signals that are either paracrine (locally active) or autocrine (acting on the same cell from which they are synthesised) and are found in almost every tissue and organ in the body. They move in and out of cells using prostaglandin receptors, also called prostaglandin transporters. The receptors are a subfamily of seven-transmembrane G-protein coupled receptors, ten of which have been described. A specific prostaglandin may have different effects depending on the cell with which it interacts. Prostaglandins are synthesised from fatty acids and are made up of 20 carbon atoms, including a five-carbon ring. Arachidonic acid, created from diacylglycerol, enters the cyclooxygenase (COX) pathway and is sequentially oxidised by the enzymes COX-1 and COX-2 and terminal prostaglandin synthases to form prostaglandins and other compounds. Specific prostaglandins are named with a letter (indicating its type of ring structure) and a number (indicating the number of double bonds in the hydrocarbon structure). For example, prostaglandin E1 is abbreviated PGE1 or PGE_1 and prostaglandin I2 is abbreviated PGI2 or PGI_2. Prostaglandins have a variety of effects, including, among others, constriction or dilation in vascular smooth muscle cells; aggregation or disaggregation of platelets; increased sensitivity of spinal neurons to pain; induction of labour in childbirth; and regulation of inflammation, hormone activities, and cell growth. They are made locally in response to injury and illness, act in small amounts, and are short-lived.

Answers

1. brain, 2. nerves, 3. lungs, 4. kidneys, 5. stomach, 6. uterus, 7. blood vessels

Endocrine Pancreas

The pancreas is located in the abdomen behind the stomach, with its head near the duodenum and the tail towards the spleen. It functions as both an exocrine and endocrine gland. The exocrine functions are served by the acinar cells, which secrete digestive enzymes into ducts that flow to the duodenum and assist in the digestion and absorption of nutrients. The endocrine portion consists of pancreatic islets (the islets of Langerhans), which are highly vascularised spherical aggregates of several different cell types that secrete hormones into the circulatory system. Alpha (α) cells secrete the polypeptide glucagon, beta (β) cells secrete the protein insulin, and delta (δ) cells secrete the polypeptide somatostatin. Together, the pancreatic hormones regulate the concentration of blood glucose and other nutrients.

Secretion of insulin is controlled by glucose levels along with hormones released by the gastrointestinal tract, termed incretins, and innervation of the pancreas by the parasympathetic and sympathetic nervous systems, which increase and decrease insulin secretion, respectively. After secretion, insulin is carried via the portal circulation to the liver, a key target organ, where it promotes storage of glucose as glycogen. In skeletal muscle and adipose tissue, insulin promotes glucose uptake and affects lipid and protein metabolism. These effects are produced when insulin binds to the insulin receptor, a large transmembrane glycoprotein composed of two α-subunits, which include the binding site for insulin, and two β-subunits, which have a tyrosine kinase domain. Receptor activation promotes tyrosine phosphorylation on a host of intracellular substrates and leads to migration of the GLUT4 glucose transporter to the cell surface, allowing increased glucose uptake. Blood glucose levels can increase dramatically when too little insulin is secreted or when insulin receptors do not respond, as in diabetes mellitus.

Glucagon is a counterregulatory hormone to insulin and is released in response to low blood glucose levels. Its primary effect is on the liver, where it promotes breakdown of glycogen and increased glucose synthesis. It acts through a G-protein coupled receptor to increase cyclic adenosine monophosphate (cAMP) levels and activate protein kinase A. Adrenaline, released under stress and exercise, triggers the same series of events as glucagon via its own receptor in the liver. It also acts on skeletal muscle and adipose tissue to increase glycogen breakdown to lactate and lipid breakdown to fatty acids, thereby providing an energy source for muscle.

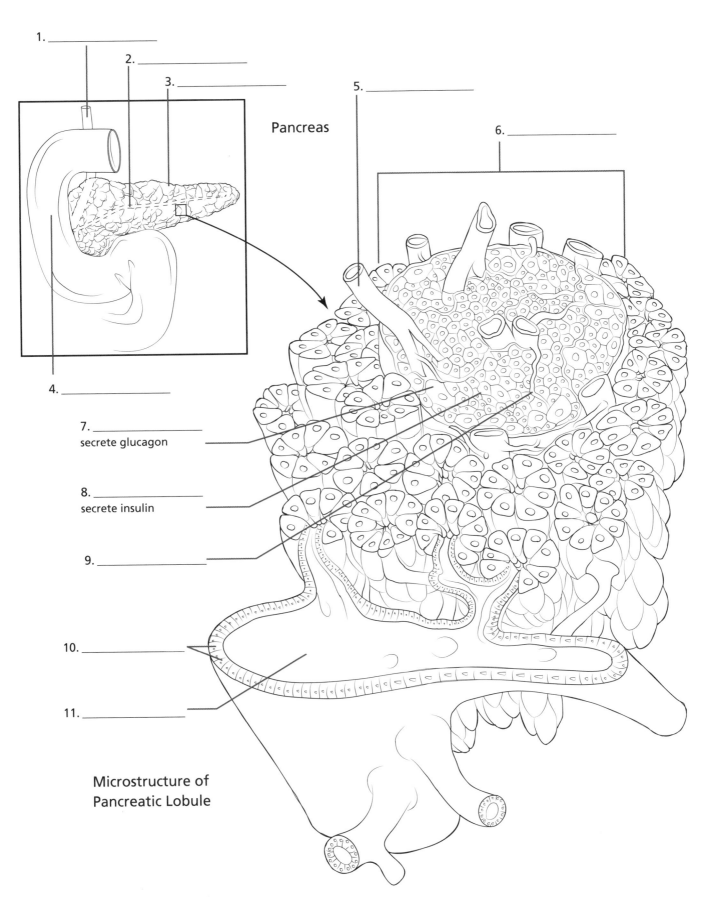

1. _____

2. _____

3. _____

Pancreas

5. _____

6. _____

4. _____

7. _____
secrete glucagon

8. _____
secrete insulin

9. _____

10. _____

11. _____

Microstructure of
Pancreatic Lobule

Answers

Adrenal Cortex: Aldosterone and Cortisol

The adrenal cortex is the outer layer of the triangular-shaped adrenal glands (or suprarenal glands), a pair of endocrine glands. Each adrenal gland is approximately 3.5 cm (1.4 inches) wide and 7.5 cm (3 inches) long and sits on top of each kidney (ad- means 'near' or 'at', and -renal means 'kidney'). The adrenal cortex comprises three main zones or layers: the zona glomerulosa, zona fasciculata, and zona reticularis. Each of these layers has distinct structural or histological characteristics, as well as distinct functions. The adrenal cortex produces two groups of corticosteroid hormones: glucocorticoids and mineralcorticoids. The glucocorticoids cortisol (hydrocortisone) and corticosterone (cortisol) are produced in the zona fasciculata, whereas the mineralcorticoid aldosterone is produced in the zona glomerulosa, the outermost layer of the adrenal cortex. The adrenal cortex also releases small amounts of male and female sex hormones from the zona reticularis. The hormones released by the adrenal cortex are necessary for life. The primary mineralcorticoid produced by the adrenal cortex is aldosterone, which functions to maintain the correct balance of salt and water to regulate blood pressure. Aldosterone is synthesised from corticosterone, a steroid derived from cholesterol, by the enzyme aldosterone synthase in the outermost layer of the adrenal cortex, the zona glomerulosa. Aldosterone is regulated by the renin-angiotensin system. Renin is secreted from the kidneys in response to variations in

1. _____

2. _____

3. _____

4. _____

Left Adrenal Gland – coronal section

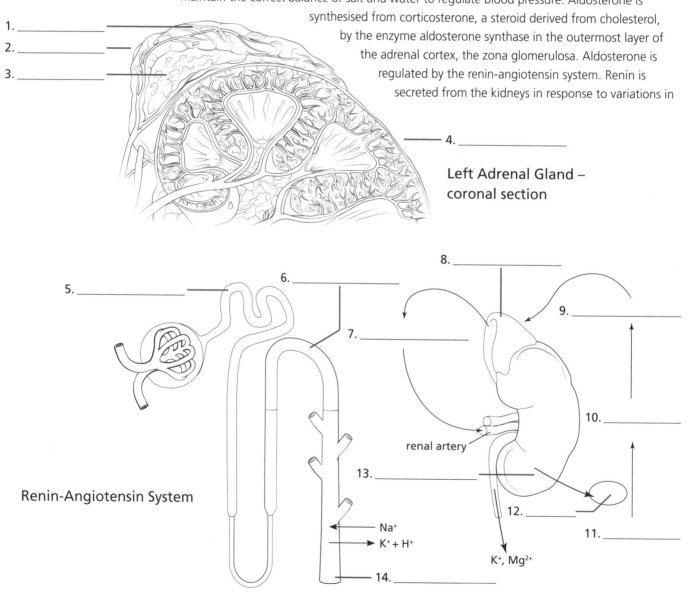

5. _____

6. _____

7. _____

8. _____

9. _____

10. _____

renal artery

13. _____

Na^+

$K^+ + H^+$

12. _____

11. _____

14. _____

K^+, Mg^{2+}

Renin-Angiotensin System

blood pressure, as well as to changes in sodium and potassium levels in the plasma. Renin acts on angiotensin I to convert it to angiotensin II, which, in turn, stimulates the release of aldosterone. Aldosterone mediates its effects through aldosterone receptor stimulation to cause increased reabsorption of sodium and water from the gut and salivary and sweat glands into the blood, and increased excretion of both potassium (by principal cells of the distal convoluted tubule) and hydrogen ions (by intercalated cells of the cortical collecting duct) in the kidney. Zona glomerulosa cells have an innate low level of electrical excitability that results in a recurrent calcium channel signal that can be controlled by angiotensin II and extracellular potassium.

Cortisol is the main secretion from the adrenal cortex and is responsible for maintaining homeostasis. It is called the 'stress hormone' due to its regulation or modulation of many responses to stress. Release of corticotropin-releasing hormone (CRH) by the hypothalamus stimulates production and release of adrenocorticotropic hormone (ACTH) by the anterior lobe of the pituitary gland. ACTH increases the concentration of cholesterol in the mitochondria of adrenal cortical cells and the synthesis of cortisol from cholesterol. Functions regulated by cortisol are blood sugar (glucose) levels, gluconeogenesis (metabolism of fat, protein, and carbohydrates to maintain blood glucose levels), immune responses, anti-inflammatory actions, blood pressure, heart and blood vessel tone, and central nervous system activation. Cortisol levels have a diurnal pattern that peaks at approximately 8 a.m. and is lowest at approximately 4 a.m. Prolonged high levels of circulating cortisol have negative effects, such as high blood pressure, sleep disruption, and lowered immune function.

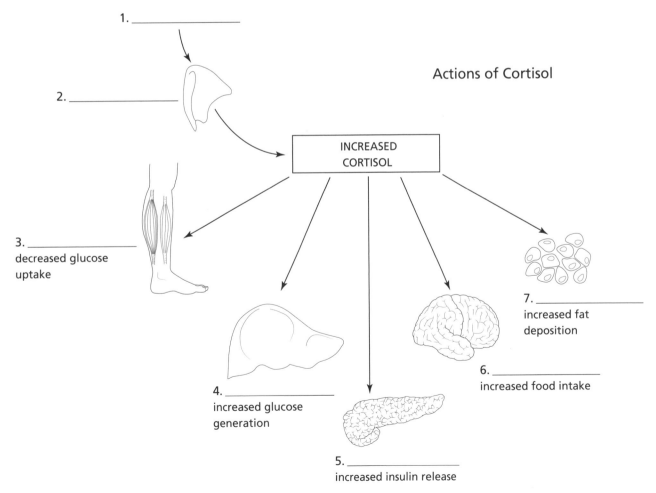

1. _____

2. _____

Actions of Cortisol

INCREASED
CORTISOL

3. _____
decreased glucose
uptake

4. _____
increased glucose
generation

5. _____
increased insulin release

6. _____
increased food intake

7. _____
increased fat
deposition

Answers

Adrenal Cortex: Sex Hormones

Gonadocorticoids (sex hormones or sex steroids) are synthesised from cholesterol in the zona reticularis in the adrenal cortex. The amounts of adrenal sex hormones released are small, and their effects are usually masked by the sex hormones produced in the testes and ovaries.

The primary male sex hormones produced are the androgens, which are responsible for the development and maintenance of reproductive function (the testes) and secondary sex characteristics in the male. They are anabolic, in that they stimulate the production of skeletal muscles, bone, and red blood cells. The most prominent androgen is testosterone. Dihydrotestosterone (DHT), a metabolite of testosterone, is also produced. A third androgen, androstenedione (Andro), is converted metabolically to testosterone and other androgens.

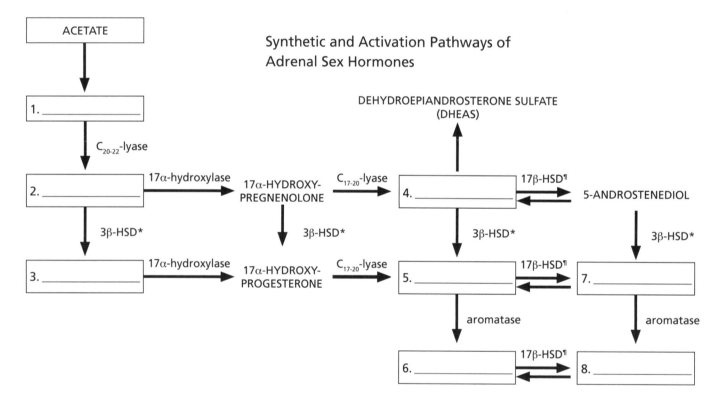

Synthetic and Activation Pathways of Adrenal Sex Hormones

*3β-HSD = 3β-hydroxysteroid dehydrogenase-$\Delta^{5,4}$-isomerase
¶ 17β-hydroxysteroid dehydrogenase

Both Andro and a fourth androgen, dehydroepiandrosterone (DHEA), are precursors to female sex hormones. Andro is the parent structure of oestrone, whereas DHEA is the primary precursor of natural oestrogens. The female sex hormones produced by the adrenal cortex are the oestrogens and the progestins. The oestrogens, the most potent of which is oestradiol, function similarly to the androgens in that they promote the development of the primary and secondary female sex characteristics and stimulate growth and skeletal maturation.

Answers

Adrenal Medulla and Catecholamines

The adrenal glands are located above the kidneys and are composed of an outer cortex layer that secretes steroid hormones and an inner medulla that secretes the catecholamines adrenaline and noradrenaline. The chromaffin cells of the medulla are innervated by sympathetic preganglionic splanchnic nerve fibres. They secrete catecholamines under conditions of stress, excitement, and low blood glucose levels, and the tissue may be considered a specialised sympathetic ganglion. Adrenaline is produced from noradrenaline by the enzyme phenylethanolamine N-methyltransferase (PNMT), present in the majority of cells, at a ratio of approximately 4:1. Noradrenaline and adrenaline interact with adrenergic receptors of the G-protein coupled receptor (GPCR) class termed α-adrenergic or β-adrenergic receptors to induce a range of physiological responses, such as increasing the heart rate and force of contraction, constriction of blood vessels to skin and viscera, dilation of blood vessels in skeletal muscle, increased hepatic glucose output, and bronchodilation. The secretion of catecholamines from the adrenal medulla prepares the body for the 'fight-or-flight' response, increasing metabolic activity and blood flow to organs required for physical activity. The effects are short-lived, lasting only a few minutes, as the catecholamines are rapidly metabolised, excreted, or taken up by tissues.

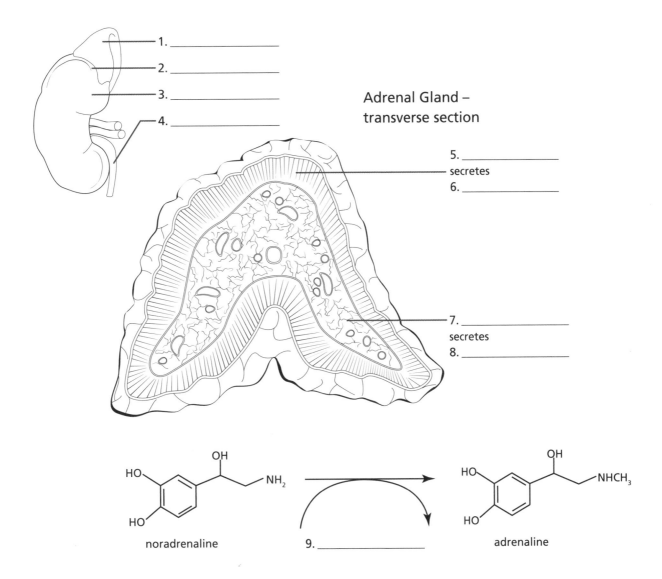

1. _____

2. _____

3. _____

4. _____

Adrenal Gland –
transverse section

5. _____
secretes
6. _____

7. _____
secretes
8. _____

noradrenaline

9. _____

adrenaline

Answers

Gonadal Hormones

Gonadal hormones are steroid hormones produced by the male and female primary reproductive organs (the testes and ovaries, respectively). They stimulate the reproductive organs, influence germ cell maturation, and are responsible for secondary sex characteristics. The primary hormones of the ovaries are oestrogens and progesterone, along with some androstenedione (Andro) and activin, a hormone that stimulates the production and release of follicle-stimulating hormone (FSH). The testes synthesise the androgens, testosterone, and Andro. Inhibins are produced by both the ovaries and testes to inhibit production and release of FSH. Steroid hormones are released into the blood after formation and are carried to various parts of the body. They enter cells through the plasma membrane, bind to intracellular receptors, and are transported to the nucleus to interact with hormone response elements (HREs) in the DNA to influence expression of specific genes. The pathway for release of sex hormones by the gonads begins with production of gonadotropin-releasing hormone (GnRH) by the hypothalamus. GnRH in turn acts on the pituitary to release the gonadotropins FSH and luteinizing hormone (LH), both of which stimulate the gonads to produce and secrete sex hormones. The pathway is regulated via negative feedback loops in which the initial stimulus (GnRH) is reduced, or inhibited, by the end product (testosterone, oestrogen, or progesterone) resulting in reduced production of LH and FSH.

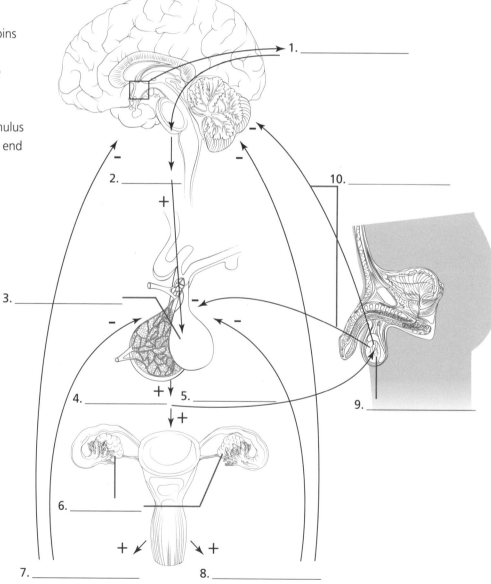

Gonadal Hormone Regulation

Answers

1. hypothalamus, 2. gonadotropin-releasing hormone, 3. pituitary, 4. luteinizing hormone, 5. follicle-stimulating hormone, 6. ovaries, 7. progesterone, 8. oestrogen, 9. testes, 10. testosterone

There are two types of female gonadal hormones, oestrogens and progesterone. The oestrogens are a group of female sex hormones responsible for growth and maturation of the uterus and vagina; breast development; widening of the pelvis; greater fat distribution in the hips, thighs, and breast; uterine changes during the menstrual cycle; and increased growth of body hair. They include oestrone and oestradiol.

Progesterone prepares the uterus for conception by regulating uterine changes during the menstrual cycle, increases sexual desire, aids in ovulation, and stimulates gland development for milk production during pregnancy. The steroid hormones are derived from cholesterol by a series of oxidative enzymes in mitochondria and endoplasmic reticulum of ovarian cells. Cholesterol is converted to pregnenolone, which is then converted to progesterone in the corpus luteum and placenta. Andro serves as the precursor to estrone, whereas testosterone is the precursor to oestradiol. Oestrone and oestradiol are interconvertible.

1. _____

2. _____

3. _____

9. _____

8. _____

7. _____

5. _____

6. _____

4. _____

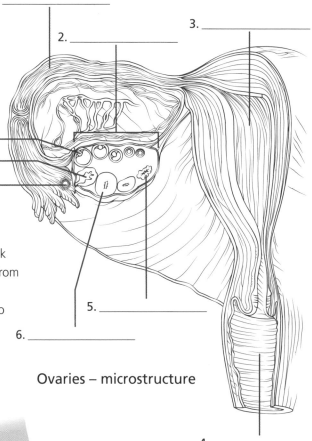

Ovaries – microstructure

Male Reproductive System – sagittal view

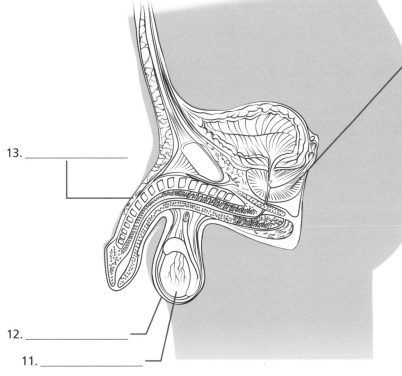

10. _____

13. _____

12. _____

11. _____

The male gonadal hormones are the androgens. The primary androgen, testosterone, is responsible for increased muscle and bone mass, increased growth of body hair, development of broad shoulders, deepening of the voice, and growth of the penis. The androgens dehydroepiandrosterone (DHEA) and Andro are derived from cholesterol through a series of reactions. These two compounds are converted into testosterone in Leydig cells in the testes. Androgens are also produced in small quantities in females and are the precursors to the female gonadal hormones.

Answers

1. uterine tube, 2. ovary, 3. uterus, 4. vagina, 5. corpus albicans, 6. corpus luteum, 7. ovum, 8. discharging follicle (at ovulation), 9. mature follicle, 10. prostate gland, 11. testis, 12. scrotum, 13. penis

Overview of the Female Reproductive System

Female Reproductive System – sagittal view

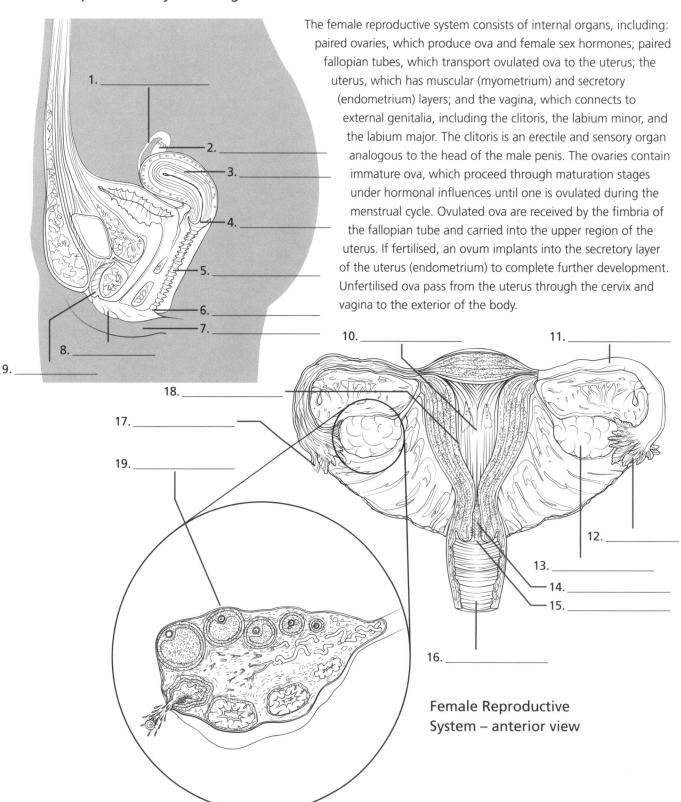

The female reproductive system consists of internal organs, including: paired ovaries, which produce ova and female sex hormones; paired fallopian tubes, which transport ovulated ova to the uterus; the uterus, which has muscular (myometrium) and secretory (endometrium) layers; and the vagina, which connects to external genitalia, including the clitoris, the labium minor, and the labium major. The clitoris is an erectile and sensory organ analogous to the head of the male penis. The ovaries contain immature ova, which proceed through maturation stages under hormonal influences until one is ovulated during the menstrual cycle. Ovulated ova are received by the fimbria of the fallopian tube and carried into the upper region of the uterus. If fertilised, an ovum implants into the secretory layer of the uterus (endometrium) to complete further development. Unfertilised ova pass from the uterus through the cervix and vagina to the exterior of the body.

1. _____
2. _____
3. _____
4. _____
5. _____
6. _____
7. _____
8. _____
9. _____

10. _____
11. _____
12. _____
13. _____
14. _____
15. _____
16. _____
17. _____
18. _____
19. _____

Female Reproductive System – anterior view

The Ovaries: Formation of the Egg and Ovulation

The female ovaries house eggs that pass through maturation stages under hormonal influences. During embryonic and fetal development, egg stem cells, called oogonia, multiply by mitosis before entering meiosis 1 as primordial follicles containing primary oocytes, which have 46 chromosomes. These oocytes become arrested in prophase 1 from birth and throughout childhood. At puberty, and monthly thereafter until menopause, one primary follicle housing a primary oocyte completes meiosis 1 and then begins meiosis 2 as a secondary follicle housing a primary oocyte. This follicle then matures into a tertiary (vesicular) follicle housing a secondary oocyte, which contains only 23 chromosomes (now halved from the original number). The secondary oocyte is ovulated from the ovary due to hormonal influence and an explosive rupture of follicular fluid within the antrum. The tertiary follicle remains behind to become a secretory corpus luteum, which, in the absence of fertilisation, slowly regresses into a corpus albicans.

Egg Development

Ovary

1. _____
2. _____
3. _____
4. _____
5. _____
6. _____
7. _____
8. _____

fetal development until birth

childhood

monthly, from puberty until menopause

9. _____
10. _____
11. _____
12. _____
13. _____
14. _____

Answers

The Ovaries: Hormone Production

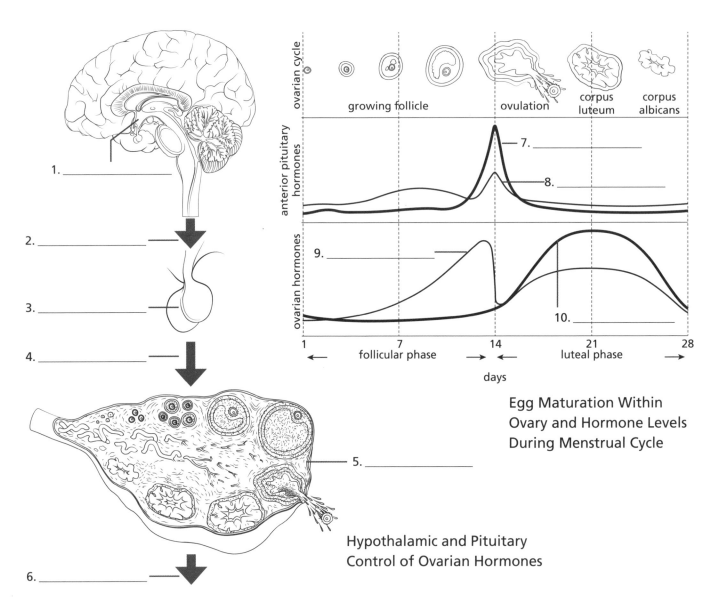

ovarian cycle

growing follicle   ovulation   corpus luteum   corpus albicans

anterior pituitary hormones

7. _____

8. _____

ovarian hormones

9. _____

10. _____

1   7   14   21   28

follicular phase   luteal phase

days

1. _____

2. _____

3. _____

4. _____

5. _____

6. _____

Egg Maturation Within Ovary and Hormone Levels During Menstrual Cycle

Hypothalamic and Pituitary Control of Ovarian Hormones

Female ovarian hormone production is regulated by the hypothalamus and anterior pituitary gland during a typical, albeit very variable, 28-day cycle, and is divided into two phases: the follicular phase and the luteal phase. During the ovarian follicular phase the hypothalamus secretes gonadotropin-releasing hormone (GnRH), which stimulates pituitary secretion of follicle-stimulating hormone (FSH) and luteinizing hormone (LH) into the blood. FSH stimulates follicle maturation, while LH stimulates thecal cells of the follicle to produce oestrogen. During ovarian follicular phase days 1–13, the follicle and oocyte within mature in response to rising FSH and LH levels, and oestrogen levels rise correspondingly. On day 14, an LH surge causes ovulation of the secondary oocyte from the tertiary follicle. This marks the beginning of the ovarian luteal phase. The tertiary follicle decreases oestrogen production and becomes a progesterone-secreting corpus luteum from days 15 to 28. Rising blood levels of progesterone inhibit further hypothalamic GnRH and pituitary FSH and LH secretion. If the ovulated egg is not fertilised, the corpus luteum regresses into a non-secretory corpus albicans. With oestrogen and progesterone levels low, GnRH secretion by the hypothalamus and FSH and LH secretion by the pituitary resume, and a new ovarian follicular phase begins.

Answers

Structure and Function of the Uterine Wall

The uterus is a dynamic organ capable of supporting and nourishing an embryo throughout fetal development and parturition. The uterine wall is composed of an inner secretory endometrium, a middle muscular smooth-muscled myometrium, and an outer membranous perimetrium. The endometrium and myometrium, sensitive to hormonal signals, undergo considerable changes associated with a monthly menstrual cycle and periodic pregnancy and childbirth. Monthly increases in follicular oestrogen stimulate the endometrial epithelium to thicken and acquire a blood lining. After ovulation, progesterone, secreted from the ovarian corpus luteum, causes even further endometrial proliferation in anticipation of implantation of a fertilised egg. If a fertilised egg implants within the endometrium, a placenta forms and provides an exchange of nutrients, hormones, and waste between the developing embryo and the mother's body. High plasma oxytocin at parturition causes strong rhythmic contractions of the myometrium, which compresses the uterine body and pushes the fetus through the cervical and vaginal canals to the exterior of the body. In the absence of fertilisation and implantation, the corpus luteum regresses and the outer endometrial layer, deprived of progesterone, disintegrates and is shed as menstrual fluid with the help of minor myometrium contractions, which are stimulated by prostaglandin secreted by the endometrium.

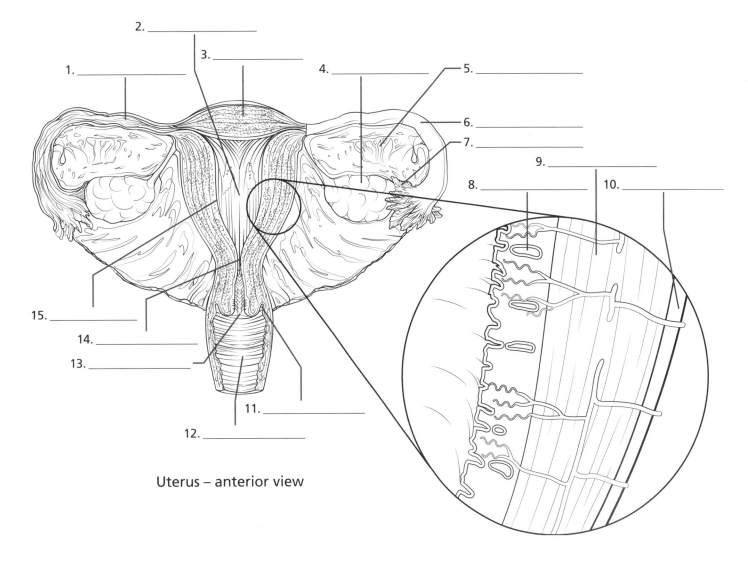

2. _____
3. _____
1. _____
4. _____
5. _____
6. _____
7. _____
9. _____
8. _____
10. _____
15. _____
14. _____
13. _____
11. _____
12. _____

Uterus – anterior view

Answers

Hormonal Regulation of the Menstrual Cycle

The menstrual cycle (typically 28 days, but varying from person to person and from cycle to cycle) is regulated by hypothalamic and pituitary hormones and is subdivided into an ovarian and a uterine cycle. The uterine cycle begins with menstruation (menses) between days 1 and 7 and overlaps with the follicular phase of the ovarian cycle between days 1 and 13. During the follicular phase, increasing hypothalamic secretion of gonadotropin-releasing hormone (GnRH) and pituitary secretion of follicle-stimulating hormone (FSH) and luteinizing hormone (LH) stimulates follicle maturation. FSH stimulates tertiary follicles to mature, and LH stimulates follicular cells to secrete oestrogen. Elevated oestrogen between days 8 and 14 marks the proliferative phase of the uterine cycle, during which the endometrium expands in cell layers. At day 14, a peak in blood LH stimulates ovulation from the dominant tertiary follicle. The luteal phase of the ovarian cycle begins post-ovulation, as the tertiary follicle becomes a corpus luteum (CL) and secretes increasing amounts of progesterone between days 15 and 26. High progesterone between days 15 and 26 overlaps with the secretory phase of the uterine cycle, marked by increased endometrial blood supply and glandular activity. If the ovulated egg is not fertilised, the CL regresses, progesterone secretion declines, and the outer endometrial layer starts degenerating by day 28.

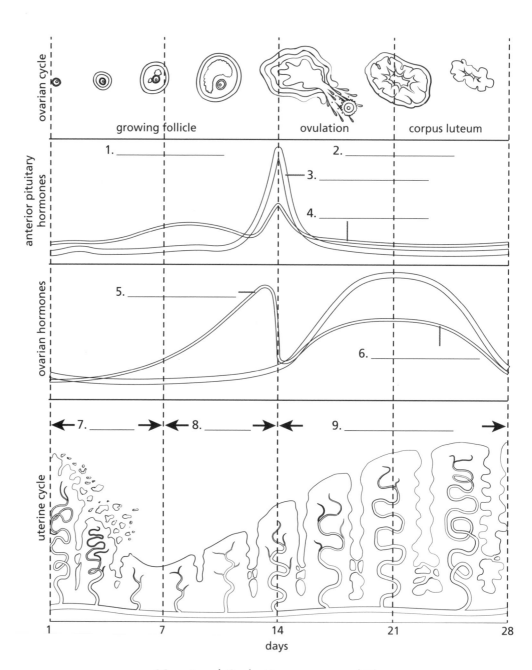

Menstrual Cycle Hormones and Phases

Physiology of the Human Sexual Response

The human sexual response consists of four phases, based on the Masters and Johnson model: arousal, plateau, orgasm, and resolution. During the arousal phase, lubricating secretions from the vaginal canal and bulbourethral glands increase, the clitoris and penis become engorged with blood, and the breasts and testes swell, in females and males, respectively. During the plateau phase, the uterus lifts up, the vaginal canal expands, and the clitoris and labia darken in females, and in males the testes become elevated and the head of the penis darkens. During the orgasm phase, females experience rhythmic contractions in the anterior vaginal wall, along with contraction of the uterus and anal sphincter, while males experience contraction of the seminal vesicles and prostate gland, the proximal urethral sphincter, and the anal sphincter, along with rhythmic contractions of the ejaculatory duct and urethra, which expel seminal fluid (ejaculation). During the resolution phase, all of the changes occurring in the previous phases gradually revert to normal. After orgasm, males experience a refractory period, during which another orgasm cannot be achieved no matter the sexual stimulation. For some females, there is no refractory period after orgasm, and another orgasm can be attained immediately after the first with continued stimulation.

Sexual Response Phases

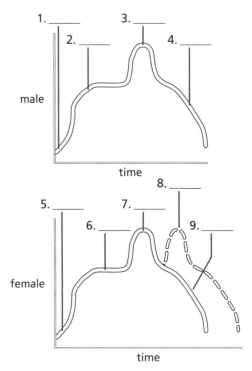

Sexual Response in Female

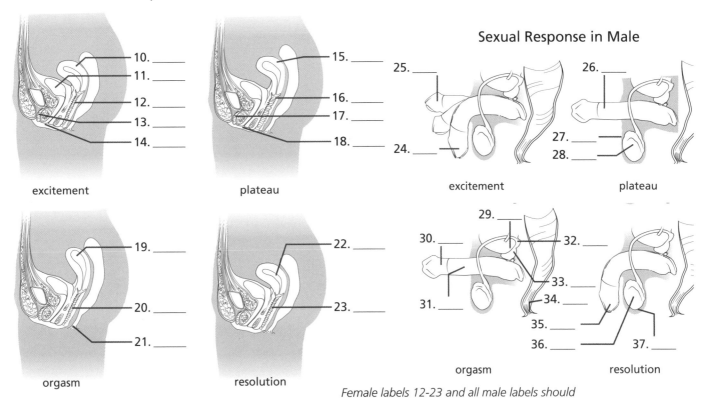

excitement

plateau

orgasm

resolution

Sexual Response in Male

excitement

plateau

orgasm

resolution

Female labels 12-23 and all male labels should include the response as well as the anatomy.

Answers

1. arousal phase, 2. plateau phase, 3. orgasm phase, 4. resolution phase, 5. arousal phase, 6. plateau phase, 7. orgasm phase, 8. multiple orgasm (in some females), 9. resolution phase, 10. uterus, 11. bladder, 12. vaginal canal (with lubricating secretions), 13. clitoris (swells), 14. labia (swells), 15. uterus (lifted up), 16. vaginal canal (expanded), 17. clitoris (darkens in colour), 18. labia (darkens in colour), 19. uterus (contracting), 20. vaginal canal (rhythmic contractions in anterior wall), 21. anal sphincter (contracts), 22. uterus (lowered to normal position), 23. vaginal canal (returned to normal size), 24. penis (unstimulated), 25. penis (erection), 26. penis (darkens in colour), 27. scrotum (swells), 28. testes (lifted up), 29. urethra (proximal sphincter contracts), 30. penis (rhythmic contractions), 31. urethra (contracts), 32. seminal vesicles (contract), 33. prostate gland (contracts), 34. anal sphincter (contracts), 35. penis (unaroused state), 36. testes (lowered to normal position), 37. scrotum (returned to normal size)

Overview of the Male Reproductive System

The male reproductive system consists of the penis, vas deferens, ejaculatory duct, urethra, seminal vesicles, prostate and bulbourethral glands, epididymis, and the scrotal sac, containing paired testes within which sperm and hormones are produced. The testes contain lobes of highly coiled seminiferous tubules, wherein testosterone and sperm production is stimulated by pituitary hormones. Sperm produced within the seminiferous tubules travel to the rete testis and then to the epididymis, where they mature. Upon ejaculation, waves of smooth muscle movement carry the mature sperm through the vas deferens. On their journey, sperm mix with secretions from the seminal vesicles, pass through the ejaculatory duct, and add prostate secretions to the seminal fluid, before exiting the body through the penile urethra. The penis consists of paired upper spongy tissue chambers, each called a corpus cavernosa, containing a penile arteriole that can vasodilate to flood the chambers with blood to cause an erection under parasympathetic regulation. The lower spongy chamber surrounding the urethra is the corpus spongiosum.

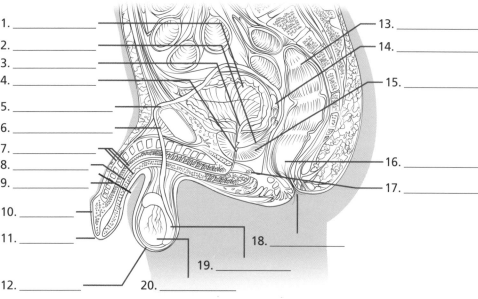

1. _____
2. _____
3. _____
4. _____
5. _____
6. _____
7. _____
8. _____
9. _____
10. _____
11. _____
12. _____
13. _____
14. _____
15. _____
16. _____
17. _____
18. _____
19. _____
20. _____

Male Reproductive System – mid-sagittal section

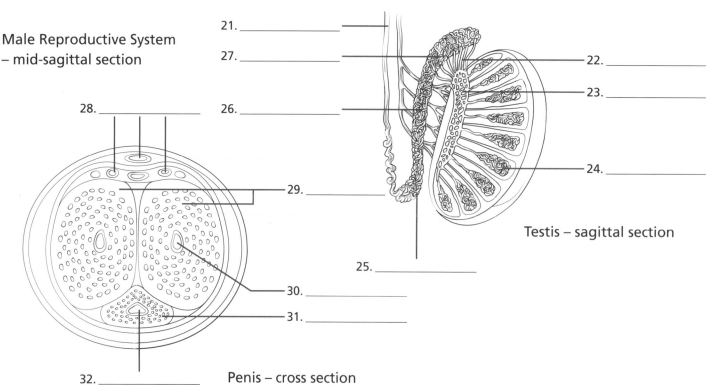

21. _____
27. _____
28. _____
26. _____
29. _____
30. _____
31. _____
32. _____
25. _____
22. _____
23. _____
24. _____

Penis – cross section

Testis – sagittal section

Answers

1. bladder, 2. ureter, 3. urethra (proximal sphincter), 4. urethra (prostatic), 5. pubis, 6. vas deferens, 7. erectile tissue of penis, 8. urethra, 9. urethra, 10. glans penis, 11. prepuce (of penis), 12. scrotum, 13. colon, 14. seminal vesicle, 15. prostate gland, 16. rectum, 17. bulbourethral gland, 18. anus, 19. epididymis, 20. testis, 21. vas deferens, 22. epididymis (efferent ductules), 23. rete testis, 24. seminiferous tubules, 25. epididymis (tail), 26. epididymis (body), 27. epididymis (head), 28. penile blood vessels, 29. corpus cavernosa, 30. arteriole (of corpus cavernosa), 31. corpus spongiosum, 32. urethra

Spermatogenesis: Components and Production of Semen

Within the testis, spermatozoa are produced within highly coiled seminiferous tubules. From here they are transported from the testicular lobules, via the rete testis and efferent ductules, to the head of the epididymis, where they mature further. During an ejaculatory event, the spermatozoa travel through the body and tail of the epididymis and enter the vas (ductus) deferens.

Testis – coronal view

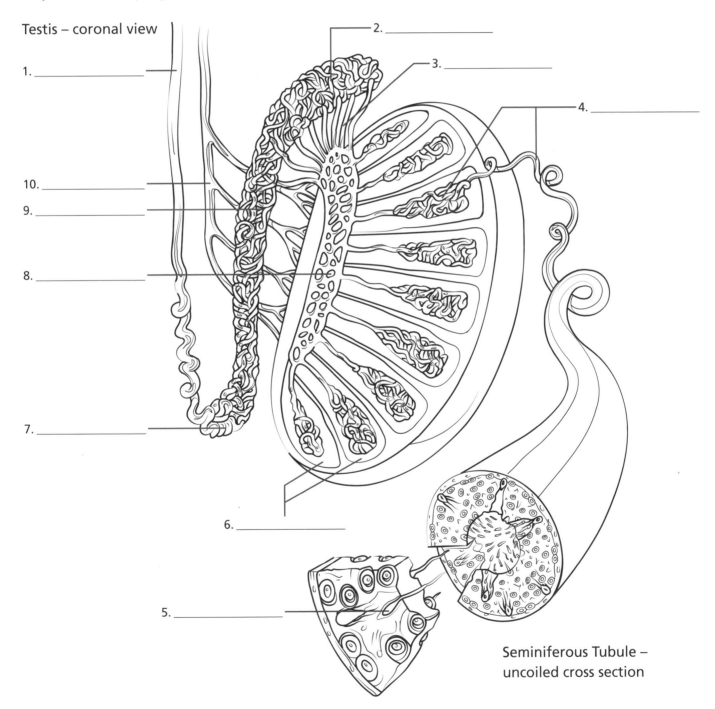

1. _____

2. _____

3. _____

4. _____

10. _____

9. _____

8. _____

7. _____

6. _____

5. _____

Seminiferous Tubule – uncoiled cross section

Answers

1. vas deferens, 2. epididymis (head), 3. efferent ductules, 4. seminiferous tubule, 5. spermatozoa, 6. lobules (of testis), 7. epididymis (tail), 8. rete testis, 9. epididymis (body), 10. testicular artery

Spermatogenesis: Components and Production of Semen

Sperm development within the seminiferous tubules begins with primordial diploid cells (i.e. with 23 pairs of chromosomes) called spermatogonia. Spermatogonia replicate by mitosis to produce primary spermatocytes, which are diploid. Primary spermatocytes undergo meiosis 1 to produce secondary spermatocytes, which are haploid (i.e. with 23 replicated chromosomes). Secondary spermatocytes complete meiosis 2 to become spermatids with 23 chromosomes, which mature into spermatozoa and are transported through the seminiferous tubule lumen to the rete testis, and eventually to the epididymis, where they mature for 20 days. At puberty approximately 1,500 sperm are produced per second within the seminiferous tubules.

During arousal, prior to ejaculation, mucous product from the bulbourethral gland is secreted from the urethra onto the glans penis for lubrication. During an ejaculation, sperm exit the epididymis via the vas deferens. Sperm combine with prostaglandin, fructose, and alkaline mucus produced from the seminal vesicles, before entering the prostate gland by way of the ejaculatory duct. The prostate adds additional mucus to the mixture, now called semen, before the seminal fluid reaches the urethra, from which semen ultimately exits the body as ejaculate.

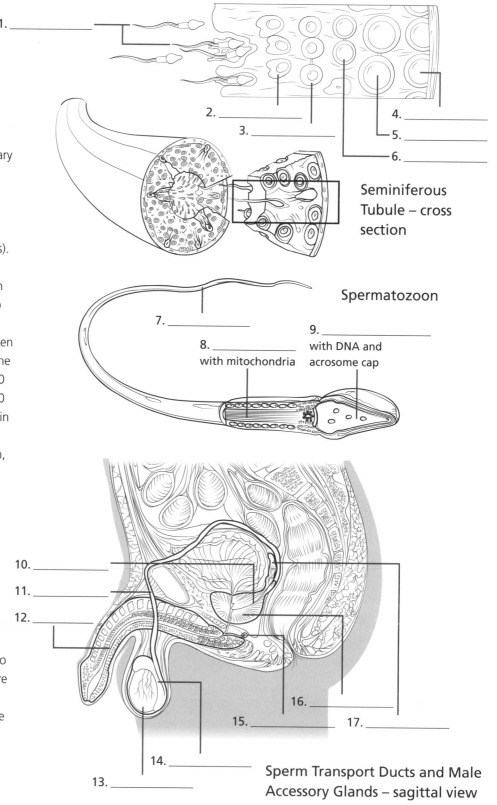

1. _____

2. _____

3. _____

4. _____

5. _____

6. _____

Seminiferous Tubule – cross section

Spermatozoon

7. _____

8. _____ with mitochondria

9. _____ with DNA and acrosome cap

10. _____

11. _____

12. _____

13. _____

14. _____

15. _____

16. _____

17. _____

Sperm Transport Ducts and Male Accessory Glands – sagittal view

Answers

1. spermatozoa, 2. spermatids (late), 3. spermatids, 4. spermatogonia, 5. primary spermatocyte, 6. secondary spermatocyte, 7. tail, 8. midpiece, 9. head, 10. ejaculatory duct (within prostate), 11. vas (ductus) deferens, 12. urethra, 13. testis, 14. epididymis, 15. bulbourethral gland, 16. prostate gland, 17. seminal vesicle

Erection and Ejaculation

An erection begins with sexual arousal and an autonomic parasympathetic release of acetylcholine (ACh) by penile nerves. ACh stimulates nitric oxide (NO) release from endothelial cells of smooth muscle lining the arteries of the penile corpora cavernosa. NO causes the smooth muscle to make cyclic guanosine monophosphate (cGMP), which in turn causes the arterial smooth muscle to relax, the arteries to vasodilate, and the corpora cavernosa sinusoidal spaces to fill with blood. The blood trapped within the sinusoids creates the hydraulic pressure that causes an erection. Ejaculation of seminal fluid consists of autonomic sympathetic regulation of two distinct phases: emission and expulsion. The emission phase begins with sympathetic release of noradrenaline and causes contraction of the proximal urethral sphincter below the urinary bladder, which prevents backflow of seminal fluid into the bladder and leakage of urine into the urethra during the emission phase. Spermatozoa travel through the vas deferens and mix with secretions from the accessory glands, and are then propelled by sympathetically stimulated contractions of smooth muscle lining the urethra. During the expulsion phase, semen is expelled from the urethra by rhythmic contractions of pelvic floor skeletal muscles (bulbospongiosus and ischiocavernosus), the urethral smooth muscle.

Erection – flaccid versus erect penis

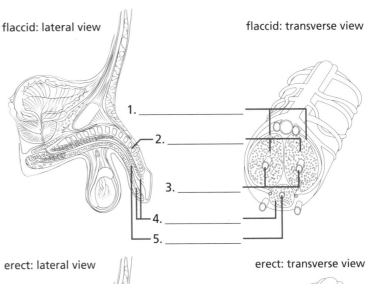

flaccid: lateral view

flaccid: transverse view

1. _____
2. _____
3. _____
4. _____
5. _____

erect: lateral view

erect: transverse view

6. _____
7. _____

Ejaculation

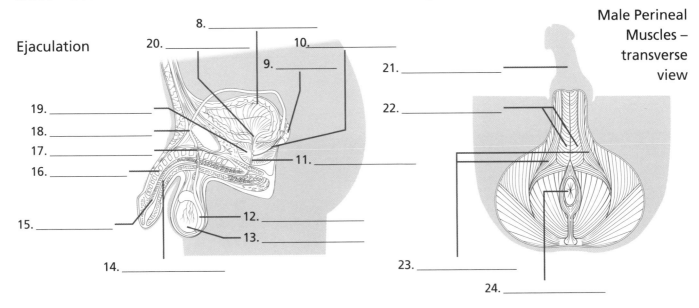

8. _____
20. _____
10. _____
9. _____
19. _____
18. _____
17. _____
16. _____
11. _____
15. _____
12. _____
13. _____
14. _____

Male Perineal Muscles – transverse view

21. _____
22. _____
23. _____
24. _____

Sperm Meets Egg: Fertilisation

Fertilisation of a secondary oocyte by a spermatozoa typically occurs within the fallopian tube of the uterus. The first spermatozoa to reach the egg releases powerful enzymes, located within its acrosome cap, in order to digest through granulosa cells (corona radiata) and a jelly coat that surround the egg. Then the sperm binds to a receptor located on the zona pellucida, which allows it to fuse with the egg plasma membrane and release its nucleus (with DNA) into the egg cell. Fusion of the sperm with the egg plasma membrane causes a sudden increase in intracellular calcium, which stimulates the release of cortical granules within the cell called the cortical reaction. The cortical granules cause intracellular water to move, by osmosis, into the perivitelline space located between the zona pellucida and egg plasma membrane. The influx of water lifts the zona pellucida from the egg cell membrane, forming a fertilisation envelope that prevents another sperm from entering the egg.

Structure of the Secondary Oocyte and Spermatozoon

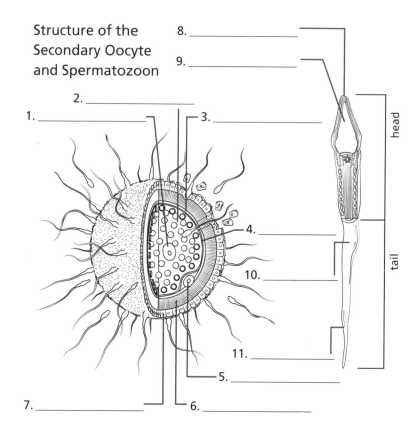

8. _____

9. _____

2. _____

1. _____

3. _____

4. _____

10. _____

11. _____

5. _____

7. _____

6. _____

head

tail

12. _____

13. _____

14. _____

15. _____

16. _____

17. _____

19. _____

18. _____

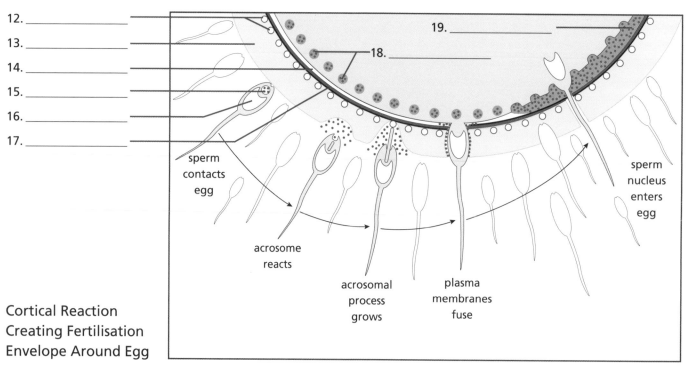

sperm contacts egg

sperm nucleus enters egg

acrosome reacts

acrosomal process grows

plasma membranes fuse

Cortical Reaction Creating Fertilisation Envelope Around Egg

Answers

1. nucleus, 2. cytoplasm, 3. zona pellucida, 4. plasma membrane, 5. polar body, 6. jelly coat, 7. corona radiata, 8. acrosome cap, 9. nucleus, 10. midpiece, 11. endpiece, 12. receptors (for sperm binding on zona pellucida), 13. jelly coat, 14. egg plasma membrane, 15. acrosome cap (of sperm head), 16. nucleus (of sperm head), 17. zona pellucida (vitelline layer), 18. cortical granules (within egg cytoplasm), 19. fertilisation envelope

Fertility and Contraception

A generalised fertility calendar for women can be estimated based on a 28-day menstrual cycle. Days 1–7 of the cycle consist of an infertile menstrual phase marked by the shedding of unfertilised egg and endometrial cells with menstrual blood. Fertile days include days 8–13, during which an egg is maturing, ovulation occurs on day 14, and post-ovulation occurs on days 15–19. Days 20–28 are post-ovulatory and are considered infertile days.

There are several different contraception categories. For the rhythm method, a woman avoids intercourse during the fertile days. Barrier contraception methods include condoms and the diaphragm. Male condoms fit over the penis, while a female condom is placed into the vagina to capture ejaculate. The diaphragm is a flexible cup that is placed over the cervix. Another form of contraception, the intrauterine device (IUD), is a flexible T-shaped device placed into the uterus by a physician. Hormonal methods of contraception include the hormonal cervical ring, placed over the cervix; the patch, placed on the skin; the pill, taken orally; or an injection. All forms of hormonal contraception function by inhibiting ovulation through negative feedback on hypothalamic gonadotropin-releasing hormone.

The Fertility Calendar

1. _____ phase

2. _____ phase

3. _____ phase

4. _____

Contraceptive Methods

13. _____

12. _____

11. _____

10. _____

9. _____

5. _____

6. _____

7. _____

8. _____

NOTES

5. <1% failure rate; 6. <1% failure rate; 7. <1% failure rate; 8. 6% failure rate; 9. <1% failure rate; 10. 2% failure rate; 11. 5% failure rate; 12. <1% failure rate; 13. 24% failure rate

Answers

1. infertile (post-ovulatory) phase, 2. infertile (menstrual) phase, 3. fertile phase, 4. ovulation, 5. patch, 6. vaginal ring, 7. pill, 8. diaphragm, 9. intrauterine device (IUD), 10. female condom, 11. male condom, 12. injection, 13. rhythm method

Early Embryogenesis and Implantation

Pre-embryonic development and implantation occurs within one week of fertilisation. After fertilisation, the zygote begins rapid mitotic divisions into two-, four-, eight-, and then 16-cell (morula) stages, followed next by formation of a blastocyst. The blastocyst is a solid ball of cells, which differentiates into two distinct areas with a central blastocyst cavity: the inner cell mass and the trophoblast. The inner cell mass becomes the embryo, while the outer layer of cells, the trophoblast, eventually becomes the placenta. The blastocyst begins secreting human chorionic gonadotropin (hCG) to signal the corpus luteum to continue secreting progesterone, while the trophoblast layer invades the endometrial wall, forming a syncytiotrophoblast or temporary pathway for nutrient exchange between embryo and mother prior to formation of the placenta. Formation of a placental connection between embryo and mother completes the implantation phase.

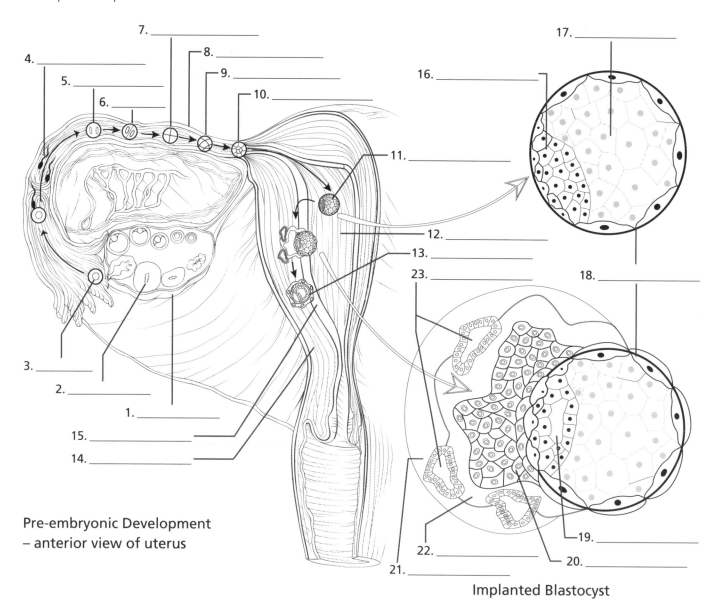

4. _____
5. _____
6. _____
7. _____
8. _____
9. _____
10. _____
11. _____
12. _____
13. _____
23. _____
16. _____
17. _____
18. _____
19. _____
20. _____
22. _____
21. _____
3. _____
2. _____
1. _____
15. _____
14. _____

Pre-embryonic Development
– anterior view of uterus

Implanted Blastocyst

Answers

Function of the Placenta

The placenta, a life-sustaining support structure between a developing fetus and the mother, has many functions. First, it produces progesterone, a hormone vital to maintaining endometrial tissues to support and continue a pregnancy. The placenta also facilitates the exchange of oxygen and nutrients from mother to fetus through transport across the maternal uterine artery into the interstitial space, where these substances are transported across fetal chorionic villi vessels and then into the umbilical vein for distribution to the fetus. Fetal metabolic wastes are removed by transport through umbilical arteries and then transported across the chorionic villi vessels into the interstitial space, and finally into the maternal uterine venous blood supply for removal. Lastly, the placenta helps protect the fetus from a potential maternal immune attack. Fetal cells contain a unique combination of paternal and maternal genetic material; thus, they express cell surface identification proteins different from the mother's own cells, and, if detected, the mother's immune system might mount an immune attack against the fetus. Fortunately, fetal cells within the placenta suppress expression of these cell-surface identification proteins, which prevents the mother's immune system from recognising them as foreign to her body.

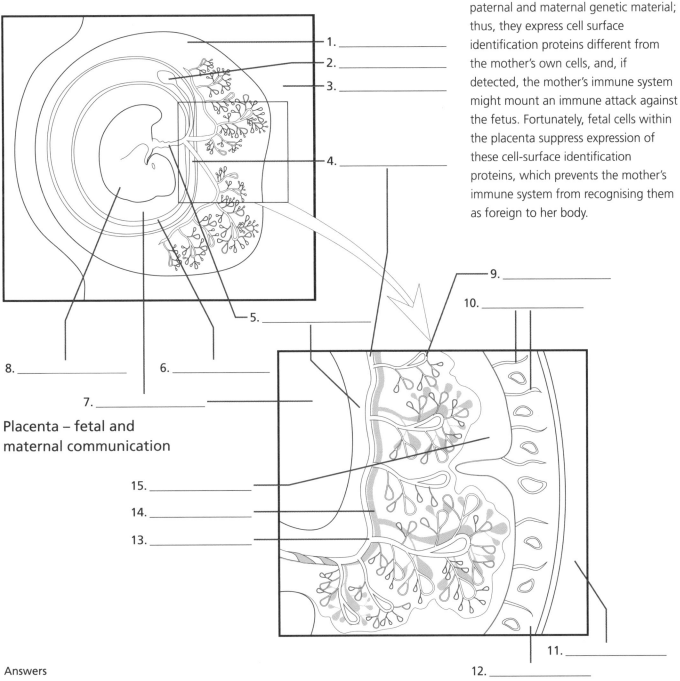

Placenta – fetal and maternal communication

1. _____
2. _____
3. _____
4. _____
5. _____
6. _____
7. _____
8. _____
9. _____
10. _____
11. _____
12. _____
13. _____
14. _____
15. _____

Answers

1. placenta, 2. yolk sac (of embryo), 3. uterus, 4. chorion (of placenta), 5. umbilical cord, 6. amnion, 7. amniotic fluid, 8. embryo, 9. chorionic villi (of placenta), 10. uterine artery and vein (in endometrium), 11. uterus, 12. placenta, 13. umbilical vein, 14. umbilical artery, 15. interstitial space

Sex Determination and Development During Pre-embryonic Life

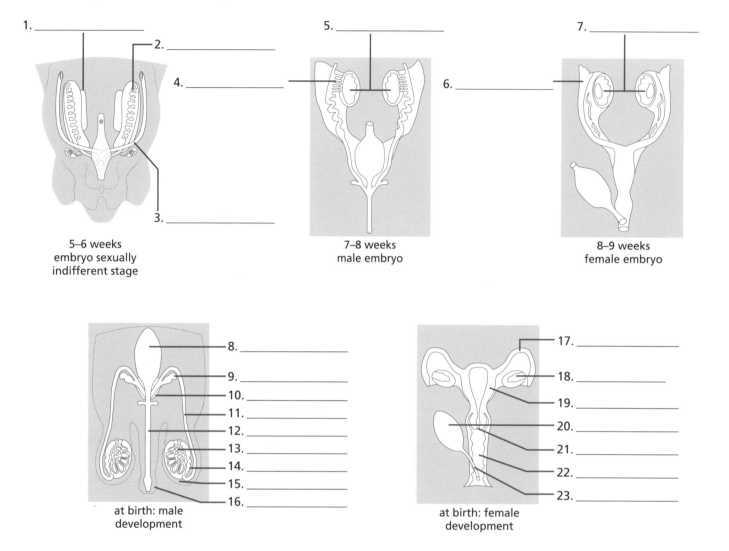

1. _____
2. _____
4. _____
3. _____

5–6 weeks
embryo sexually
indifferent stage

5. _____
6. _____

7–8 weeks
male embryo

7. _____

8–9 weeks
female embryo

8. _____
9. _____
10. _____
11. _____
12. _____
13. _____
14. _____
15. _____
16. _____

at birth: male
development

17. _____
18. _____
19. _____
20. _____
21. _____
22. _____
23. _____

at birth: female
development

Note: 11 = formerly Wolffian duct and 19, 21, 22, and 23 = formerly Müllerian duct.

Sex Differentiations – internal organs

Human sex determination is based on sex chromosomes, with males being XY and females being XX. During week five of embryonic development, paired gonadal ridges, a genital tubercle, and labial folds form, having the potential to become either testes or ovaries, a glans penis or glans clitoris, and a scrotal sac or labia minor and major, respectively. During week seven in a male embryo, the sex-determining region of the Y chromosome activates and stimulates the gonadal ridges to become testes, which secrete testosterone and Müllerian-inhibiting hormone (MIH) by week eight. MIH regresses the Müllerian ducts, while testosterone causes formation of the epididymis, male accessory glands, penile shaft, and a urethral opening on the glans penis, and the Wolffian ducts become the vas deferens and ejaculatory duct. In a female embryo at week eight of development, activation of X chromosome genes stimulates the gonadal ridges to become ovaries, which secrete oestrogen. Oestrogen stimulates differentiation of the Müllerian ducts into the vagina, separate urethral and vaginal canal, fallopian tubes, uterus, and cervix, and also formation of the clitoris and labia minor and major from the genital tubercle and labial folds, respectively.

Answers

1. gonadal ridge, 2. Wolffian duct, 3. Müllerian duct, 4. Wolffian duct, 5. testes (embryonic), 6. Müllerian duct, 7. ovaries (embryonic), 8. bladder, 9. seminal vesicle, 10. prostate gland, 11. vas deferens, 12. urethra, 13. efferent ductules, 14. epididymis, 15. testis, 16. glans penis, 17. fallopian tubes, 18. ovary, 19. uterus, 20. bladder, 21. cervix, 22. vagina, 23. urethra

Regulation of Pregnancy

Regulation of pregnancy is a complex communication of hormone signals between fetus and mother. Early in embryonic development the blastocyst secretes human chorionic gonadotropin (hCG), which prevents the ovarian corpus luteum from self-destructing until the placenta forms and takes over progesterone and oestrogen production to maintain the uterus for pregnancy. Increasing levels of oestrogen and progesterone from the placenta have a negative feedback on the maternal brain, inhibiting hypothalamic gonadotropin-releasing hormone (GnRH), which inhibits anterior pituitary luteinizing hormone (LH) and follicle-stimulating hormone (FSH) from stimulating the ovaries to mature and ovulate a new egg. Placental oestrogen also increases maternal uterine blood flow to assist fetal development, while placental progesterone also prevents premature uterine contraction. Placental relaxin stimulates the maternal pubic symphasis to become more flexible in anticipation of a baby passing through the birth canal. Placental human placental lactogen (hPL) promotes maternal mammary gland development, as well as increased blood glucose and fatty acids to aid fetal development. Lastly, placental corticotropin-releasing hormone (CRH) stimulates the fetal anterior pituitary gland to secrete adrenocorticotropic hormone (ACTH), which stimulates the fetal adrenal cortex to secrete cortisol. Fetal cortisol is necessary to aid lung maturation and surfactant production later in gestation.

Hormonal Regulation of Pregnancy

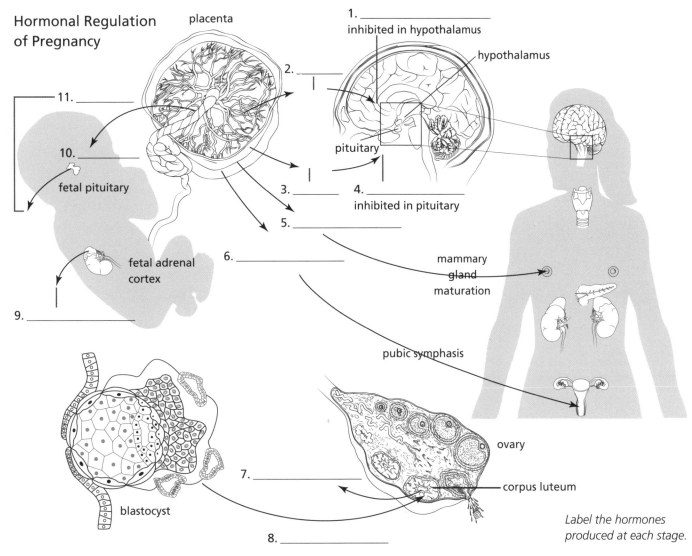

Label the hormones produced at each stage.

Answers

Mechanisms and Control of Parturition

Parturition is a complex interplay of hormonal signals between the placenta and fetal and maternal hormones. The hormonal cascade regulating parturition begins when corticotropin-releasing hormone (CRH) is secreted from the placenta late in gestation. CRH stimulates the fetal anterior pituitary gland to secrete adrenocorticotropic hormone (ACTH), which then stimulates the fetal adrenal gland cortex to secrete cortisol. As the end of gestation approaches, increasing placental CRH leads to a corresponding increase in fetal ACTH and cortisol. Cortisol is necessary for maturation of fetal lungs and production of surfactant. Cortisol also crosses the placenta, enters the maternal bloodstream, and stimulates the release of hypothalamic oxytocin from the posterior pituitary. Oxytocin causes powerful contractions of the uterine myometrium, compressing the fetus against the cervix, and stimulating cervical stretch receptors. Cervical stretching sends a positive feedback signal to the hypothalamus to release more oxytocin, which causes more uterine contractions, thereby causing more stretching of the cervix by the fetus. This positive feedback loop between fetal cortisol, maternal hypothalamic oxytocin release, uterine contractions, and cervical stretching continues until the fetus has cleared the birth canal, and the absence of fetal cortisol and cervical stretching ends stimulation of hypothalamic oxytocin secretion.

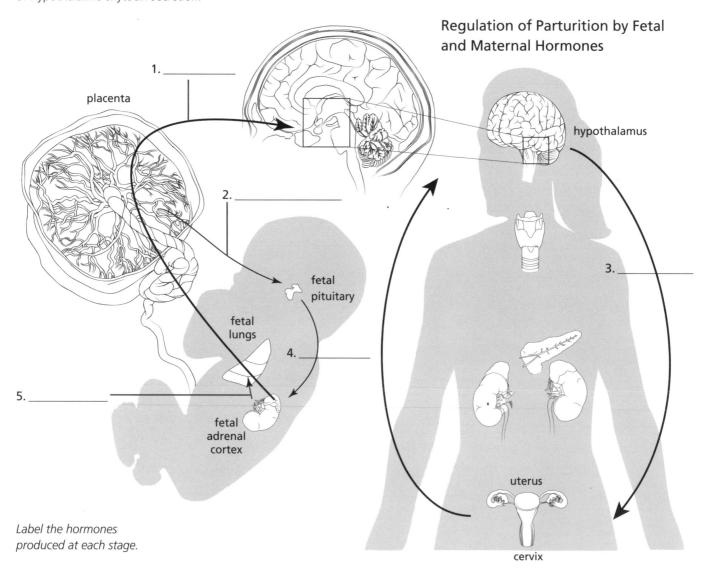

Regulation of Parturition by Fetal and Maternal Hormones

placenta

1. _____

2. _____

hypothalamus

3. _____

fetal pituitary

fetal lungs

4. _____

5. _____

fetal adrenal cortex

uterus

cervix

Label the hormones produced at each stage.

Answers

1. cortisol, 2. corticotropin-releasing hormone, 3. oxytocin, 4. adrenocorticotropin hormone, 5. cortisol

Mammary Gland Growth and Lactation

Growth and preparation of the female breast for lactation starts during puberty and ends with parturition. Each breast contains a mammary gland with 10–20 lobules. Each lobule has clusters of alveoli, or hollow cavities, lined with secretory epithelial cells. Growth and maturation of the mammary gland, or mammogenesis, occurs at puberty and is completed during pregnancy. During pregnancy lactogenesis begins, rendering the glands capable of producing and secreting milk. Breast milk is a complex fluid that provides nutrition and protection for rapidly growing infants. The first stage of lactogenesis, occurring in midpregnancy, involves gland differentiation and production of lactase, proteins, and immunoglobulins by the alveolar cells. Stage two of lactogenesis occurs at the time of parturition, when milk production actively begins in the alveoli in response to the release of prolactin hormone from the anterior pituitary and decreased levels of progesterone when the placenta is expelled with afterbirth. When the nipple undergoes tactile stimulation from a baby suckling, it sends afferent signals to the maternal hypothalamus, which produces oxytocin that is released by the posterior pituitary. Oxytocin causes alveolar smooth muscle to contract and eject milk from alveoli into the duct, and then into the lactiferous sinus and out through the nipple.

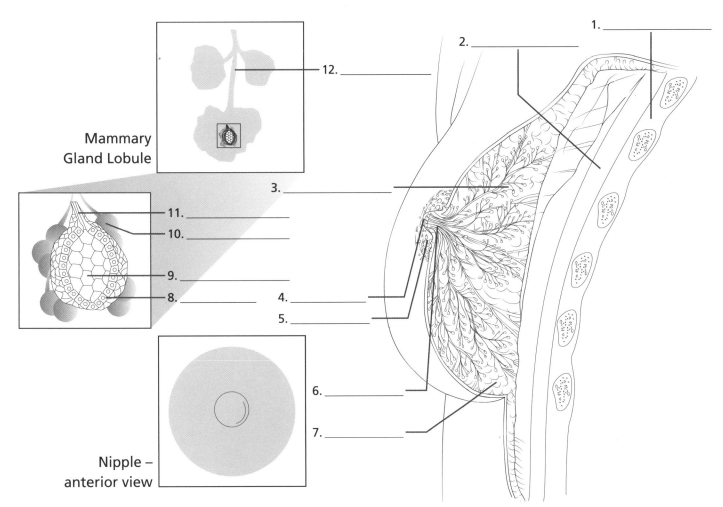

Mammary Gland Lobule

1. _____
2. _____
12. _____
3. _____
11. _____
10. _____
9. _____
8. _____
4. _____
5. _____
6. _____
7. _____

Nipple –
anterior view

Breast with Mammary Gland – sagittal view

Answers

1. chest wall (ribcage), 2. pectoralis muscles, 3. lobule, 4. nipple, 5. areola, 6. lactiferous sinus, 7. fat, 8. secretory cell, 9. cavity, 10. alveoli, 11. duct, 12. lactiferous sinus

Reproductive System

Puberty and sexual maturation

At puberty the hypothalamus increases production of gonadotropin-releasing hormone (GnRH), which stimulates the pituitary to increase secretion of luteinizing hormone (LH) and follicle-stimulating hormone (FSH). At puberty in females, FSH stimulates ovarian follicle and egg maturation, while LH stimulates oestrogen secretion from the dominant follicle thecal cells and also stimulates ovulation of a secondary oocyte. High levels of blood oestrogen cause the formation of female secondary sexual characteristics, such as fat deposition in the breast and on the hips, growth of pubic and armpit hair, and increased sebaceous secretions. At puberty in males, FSH stimulates testicular seminiferous tubules to produce sperm, while LH causes Leydig cells in the tubules to produce testosterone. High levels of blood testosterone cause formation of male secondary sex characteristics such as increased muscle mass; lengthening of the vocal chords and a deepening of the voice; increased sebaceous gland secretions; and growth of facial, chest, pubic, and armpit hair. High testosterone and oestrogen also cause psychological changes, such as increased libido in males and females, respectively.

Hormonal Regulation of Puberty – the hypothalamic-pituitary-gonadal axis

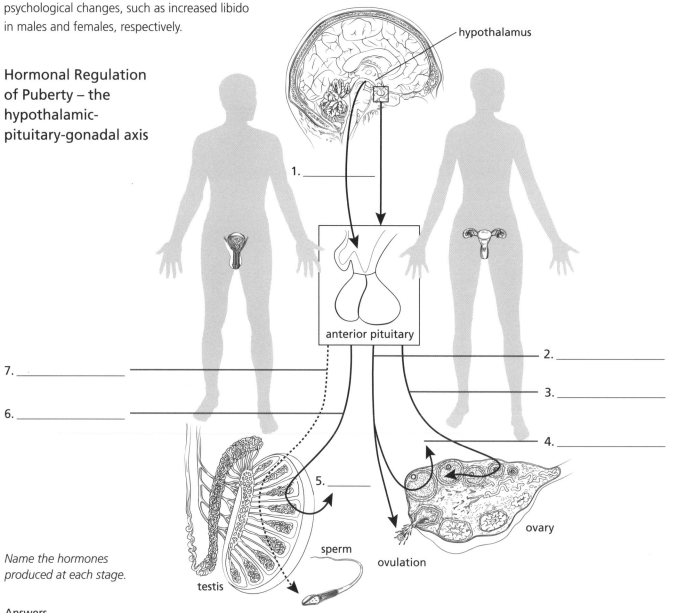

Name the hormones produced at each stage.

Answers

Types of White Blood Cells

White blood cells (leukocytes) are immune cells. They are produced in the bone marrow and thymus and are transported to other tissues via the bloodstream. There are three main types of leukocytes in the blood: granulocytes, monocytes, and lymphocytes.

Granulocytes (neutrophils, eosinophils, basophils, and mast cells) are inflammatory cells that are involved in killing microbes and in allergic reactions. They have large numbers of intracellular vesicles called granules, which contain degradative enzymes, antimicrobial peptides, and inflammatory mediators that can be released by degranulation to kill extracellular pathogens and mobilise other immune cells.

Monocytes enter tissues, where they become macrophages. They engulf microbes and clear tissue debris by phagocytosis. Lymphocytes include B cells and T cells. B cells produce antibodies, while T cells can activate other immune cells or kill infected cells.

Granulocytes and monocytes are innate immune cells. They are particularly important in the early stages of immune responses against invading microbes. Other innate immune cells include dendritic cells (which activate T cells) and natural killer cells (which release their granules to kill infected cells). Lymphocytes are adaptive immune cells. They are mobilised more slowly but are responsible for the long-lasting immune memory that confers protection against re-infection.

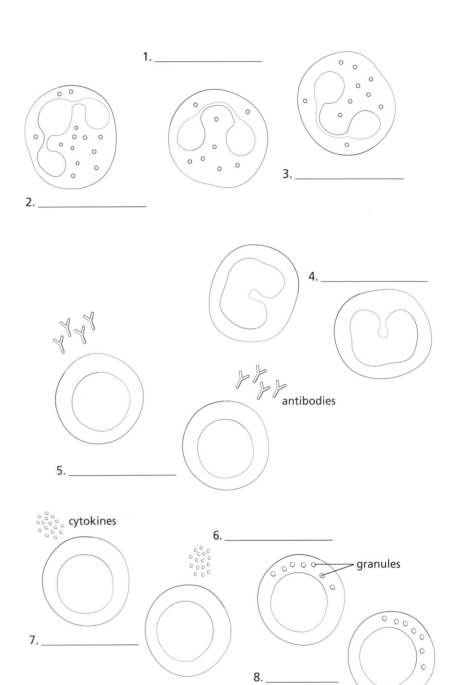

1. _____

2. _____

3. _____

4. _____

antibodies

5. _____

cytokines

6. _____

granules

7. _____

8. _____

Answers

Function of Macrophages and Granulocytes

Macrophages patrol tissues, where they clear debris and monitor for invading microbes. They employ phagocytosis to engulf and internalise dead cells and small microbes such as bacteria. Macrophages kill and degrade internalised microbes in acidic intracellular compartments using enzymes and reactive oxygen and nitrogen compounds. When they detect invading microbes, macrophages also produce inflammatory mediators to attract other immune cells.

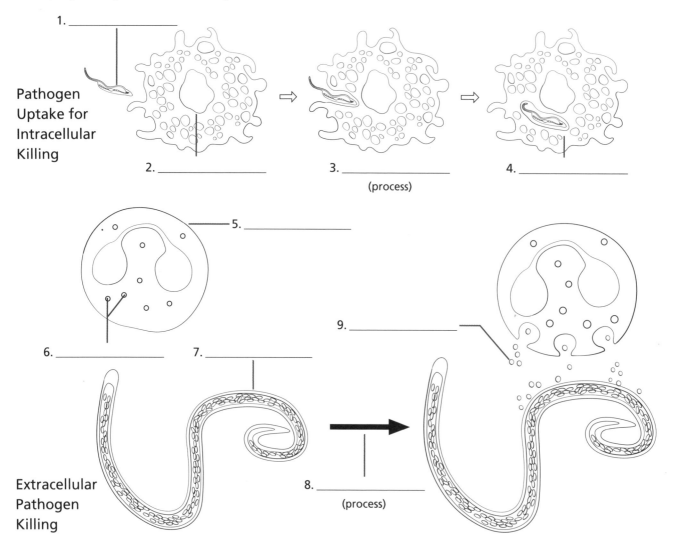

1. _____

Pathogen
Uptake for
Intracellular
Killing

2. _____

3. _____
(process)

4. _____

5. _____

6. _____

7. _____

9. _____

Extracellular
Pathogen
Killing

8. _____
(process)

Neutrophils are usually the first immune cells recruited to infected tissues. Like macrophages, they undergo phagocytosis to capture and kill small microbes, but they can also kill microbes that are too big to be internalised. Neutrophils undergo degranulation to release the contents of their intracellular granules (including enzymes and antimicrobial peptides) onto extracellular targets. They can also catch extracellular microbes in a web of extruded DNA known as a neutrophil extracellular trap (NET).

The other granulocytes – eosinophils, basophils, and mast cells – also release the contents of their granules. They are particularly important for killing parasitic worms. In addition, they release histamine, which increases the permeability of blood vessels to allow more leukocytes to enter the tissues to kill invading microbes. Histamine release by these cells also triggers many of the symptoms associated with allergies and asthma.

Answers

1. microbe, 2. macrophage, 3. phagocytosis, 4. phagosome, 5. eosinophil/basophil/mast cell, 6. granules, 7. parasite, 8. degranulation, 9. cytotoxic granule proteins

Humoral Defence: B Lymphocytes and Antibody Production

B cells are lymphocytes that use immunoglobulins to detect molecular structures known as antigens (e.g. components of bacteria or viruses). Immunoglobulins (IgA, IgD, IgE, IgG, IgM) exist both as B cell receptors on the cell surface and as secreted molecules known as antibodies.

B cells are activated when their B cell receptors detect specific antigens. Activated B cells (known as plasma cells) produce antibodies, which recognise the same antigens as the B cells that produced them. Antibodies therefore coordinate immune responses against specific targets.

IgA is secreted in mucosal tissues (e.g. intestinal, respiratory, and urogenital tracts). IgG plays several important roles in protection from infection. For example, it can neutralise viruses to limit their spread, attach to bacteria to promote their uptake by macrophages and neutrophils, or identify cells infected with viruses to promote their destruction by cytotoxic T cells and natural killer cells. IgG can also cross the placenta to protect the unborn child. IgE marks extracellular targets such as parasitic worms for destruction by eosinophils and is also responsible for triggering allergic reactions.

Some activated B cells become memory cells, which can be reactivated months or even years later if a specific threat is detected again.

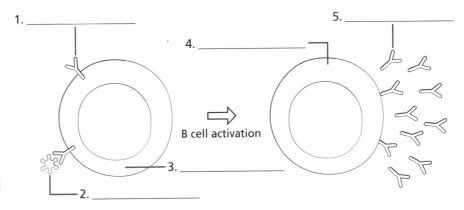

B Cell Activation

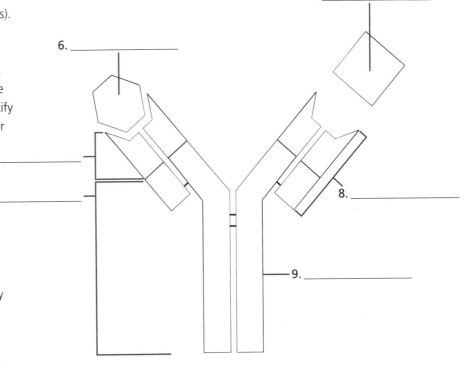

Immunoglobulin

Cellular Defence: T Lymphocytes and Cell-Mediated Immunity

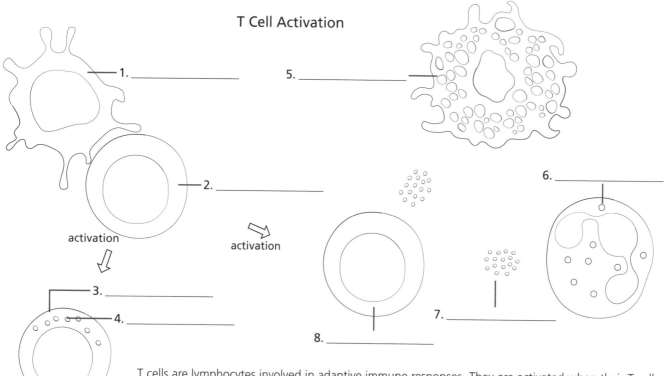

T Cell Activation

1. _____

2. _____

activation

activation

3. _____

4. _____

5. _____

6. _____

7. _____

8. _____

T cells are lymphocytes involved in adaptive immune responses. They are activated when their T cell receptors detect specific antigens, but the antigens must be presented to T cells by antigen-presenting cells such as dendritic cells. T cells mature in the thymus and are stored in lymphoid tissues (spleen and lymph nodes). They can be effector cells, memory cells, or regulatory cells. Effector T cells can be helper cells or cytotoxic cells. Helper T cells orchestrate cell-mediated immune responses by releasing inflammatory mediators such as chemokines and cytokines, which attract and activate other immune cells, including macrophages and neutrophils. In addition, helper T cells assist in the activation of cytotoxic T cells and B cells.

Cytotoxic T cells undergo degranulation to release their granule contents to kill targets such as tumour cells or cells infected with viruses. Some activated T cells become memory T cells, which can be reactivated upon subsequent detection of the same threat. Along with memory B cells, they are responsible for the long-lasting immunoprotective effects of vaccines. T cells that recognise self-antigens rather than foreign antigens are deleted in the thymus to avoid autoimmunity. Regulatory T cells also prevent autoimmunity by suppressing immune responses.

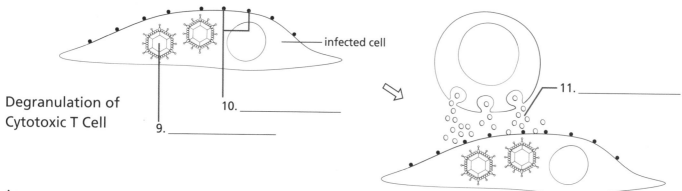

Degranulation of Cytotoxic T Cell

infected cell

9. _____

10. _____

11. _____

Answers

Response to Exercise: Metabolism

The regulation of metabolism during exercise is complex and is influenced by a number of factors, including the duration and intensity of exercise (% VO_2 max). In general, low-intensity exercise is primarily reliant on lipid (fat) as a fuel source, and as exercise intensity increases, carbohydrates (glucose) become the primary fuel source. In contrast, proteins play a small role as a fuel source during exercise and must first be degraded into amino acids. Proteases may be activated during extended exercise periods (two hours or more), and amino acids may contribute as a fuel source during such times.

Accordingly, during low-intensity exercise, plasma free fatty acids (FFAs) are the primary source of fuel. As exercise intensity increases from low to moderate, the contribution of plasma FFAs declines and there is an increased reliance upon muscle triglycerides. At higher exercise intensities, the contribution of plasma FFAs and muscle triglycerides are equal and much smaller in comparison to that of muscle glycogen.

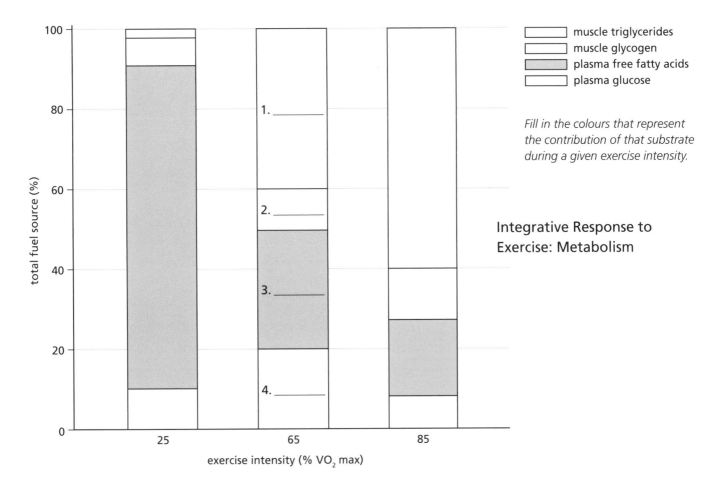

Legend:
- muscle triglycerides
- muscle glycogen
- plasma free fatty acids
- plasma glucose

Fill in the colours that represent the contribution of that substrate during a given exercise intensity.

Integrative Response to Exercise: Metabolism

Glucose is stored in the liver and skeletal muscle as glycogen. Muscle glycogen stores are affected by training status such that aerobically trained individuals are able to store a greater amount of muscle glycogen to serve as a muscle fuel source. Liver glycogen stores primarily serve to maintain blood glucose levels at rest and during low-intensity exercise, and this plasma glucose can serve as a fuel source for muscle. As exercise intensity increases, there is a large increase in the reliance upon muscle glycogen stores as a fuel source. The contribution of skeletal muscle glycogen as a fuel source for exercising muscle is an intensity-dependent relationship.

Answers

1. muscle glycogen, 2. plasma glucose, 3. plasma free fatty acids, 4. muscle triglycerides

Response to Exercise: Cardiovascular

During acute exercise, there is an elevated demand for oxygen from the working muscles. As a means to meet this elevated oxygen demand, blood flow and oxygen delivery increase to the working tissues, in part by elevating cardiac output and redistributing blood flow away from non-working muscles and the viscera, and towards exercising muscles via local vasodilation. In addition to a redistribution of blood in the periphery, there appears to be significant increase in brain blood flow associated with exercise.

Ventilation increases with exercise intensity as a means of oxygenating the blood. Further, a greater surface area of the lung is both ventilated and perfused with blood to maximise loading of oxygen and unloading of carbon dioxide; this is reported as improved matching of ventilation and perfusion within the lung. Increased cardiac output facilitates the increased delivery of oxygenated blood to the periphery, mainly through an elevated heart rate. This increased work of the heart leads to an elevated metabolic demand on the cardiac tissue and a subsequent increase in oxygen demand. Accordingly, blood flow within the heart muscle is also elevated to facilitate the matching of oxygen delivery to demand. Skeletal muscle blood flow can increase 100-fold during high-intensity exercise, due to elevations in cardiac output and blood flow redistribution. Another adaption that occurs during exercise is a reduction in plasma volume through a loss of water to the contracting skeletal muscle. This leads to haemoconcentration of red blood cells, which facilitates extraction of oxygen by the tissue (contracting muscle).

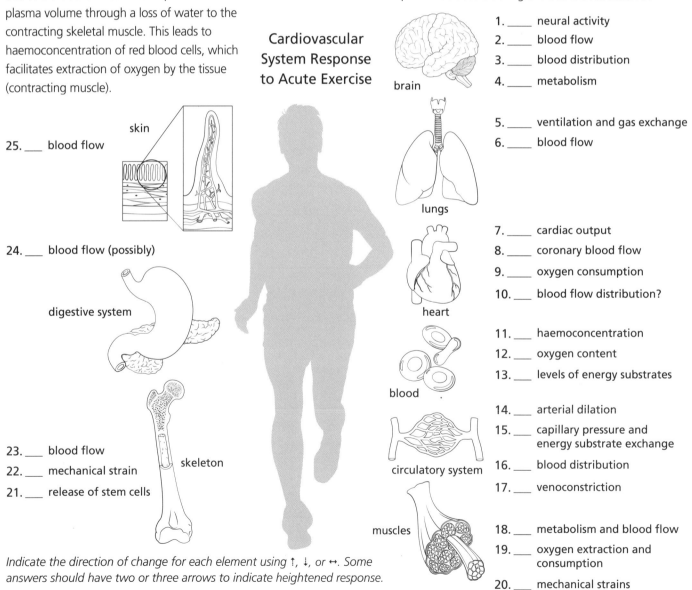

Cardiovascular System Response to Acute Exercise

brain

1. ____ neural activity
2. ____ blood flow
3. ____ blood distribution
4. ____ metabolism

lungs

5. ____ ventilation and gas exchange
6. ____ blood flow

heart

7. ____ cardiac output
8. ____ coronary blood flow
9. ____ oxygen consumption
10. ___ blood flow distribution?

blood

11. ___ haemoconcentration
12. ___ oxygen content
13. ___ levels of energy substrates

circulatory system

14. ___ arterial dilation
15. ___ capillary pressure and energy substrate exchange
16. ___ blood distribution
17. ___ venoconstriction

muscles

18. ___ metabolism and blood flow
19. ___ oxygen extraction and consumption
20. ___ mechanical strains

skin

25. ___ blood flow

24. ___ blood flow (possibly)

digestive system

skeleton

23. ___ blood flow
22. ___ mechanical strain
21. ___ release of stem cells

Indicate the direction of change for each element using ↑, ↓, or ↔. Some answers should have two or three arrows to indicate heightened response.

Answers

1. ↑↑, 2. ↔↑, 3. ↑, 4. ↑, 5. ↑↑↑, 6. ↑↑↑, 7. ↑↑↑, 8. ↑↑↑, 9. ↑↑↑, 10. ↑, 11. ↑, 12. ↑, 13. ↑, 14. ↔↑, 15. ↑↑↑, 16. ↑, 17. ↑, 18. ↑↑↑, 19. ↑↑↑, 20. ↑, 21. ↑, 22. ↑↑, 23. ↑↑, 24. ↑↔↑, 25. ↑, ↔↑↓

Response to Exercise: Endocrine

As exercise ensues there is withdrawal of the parasympathetic nervous system and activation of the sympathetic nervous system (SNS), and the increase in this branch of the nervous system is graded with exercise intensity. At approximately 60 per cent of VO_2 max, there is a marked increase in SNS activity, resulting in elevated catecholamines concentration (noradrenaline and adrenaline). These catecholamines increase heart rate and help redistribute blood flow to the working muscles by evoking peripheral vasoconstriction. Additionally, the catecholamines work to help mobilise fuel sources by stimulating glycogenolysis and lipolysis. Another hormone that aids in mobilising fuels for exercise is cortisol. Released from the adrenal cortex, cortisol increases gluconeogenesis and lipolysis. Additionally, the SNS suppresses insulin secretion during exercise in an effort to maintain blood glucose levels. During exercise, skeletal muscle glucose uptake occurs in an insulin-independent manner and the rate of glucose uptake during exercise far exceeds that observed during rest. It is believed that increases in intracellular calcium associated with skeletal muscle contractions drive the insulin-independent uptake of glucose observed with exercise. Additionally, the kidney is innervated by the SNS and upon activation, blood flow to the organ will decrease in an effort to redistribute blood to working muscles. Additionally, SNS stimulation increases the secretion of renin from the kidney which, along with aldosterone and angiotensin II, work to maintain blood pressure over the long term by affecting fluid and electrolyte balance.

Label the hormones in each graph.

Endocrine System   4. _____ □
Response During   5. _____ △
Acute Exercise   6. _____ ○

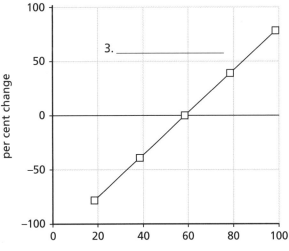

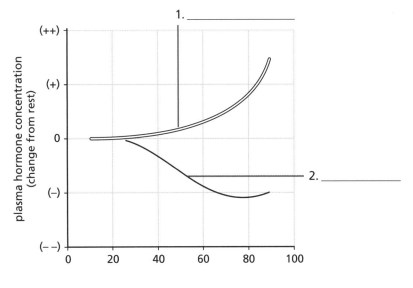

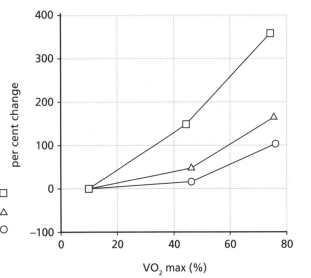

Answers

Index

Major topics are indicated with **bold** page numbers.